McGRAW-HILL TECHNICAL EDUCATION SERIES

Norman C. Harris, Series Editor

Introduction to Electron Tubes and Semiconductors • Alvarez and Fleckles

Architectural Drawing and Planning • Goodban and Hayslett

Introductory Applied Physics, 2d ed. • Harris and Hemmerling

Experiments in Applied Physics • Harris

Elementary Mathematics: Arithmetic, Algebra, & Geometry • Hemmerling

Pulse and Switching Circuits • Ketchum and Alvarez

Introduction to Microwave Theory and Measurements • Lance

Specifications Writing for Architects and Engineers • Watson

(Other volumes in preparation.)

Other McGraw-Hill books by
Edwin M. Hemmerling

MATHEMATICAL ANALYSIS

INTRODUCTORY APPLIED PHYSICS, *Second Edition*
(with Norman C. Harris)

ELEMENTARY MATHEMATICS

Arithmetic

Algebra &

Geometry

EDWIN M. HEMMERLING

CHAIRMAN OF MATHEMATICS-ENGINEERING-
TECHNICAL-SCIENCE DIVISION
BAKERSFIELD COLLEGE

McGRAW-HILL BOOK COMPANY

NEW YORK, ST. LOUIS, SAN FRANCISCO,
LONDON, TORONTO, SYDNEY

Preface

It has been the author's observation that too often an otherwise capable and competent student will attempt to study mathematical concepts at a level not commensurate with his inadequate background. He has seen the devastating effect of the student's attempting the study of a course for which he is not prepared. On the other hand, he has seen many students with weak mathematical foundations transfer from high schools to technical institutes, junior colleges, and senior colleges and succeed admirably after first repairing their deficiencies.

It is for such students that this book is written. Vocational, technical, and nontechnical students should find it equally suitable. The student who has mastered the contents of this book should be well prepared for the technical mathematics, intermediate algebra, and trigonometry courses.

This text provides a foundation course covering the essential parts of arithmetic, slide rule, elementary algebra, basic concepts of plane geometry, and mensuration of elementary solids. It presupposes little or no background of the courses normally taught in secondary schools.

The concept of place value and degrees of accuracy of measured quantities is introduced early and used throughout the text. The student is taught to check the reasonableness of his answers, not only with respect to the magnitudes of the numerical answers but also to their indicated degrees of accuracy.

Use of the slide rule is covered early in the book so the student can use the rule throughout to solve the more complex problems involving multiplication, division, powers, and roots.

Algebra has been developed as a natural extension of arithmetic. Careful explanations of the reasons behind the various arithmetic and algebraic operations are developed. The emphasis throughout the book is on understanding before memorizing. The student is led to determine the reasonableness of rules before applying them in solving problems.

Since mathematical theory is combined closely with its use, stated problems are drawn from experiences familiar to the student or within the sphere of his daily living and reading. Students are taught to solve these problems by careful analysis and clear thinking, not by blind substitution in formulas.

No effort is made to prove geometric propositions. The aim is to show how the propositions can be used in determining properties of familiar geometric figures as they may be applied in daily observations and studies. Special concepts and mensuration formulas are developed in Chapter 16.

The illustrative problems have been carefully selected to illustrate the various mathematical principles. At the same time, the author has avoided the practice of having one or two ridiculously easy problems solved for the student and then including in the sets of exercises problems of a much more complex nature. The illustrative problems show how to solve difficult problems as well as elementary ones.

The book contains an abundant supply of problems so that the instructor may vary his assignments from class to class, if he chooses. The easier problems are given at the beginning of each exercise. The more difficult ones are listed at the end of each exercise.

Edwin M. Hemmerling

Contents

ELEMENTARY MATHEMATICS:

Arithmetic, Algebra, & Geometry

CHAPTER 1

Operations with Numbers

1-1 Developing a Number System. Man's development from his primitive background to his present status of civilization is directly related to his progress in developing mathematics as a language. Primitive man took a great step forward when he was able to distinguish between a single object and several objects of the same kind. For thousands of years these people carried on simple conversations involving bartering and trading by means of gestures involving their fingers or hands. But their concepts of numbers did not go beyond two or three. Any quantity greater than two or three was treated as a group whose magnitude was roughly recognized by the size of the group.

The history of the evolution of number systems is a fascinating study which is beyond the scope of this text. The development of names and symbols for numbers led to many number systems. With these number systems man was able to keep written records of his countings.

The present number system used by most civilized nations is known as the *Hindu-Arabic* system. It had its origin in India about 500 B.C. There are two unique features of this system which make it superior to all other systems. The introduction of the symbol for zero to represent the absence of quantity did not appear in the other notations that had been developed. The inclusion of the zero symbol in the number system made possible the feature which makes for the genius of the system, that of the *principle of place value.* Thus, for the number represented by

1

444, the right-hand 4 represents 4 units, the next 4 represents ten times as much, and the left 4 represents one hundred times the right 4. Thus $444 = 4(10)^2 + 4(10) + 4(1)$. Each digit in an Arabic number has not only its *face value* but also its *place* or *position value*.

The principle of digits having both face and position values makes it possible to represent any quantity, no matter how large, by using only 10 symbols, 0, 1, 2, 3, 4, 5, 6, 7, 8, and 9. This system also permits the development of easy rules for performing the four fundamental processes of addition, subtraction, multiplication, and division.

It should be noted that the system in common use today has 10 as its base. However, equally effective systems could, and have been, developed using other numbers as bases. Our modern high-speed computers have 2 as the base of the system used.

1-2 Mathematics as a Language. The student should realize that the symbols for concepts and operations that are used in mathematical computations are essentially a form of communication. Therefore, their use must be just as precise, understandable, and convincing as is the use of words. Every mathematical statement or operation expressed in symbolic form must be a complete and true statement. These statements must be understandable to any person who is familiar with the symbolisms and algorithms used. In solving a problem, the mere answer to the problem is not sufficient. The explanation, in symbolic form, of how it was determined is necessary. The student's written work should be a clear record of the method used to solve the problem.

The student is urged to analyze the processes in the solution of a problem into its constituent parts. Each step in the solution must be clearly understood. Each step should be related to the complete solution. Often a student is able to get the correct answer to a problem by following certain rules of procedure, but unless he understands why these rules are applied, he does not truly understand the process. One of the best tests for understanding a process is that of attempting to explain the process to another person. If the other person comprehends your explanation, you must understand it. Throughout the study of this text, the student should stress *understanding* the fundamental concepts. Facts that are forgotten can easily be found in books, but the understanding of facts and concepts cannot be looked up.

1-3 Addition of Numbers. Addition is a procedure based upon the process of counting, where one seeks the total number of objects contained in several sets of objects. Thus, the child might add 5 and 5 by counting the number of fingers on both hands. A person might add the number of girls and boys in a given class by counting all the students in the class. It is important that the student recognize that only *like* quantities can be added. Thus one could not add 2 feet (ft) and 3 quarts (qt).

To find the sum of two or more numbers one utilizes the principle of place value and adds only numbers which have the same place value. For example, when we add

$$
\begin{array}{ll}
2,317 & 2(1,000) + 3(100) + 1(10) + 7(1) \\
584 \quad \text{we are} & 5(100) + 8(10) + 4(1) \\
\overline{6,903} \quad \text{saying} & \overline{6(1,000) + 9(100) + 0(10) + 3(1)}
\end{array}
$$

We then can add the units, the tens, the hundreds, and the thousands to get $(8(1,000) + 17(100) + 9(10) + 14(1))$. This can be written

$$
\begin{array}{lll}
2,317 & & \\
584 & & \\
\underline{6,903} & & \\
14(1) & = & 1(10) + 4(1) \\
9(10) & = & 9(10) \\
17(100) & = 1(1,000) + 7(100) & \\
\underline{8(1,000)} & - 8(1,000) & \\
\text{Total} & = \overline{9(1,000) + 7(100) + 10(10) + 4(1)}
\end{array}
$$

Replacing 10(10) by 1(100), we get

$$
\begin{aligned}
\text{Total} \quad &= 9(1,000) + 7(100) \qquad\qquad + 4(1) \\
&\qquad\qquad\qquad + 1(100) \\
\hline
&= 9(1,000) + 8(100) + 0(10) + 4(1)
\end{aligned}
$$

In actual practice the process is simplified by "carrying (the number) in your head" from one column to the next one to the left, either by writing down the number carried in the proper column or by performing the task mentally.

Thus we might write the addition algorithm

$$
\begin{array}{r}
{\scriptstyle 1\quad 1\ 1} \\
2\,,3\,1\,7 \\
5\,8\,4 \\
6\,,9\,0\,3 \\
\hline
9\,,8\,0\,4
\end{array}
$$

A good way to check addition is to start at the bottom of a column and add upward once and then start at the top of the column and add downward. If the same answer is obtained using both methods, the answer is probably correct.

Example 1-1. Combine into a single number $2,863 + 92 + 845 + 107$.

Solution. The symbol $+$ indicates addition. Writing the numbers in a vertical column and adding, we get

$$
\begin{array}{r}
{\scriptstyle 1\quad 2\ 1} \\
2\,,8\,6\,3 \\
9\,2 \\
8\,4\,5 \\
1\,0\,7 \\
\hline
3\,,9\,0\,7
\end{array}
$$

Example 1-2. Find the perimeter of $ABCD$.

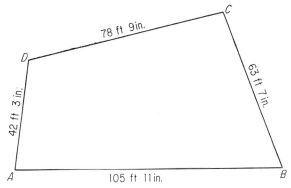

Fig. 1-1

Solution. The sum of the sides is the perimeter of the figure.

$$\begin{array}{r} 42 \text{ ft } \ \ 3 \text{ in.} \\ 78 \text{ ft } \ \ 9 \text{ in.} \\ 63 \text{ ft } \ \ 7 \text{ in.} \\ \underline{105 \text{ ft } 11 \text{ in.}} \\ 288 \text{ ft } 30 \text{ in.} \end{array}$$

Replacing 30 in. by 2 ft 6 in., we get

$$\begin{array}{r} 288 \text{ ft} \\ \underline{2 \text{ ft } \ \ 6 \text{ in.}} \\ \text{Perimeter } = 290 \text{ ft } \ \ 6 \text{ in.} \end{array}$$

PROBLEMS

Add:

1-1. 2,135 716 8,032 544	**1-2.** 6,930 853 1,468 79	**1-3.** 4,671 50 679 8,523
1-4. 5,382 12,568 24 348 5,511	**1-5.** 95,057 1,983 3,624 807 99	**1-6.** 792,886 553 60,248 44 5,238,716

1-7. 8,560,243
1,799,207
4,153,648
7,134,089
5,624,107

1-8. $5,828 + 916 + 6,599$

1-9. $16 + 9,564 + 387 + 87$

1-10. $336 + 65 + 89,638 + 1,009$

1-11. Find the sum of 649; 87,853; 22; 1,001; 8.

1-12. Find the sum of 26; 3,006; 3,600; 306; 6.

1-13. Find the total length of fence required to enclose the parcel of land whose dimensions are shown in the figure.

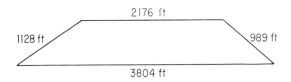

Problem 1-13

1-14. The floor plan of a building is illustrated in the accompanying figure. What is the distance around the building?

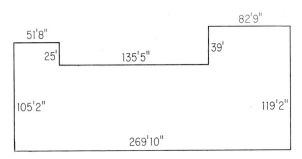

Problem 1-14

1-15. Find the perimeter of the symmetric figure if $a = 78$ ft, $b = 48$ ft, $c = 123$ ft, $d = 39$ ft, $e = 107$ ft, $f = 64$ ft, $g = 65$ ft, $h = 54$ ft, $i = 98$ ft, $j = 40$ ft, $k = 46$ ft.

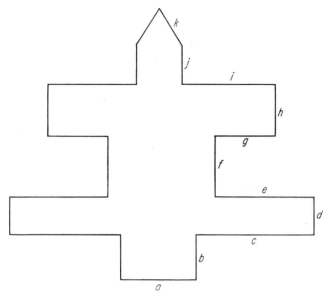

Problem 1-15

1-16. Find the sum of 18 gallons (gal) and 3 qt, 7 gal and 1 qt, 2 qt and 5 gal. (Hint: 1 gal is equivalent to 4 qt.)

1-17. California has an area of 156,803 square miles; Oregon has 96,350 square miles; Washington has 66,977 square miles. What is the total area of these three states that border the Pacific Ocean?

1-18. A cargo plane checked in loads of 2,867, 4,310, 5,862, 6,003 and 505 lb. What is its total pay load?

1-19. A salesman in the parts department of a television store had a sales record for a given week as follows: Monday, \$392.76; Tuesday, \$235.43; Wednesday, \$109.82; Thursday, \$85.07; Friday, \$293.87; Saturday, \$401.08. What were his total sales for the week?

1-20. Find the sum of the following time intervals: 3 hours (hr) 12 minutes (min), 22 hr 45 min, 15 hr 30 min, 9 hr 8 min. (Leave answer in a form that will have not more than 60 min in the total.)

1-4 Subtraction of Numbers. The process which is the inverse of addition is called *subtraction.* Subtraction consists of finding the *difference* between two numbers. The symbol $-$, called the minus sign, indicates subtraction. For example, we subtract 5 from 9 to get 4. To subtract 5 from 9 means to find the number which must be added to 5 to get 9. Thus, $9 - 5 = 4$, because $4 + 5 = 9$. The number to be subtracted is called the *subtrahend.* The number from which it is subtracted is called the *minuend.* The result is called the *remainder* or *difference.*

To prove a subtraction, one adds the subtrahend and the remainder. If their sum is equal to the minuend, the subtraction is correct.

In subtraction, the subtrahend is written directly under the minuend, with the units, tens, hundreds, etc., digits aligned in proper columns. In subtracting, we can subtract only units digits from units digits, only tens digits from tens digits, only hundreds digits from hundreds digits, etc. When the digits are subtracted from smaller digits, we use the borrowing method of subtraction. For example, when we write

Subtract

$$683$$
$$\underline{247}$$

$$\begin{aligned}
\text{Since } 83 &= 8 \text{ tens} + 3 \text{ units} \\
&= 7 \text{ tens} + 1 \text{ ten} + 3 \text{ units} \\
&= 7 \text{ tens} + 10 \text{ units} + 3 \text{ units} \\
&= 7 \text{ tens} + 13 \text{ units,}
\end{aligned}$$

$$\begin{aligned}
\text{we think } 683 &= 6 \text{ hundreds} + 7 \text{ tens} + 13 \text{ units} \\
\underline{247} &= \underline{2 \text{ hundreds} + 4 \text{ tens} + 7 \text{ units}} \\
\text{Difference} = 436 \text{ or } & 4 \text{ hundreds} + 3 \text{ tens} + 6 \text{ units}
\end{aligned}$$

In the solution we "borrow" one of the tens digits in the minuend and replace it with 10 units, which added to the 3 units makes 13 units. The answer will be 4 hundreds + 3 tens +

6 units, or 436. Thus we write

Subtract   *Check (add)*

```
    6 8 3                                               2 4 7
    2 4 7                                               4 3 6
    4 3 6                                               6 8 3
```

EXAMPLE 1-3. How much longer is 2,847 ft 3 in. than 1,563 ft 7 in.?

Solution

Subtract

```
    2 , 9 4 7 ft   3 in.
    1 , 5 6 3 ft   7 in.
```

Rewrite the problem:

Subtract

```
    2 , 9 4 6 ft 1 5 in.
    1 , 5 6 3 ft     7 in.
    1 , 3 8 3 ft     8 in.
```

Check

Add

```
    1 , 5 6 3 ft     7 in.
    1 , 3 8 3 ft     8 in.
    2 , 9 4 6 ft 1 5 in.
```
or
```
    2 , 9 4 7 ft     3 in. (sum)
```

PROBLEMS

Subtract and prove each answer by addition:

1-21.	9 8	1-22.	7 6 4	1-23.	8 7 6
	4 6		2 3 1		5 9

1-24. 6 , 8 4 2
        3 , 5 1 8

1-25. 3 , 5 6 7
        1 , 0 8 5

1-26. 8 , 4 3 9
          5 8 2

1-27. 6 3 , 8 5 4
          2 , 5 4 9

1-28. 4 9 , 0 0 9
        2 5 , 5 1 2

1-29. 8 0 , 8 0 8
        2 4 , 2 4 2

1-30. 3 0 , 0 2 8
          5 , 7 0 6

1-31. 8 5 3 , 0 8 6
        3 8 4 , 7 0 7

1-32. 7 , 0 0 5 , 3 0 0
        2 , 9 9 0 , 0 3 1

1-33. How much larger is 90,000 than 3,849?

1-34. From 8,349 subtract 5,761.

1-35. The electric meter at Mr Brown's house read 82,763 kilo-watthours (kwhr) on July 31. On Aug. 31 it read 84,108 kwhr. How much electricity was used during the month of August?

1-36. Mr. Smith bought a house valued at $25,350. Ten years later the house was valued at $21,780. How much did the property depreciate in value during the 10 years?

1-37. The stadium at Belleview High School has a seating capacity of 22,000. During a recent game all seats were occupied but a block containing 1,750 seats. How many were seated in the stadium?

1-38. The number of cars of a certain make sold during the first 3 months of this year were: January, 57,864; February, 42,357; March, 61,008. Last year's sales of the same car were: January, 49,038; February, 35,705; March, 53,444. Find the increase of sales for the first 3 months of this year over the comparable period last year.

1-39. Mr. Evans has $18,750 in the bank with which to build a home. His cost will be: lot, $3,475; house, $16,600; garage, $1,785; landscaping, $1,035; incidentals, $250. How much will he need to borrow before he can complete the home?

1-40. At the beginning of the day, the owner of an appliance store had $350 cash on hand. During the day he sold the following for cash: a television set, $212.50; one radio, $39.75; a second radio, $115.95; a toaster, $19.98; a percolator,

$23.99. He paid out in cash: $237.50 to a bill collector, $112 for advertising, $50 to charity. How much cash should the owner have on hand at the end of the day?

1-41. A computing machine subtracted 48 from a certain number 16 times in succession leaving a final remainder of 19. Find the number from which the 48s were subtracted.

1-5 Multiplication. Multiplication is a short-cut for adding equal numbers. Thus, instead of adding

$$3 + 3 + 3 + 3 = 12$$

we can write the same fact $4 \times 3 = 12$. We say that we have *multiplied* 3 by 4 and that 12 is the *product* of 4 and 3. The 4 and 3 are *factors* of 12. The $\times$ sign indicates *multiplication*.

The *multiplicand* is the number which is multiplied by a second number, called the *multiplier*. That is,

Multiplicand $\times$ multiplier = product

In multiplying, we usually place the units of the multiplier under the units of the multiplicand, the tens under the tens, etc. The procedure of multiplication is easier to illustrate than to describe. Consider the following:

EXAMPLE 1-4. Multiply 347 by 56.

Solution

$$
\begin{array}{r}
3\ 4\ 7 \text{ (multiplicand)} \\
5\ 6 \text{ (multiplier)} \\
\hline
2\ \ 0\ 8\ 2 \text{ (multiplicand} \times 6) \\
1\ 7\ \ \ 3\ 5 \text{ (multiplicand} \times 5) \\
\hline
1\ 9\ ,4\ 3\ 2 \text{ (product)}
\end{array}
$$

The 2,082 above, called partial product, represents 2,082 units, while the partial product 1,735 represents 1,735 tens or 17,350 units. Thus the product is the sum of 2,082 and 17,350. The zero is usually deleted from the second partial product in the solution of the problem.

1-6 Laws of Multiplication. Three important laws of multiplication will help us in solving and checking problems.

Commutative Law. In finding the product of two numbers, either number can be chosen as the multiplicand or multiplier. This law is often used in checking problems of multiplication. Thus, the product obtained in the example above can be checked by showing that $347 \times 56 = 56 \times 347 = 19{,}432$.

Associative Law. The product of three or more numbers does not depend upon the way in which the factors are grouped. Thus, $5 \times 6 \times 4 = (5 \times 6) \times 4 = 5 \times (6 \times 4) = (5 \times 4) \times 6$, etc.

Distributive Law. The sum of two or more numbers may be multiplied by a given number by multiplying each of them by that number and then adding the products. For example, $4(5 + 2) = 20 + 8 = 28$, where the parentheses have been used as a symbol of multiplication. It should be noted that $4(5 \times 2)$ does not equal (written $\neq$) $20 \times 8 = 160$.

Thus,

$$4(5 + 2) = 20 + 8 = 28$$
$$4(5 \times 2) \neq 20 \times 8 = 160$$
$$4(5 \times 2) = 4 \times 5 \times 2 = 40$$

EXERCISES

Multiply:

1-42. 3 8 4
        7
	1-43. 2 9 5
	       3 6
		1-44. 5 7 3
		       1 0 8

1-45. 2 , 1 5 6
         3 8 4
	1-46. 7 , 8 3 4
	       2 , 5 9 1
		1-47. 6 , 0 1 9ᵗ
		       5 , 2 0 3

1-48. 7 2 , 0 0 3
          5 , 0 0 4
	1-49. 8 0 , 4 0 2
	        5 0 , 3 0 1
		1-50. 9 8 , 7 5 6
		          3 , 0 4 7

1-51. 5 8 , 9 7 1 2 4 , 0 3 6	**1-52.** 8 $\times$ 7 $\times$ 5	

1-53. 30 × 15 × 20

1-54. Show that 36 × 25 × 24 = 36 × 24 × 25.

1-55. Find the value of 7(8 + 5).

1-56. Find the value of 8(6 + 3 + 4).

1-57. Mr. Brandt's monthly water bill is $7.60. If he is charged the same rate each month, what is his annual water bill?

1-58. A wheel turns at a constant rate of 3,600 revolutions per minute (rpm). How many revolutions will it make in 24 hr?

1-59. Joe Turner is a traveling salesman who is given a travel allowance of 8 cents per mile. If he travels an average of 400 miles per week, what is his annual travel allowance?

1-60. In the figure, *A* and *B* represent plots of two parcels of land. Which has the larger area? How much larger?

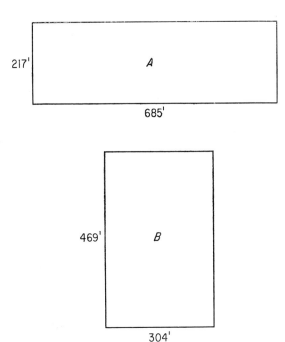

Problem 1-60

(HINT: The area of a rectangle is the product of its length and its width.)

1-61, Car X will travel 18 miles on a gallon of gasoline. Car Y will travel 15 miles on a gallon of gasoline. Car X holds 17 gal. Car Y holds 20 gal. Which car can travel farther on a full tank? How much farther?

1-7   Division. The fourth fundamental process with numbers is called division. Just as subtraction is the inverse of addition, so division is the inverse of multiplication. Thus to divide 12 by 3 is to determine the number (called the *quotient*) which multiplied by 3 (called the *divisor*) gives 12 (called the *dividend*).

There are several signs of division, among them $\div$, $/$, $-$, $\overline{)\ }$. Each symbol is read "divided by." Thus $12 \div 3 = 4$; $12/3 = 4$; $\frac{12}{3} = 4$; $3\,\overline{)12}^{\,4}$. We can state: The quotient of two numbers is that number which when multiplied by the divisor gives the dividend. We know that $12 \div 3 = 4$ because $4 \times 3 = 12$.

Just as multiplication can be thought of as continued addition, division can be interpreted as continued subtraction. For example, $12 \div 3 = 4$ can be interpreted as follows:

$$
\begin{array}{r}
12 \\
- \ 3 \\
\hline
9 \\
- \ 3 \\
\hline
6 \\
- \ 3 \\
\hline
3 \\
- \ 3 \\
\hline
0
\end{array}
$$

This tells us that there are exactly four 3s in 12. This operation is sometimes called measuring. Our problem solution also tells us that if we divided 12 into three equal parts, the size of each part is 4. This operation is called *partition*.

Thus division can be interpreted as:

1. The inverse of multiplication
2. Continued subtraction or measuring
3. Partition

1-8 Long Division. Consider the problem $38,695 \div 42$. This problem can be solved by the long-division method as follows.

Example 1-5

$$
\begin{array}{r}
9\,2\,1 \\
4\,2\overline{)3\,8\,,6\,9\,5} \\
\end{array}
$$

$$
\left.
\begin{array}{rcl}
3\,7\ \ 8\,0\,0 &=& 9\,0\,0 \times 4\,2 \\
\overline{8\,9\,5} & & \\
8\,4\,0 &=& 2\,0 \times 4\,2 \\
\overline{5\,5} & & \\
4\,2 &=& 1 \times 4\,2 \\
\end{array}
\right\} = (900 + 20 + 1)42 = 921 \times 42
$$

$$
\overline{1\,3}\ \text{(remainder)}
$$

It will be noted that we have found that there are exactly nine hundred 42s plus twenty 42s plus one 42 (total 921) in the dividend 38,695 with a *remainder* of 13 "left over." The process is shortened by deleting from the solution the zeros in 37,800 and 840. These zeros are "understood" but not written down. The complete solution (quotient) of the division is $921\frac{13}{42}$.

To check the result of a division, multiply the whole part of the quotient by the divisor and add the remainder to this product. If the result is equivalent to the dividend, the solution is correct. Thus, for the example above we have

Check

$$
\begin{array}{r}
9\,2\,1 \\
\times\ \ \ \ 4\,2 \\
\hline
1\ \ 8\,4\,2 \\
3\,6\ \ 8\,4 \\
\hline
3\,8\,,6\,8\,2 \\
\end{array}
\qquad
\begin{array}{r}
3\,8\,,6\,8\,2 \\
+\ \ \ \ 1\,3 \\
\hline
3\,8\,,6\,9\,5 \\
\end{array}
$$

PROBLEMS

Divide and check by multiplication:

1-62. $9,800 \div 35$ **1-63.** $1,898 \div 26$

1-64. $32,724 \div 81$ **1-65.** $12,285 \div 273$

1-66. $\dfrac{66,468}{382}$ **1-67.** $\dfrac{81,621}{404}$

1-68. $\dfrac{522,252}{572}$ **1-69.** $\dfrac{229,329}{8,493}$

1-70. $\dfrac{19,272,708}{60,606}$ **1-71.** $\dfrac{27,484,392}{274}$

1-72. $222\overline{)1,001001}$ **1-73.** $309\overline{)9,284,576}$

1-74. $3,704\overline{)19,013,501,714}$ **1-75.** $653\overline{)65,565,680}$

1-76. $4,309\overline{)1,771,503,153}$ **1-77.** $38,072\overline{)17,475,048}$

1-78. Determine the rate of gas consumption (miles per gallon) for a car which travels 2,834 miles on 177 gal.

1-79. Bruce Marolf received the following monthly commissions for selling cars: January, \$684.27; February, \$513.24; March, \$688.33; April, \$591.34; May, \$575.75; June, \$521.17; July, \$466.24; August, \$450.85; September, \$967.84; October, \$1,358.84; November, \$887.36; December, \$581.26. What was his average monthly commission?

1-80. How many 80-pound (lb) sacks of fertilizer can be purchased for \$201.75 if each sack costs \$43.75?

1-81. Sixty four nails of a certain size weigh 1 lb. How many pounds of nails must be purchased to surely obtain 2,750 nails? Express answer to the nearest whole number.

1-9 Operations with Zero. We have noted the value of the symbol 0 in our number system. Sometimes students refer to zero as "nothing." This is an unfortunate mistake. The word "nothing" refers to a nonexistence. Zero does exist. Zero is a number which indicates the absence of any quantity. Zero also has a positional value as has any of the other nine digits in the Hindu-Arabic number system. Thus, the zero in the number 304 indicates the absence of any tens and also is used to place the 3 and 4 in the proper hundreds and units position.

The number zero has some unique properties and obeys certain special laws which we shall list. The letter N will be used to represent any real number in the following.

▶ 1. If zero is added to a number, the sum is equal to the original number. For this reason it is often called the *additive identity element.*

ILLUSTRATIONS. $3 + 0 = 3$ $\quad N + 0 = N$
$0 + 0 = 0$ $\quad 0 + N = N$

▶ 2. If zero is subtracted from a number, the difference is equal to the original number.

ILLUSTRATIONS. $5 - 0 = 5$ $\quad N - 0 = N$

▶ 3. A number subtracted from itself is zero.

ILLUSTRATIONS. $7 - 7 = 0$ $\quad N - N = 0$

▶ 4. If a number is subtracted from zero, the difference is the negative of that number.

ILLUSTRATIONS. $0 - 6 = -6$ $\quad 0 - N = -N$

▶ 5. The product of zero and any quantity is zero.

ILLUSTRATIONS. $0 \times 4 = 0$ $\quad 0 \times N = 0$
$4 \times 0 = 0$ $\quad 0 \times 0 = 0$

▶ 6. If the product of two numbers is equal to zero, one of the numbers must be equal to zero.

ILLUSTRATIONS. If $a \cdot b = 0$, then $a = 0$ or $b = 0$ (or both). If $(x - a)(x - b) = 0$, then $x - a = 0$ or $x - b = 0$ (or both).

▶ 7. If zero is divided by any number except zero, the quotient is zero.

ILLUSTRATIONS. $0 \div 5 = 0$ $\quad 0 \div N = 0$ if $N \neq 0$

We have stated that to divide a number a by a number b is to find a number q, called *quotient*, such that b multiplied by q gives a. That is, $a/b = q$ if, and only if, $a = b \cdot q$. If $b = 0$

and $a \neq 0$, there is no number q which satisfies the condition $a = 0 \cdot q$. If $a = 0$ and $b = 0$, we find there are many numbers q which satisfy the condition $0 = 0 \cdot q$. Thus, $\frac{0}{0}$ does not represent a *single* real number. It is said to be *indeterminate*. We must exclude division by zero in our operations, since division by zero is meaningless.

1-10 Combinations of the Four Fundamental Operations. Usually arithmetic and algebraic problems involve some combinations of the four fundamental operations. The order in which these operations are performed is critical. The following rules should be followed.

1. *A series of additions may be taken in any order.* For example, $2 + 5 + 3 + 7 = 7 + 2 + 5 + 3 = 3 + 7 + 5 + 2 = 17$.

2. *A series of subtractions must be performed in the order given.* Thus, $25 - 13 - 3 = 12 - 3 = 9$. It would be wrong first to subtract 3 from 13 to get 10 and then to subtract the 10 from 25.

3. *A series of multiplications may be taken in any order.* Thus, $8 \times 2 \times 5 = 8 \times 5 \times 2 = 2 \times 5 \times 8 = 80$.

4. *A series of divisions must be taken in the order given.* Thus, $480 \div 24 \div 4 = 20 \div 4 = 5$. But $480 \div 24 \div 4 \neq 480 \div 6$.

5. When a problem involves the four fundamental operations, there is a definite order that must be followed in performing the operations. Common usage dictates the following rule: *Perform all the multiplications and divisions first in the order in which they are given. Then perform additions and subtractions in the remaining order.*

EXAMPLE 1-6. Simplify $156 - 56 \div 7 \times 2 + 34$.

Solution

$$156 - 56 \div 7 \times 2 + 34 =$$
$$156 - 8 \times 2 + 34 =$$
$$156 - 16 + 34 =$$
$$140 + 34 = 174$$

EXAMPLE 1-7. Simplify $64 + 36 \times 8 \div 4 \times 2 - 2$.

Solution

$$64 + 36 \times 8 \div 4 \times 2 - 2 =$$
$$64 + 288 \div 4 \times 2 - 2 =$$
$$64 + 72 \times 2 - 2 =$$
$$64 + 144 - 2 =$$
$$208 - 2 = 206$$

1-11 Symbols of Grouping. It is often necessary or desirable to consider several terms as a single group upon which operations may be performed. In such cases, a symbol of grouping is used. Symbols for grouping include the parentheses ( ), the brackets [ ], the braces { }, and the bar, or vinculum, ————. Frequently, several symbols are used to indicate grouping of terms within a second group. If different symbols are used, it is easier to tell which terms are combined.

When no number is written before a symbol of grouping, it is understood to be $+1$ or -1 according to whether the sign preceding the symbol is plus or minus. Symbols are removed from or placed about a group according to the following rules:

▶ 1. Symbols of grouping preceded by a plus sign may be removed or inserted without changing the signs of the enclosed terms.

▶ 2. Symbols of grouping preceded by a minus sign may be removed or inserted if the sign of each of the enclosed terms is changed.

▶ 3. Symbols of grouping are generally removed by first removing the innermost pair according to the above rules, next the innermost pair of all that remain, and so on.

EXAMPLE 1-8. Simplify $4 + \{9 - [-5 - (4 - 7) - 3]\}$.

Solution

$$4 + \{9 - [-5 - (4 - 7) - 3]\} =$$
$$4 + \{9 - [-5 - 4 + 7 - 3]\} =$$
$$4 + \{9 + 5 + 4 - 7 + 3\} =$$
$$4 + 9 + 5 + 4 - 7 + 3 = 18$$

EXAMPLE 1-9. Simplify

$$(6 - 2) - 3\{2 - [5 + 7 - \overline{1 - 2} + 8]\}$$

Solution

$$(6 - 2) - 3\{2 - [5 + 7 - \overline{1 - 2} + 8]\} =$$
$$(6 - 2) - 3\{2 - [5 + 7 - 1 + 2 + 8]\} =$$
$$(6 - 2) - 3\{2 - 5 - 7 + 1 - 2 - 8\} =$$
$$6 - 2 - 6 + 15 + 21 - 3 + 6 + 24 = 61$$

PROBLEMS

Simplify the following:

1-82. $112 + 48 \div 8 \times 3 - 67$

1-83. $120 \times 4 \div 4 - 4 + 4$ **1-84.** $263 - 63 \div 9 \times 7 - 8$

1-85. $18 \times 14 - 4 + 6 \div 5$ **1-86.** $288 \div 4 \div 6 \div 4$

1-87. $8 \times 4 \times 9 \div 3 \times 12$ **1-88.** $6 \div 6 \times 6 \times 6 \div 6$

1-89. $6 \div 6 \times 6 \div 6 \times 6$ **1-90.** $9 + (7 - 3)$

1-91. $4 - (7 - 5)$ **1-92.** $8 - 0(6 - 3)$

1-93. $(13 - 6) - 5$ **1-94.** $(8 - 4) - (3 - 7)$

1-95. $11 - [7 - (5 - 4)]$ **1-96.** $11 - [7 - 0(9 - 5) + 4]$

1-97. $6[9 - 5(11 - 8) + 2(8 - 4)]$

1-98. $25 - [9 - (7 + 2) + 2(5 - 2)]$

1-99. $28 - 2\{34 - 5[9 - (5 - 1)]\}$

1-100. $\{85 - [12 - 0(8 - 3)]\} - 2[10 - 5(2 - 4)]$

1-101. $42 - 2[17 - 6(5 - 4) - 11] + 3(6 - 2)$

CHAPTER **2**

Fractions

2-1 Common Fractions. For many years the natural numbers, called *whole numbers* or *integers*, were sufficient for the needs of our ancestors. But as civilization advanced, there came a time when the idea of a part of a whole had to be considered. Lands and produce were partitioned, and concepts for these parts needed to be developed. This resulted first in the concepts of unit fractions, which we recognize as $\frac{1}{2}$, $\frac{1}{3}$, $\frac{1}{4}$, and so on. Symbols for these concepts have been found in the books used by Egyptians as early as 1650 B.C. Thus, if a board is divided into three equal parts, the fraction $\frac{1}{3}$ represents one of those equal parts (see Fig. 2-1). If a circle is partitioned into four equal parts (see Fig. 2-2), one of the equal parts is represented by the unit fraction $\frac{1}{4}$.

In Fig. 2-1 the unshaded portion of the figure, which is made up of two of the equal parts, is represented by $\frac{2}{3}$. The unshaded

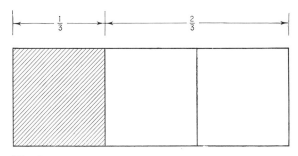

Fig. 2-1

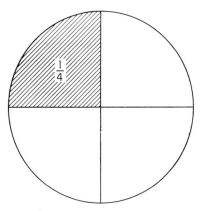

Fig. 2-2

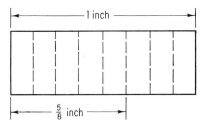

Fig. 2-3

portion of Fig. 2-2 represents $\frac{3}{4}$ of the area of the circle. $\frac{5}{8}$ inch represents the length of five of eight equal parts into which an inch is divided (see Fig. 2-3).

The number above the line of a fraction is called the *numerator* of the fraction.   The number below the line is called the *denominator*.   In the fraction $\frac{5}{8}$, the 5 is the numerator and the 8 is the denominator.   Thus,

A fraction $= \dfrac{\text{numerator}}{\text{denominator}}$

$= \dfrac{\text{number of parts}}{\text{number of (equal) partitions of whole}}$

A *proper* fraction is a fraction whose numerator is smaller than its denominator. $\frac{1}{2}, \frac{3}{4}, \frac{7}{9}$ are proper fractions.

An *improper* fraction is a fraction whose numerator is equal to or larger than its denominator. $\frac{3}{3}, \frac{5}{5}, \frac{7}{6}$, and $\frac{11}{8}$ are improper fractions.

The numerator and denominator taken together are called the terms of the fraction.

2-2 Changing the Form of a Fraction. *Equivalent fractions* are fractions which represent the same part of a whole quantity. For example, $\frac{3}{4}$ of an inch is equivalent to $\frac{6}{8}$ of an inch. Eight-twelfths of a dozen is equivalent to $\frac{2}{3}$ of a dozen. Equivalent fractions can be obtained by applying the following fundamental principle of fractions: *The value of a fraction is unchanged if both the numerator and the denominator are multiplied (or divided) by the same number, excepting zero.*

EXAMPLES

1. $\dfrac{3}{5} = \dfrac{3 \times 4}{5 \times 4} = \dfrac{12}{20}$

2. $\dfrac{12}{20} = \dfrac{12 \div 4}{20 \div 4} = \dfrac{3}{5}$

A mixed number consists of a number plus a fraction. The mixed number $4\frac{2}{3}$ means $4 + \frac{2}{3}$. In working with fractions it is often necessary to convert mixed numbers to improper fractions and improper fractions to mixed fractions. Examples of the processes follow.

EXAMPLES

1. $5\frac{2}{3} = 5 + \dfrac{2}{3} = \dfrac{5 \times 3}{1 \times 3} + \dfrac{2}{3} = \dfrac{15}{3} + \dfrac{2}{3} = \dfrac{17}{3}$

2. $\dfrac{18}{7} = 18 \div 7 = 2\frac{4}{7}$

2-3 Reduction to Lowest Terms. A fraction is said to be in its *lowest terms* if the numerator and denominator have no common divisor except 1. Thus, the fraction $\frac{12}{20}$, above, has been reduced to its lowest terms $\frac{3}{5}$ by dividing both the numerator and denominator by 4. Such a fraction is called a *prime fraction*. Reduction to lowest terms does not mean reducing to a mixed number. Thus, $\frac{18}{8}$ in lowest terms is $\frac{9}{4}$, not $2\frac{1}{4}$.

2-4 Conversion to Higher Terms. A fraction can be converted to higher terms by multiplying both the numerator and the denominator by the same constant greater than unity. This process will be found useful in adding and subtracting fractions. The fraction $\frac{3}{7}$ is converted to the higher termed fraction $\frac{6}{14}$ by multiplying both the numerator and denominator by 2.

PROBLEMS

Change each of the following fractions to equivalent fractions (fill in the blank spaces):

2-1. $\dfrac{3}{5} = \dfrac{}{25}$ **2-2.** $\dfrac{5}{8} = \dfrac{}{24}$ **2-3.** $\dfrac{3}{8} = \dfrac{12}{}$

2-4. $\dfrac{2}{3} = \dfrac{}{18}$ **2-5.** $\dfrac{16}{48} = \dfrac{1}{}$ **2-6.** $\dfrac{12}{64} = \dfrac{3}{}$

2-7. $\dfrac{13}{23} = \dfrac{}{92}$ **2-8.** $\dfrac{13}{18} = \dfrac{}{126}$ **2-9.** $\dfrac{705}{1{,}245} = \dfrac{}{83}$

2-10. $\dfrac{7{,}896}{6{,}237} = \dfrac{376}{}$

Change to equivalent mixed numbers:

2-11. $\frac{19}{3}$ **2-12.** $\frac{27}{4}$ **2-13.** $\frac{45}{4}$

2-14. $\frac{64}{15}$ **2-15.** $\frac{34}{24}$ **2-16.** $\frac{69}{48}$

2-17. $\frac{43}{12}$ **2-18.** $\frac{77}{42}$ **2-19.** $\frac{117}{36}$

2-20. $\frac{136}{56}$

Change to equivalent improper fractions:

2-21. $1\frac{7}{8}$ **2-22.** $3\frac{4}{7}$ **2-23.** $4\frac{6}{11}$

2-24. $5\frac{8}{13}$ **2-25.** $2\frac{7}{9}$ **2-26.** $6\frac{9}{16}$

2-27. $7\frac{3}{4}$ **2-28.** $8\frac{1}{8}$ **2-29.** $9\frac{3}{5}$

2-30. $5\frac{11}{12}$

Reduce to lowest terms:

2-31. $\frac{18}{30}$ **2-32.** $\frac{48}{60}$ **2-33.** $\frac{160}{192}$

2-34. $\frac{252}{288}$ **2-35.** $\frac{56}{252}$ **2-36.** $\frac{159}{198}$

2-37. $\frac{140}{252}$ **2-38.** $\frac{288}{432}$ **2-39.** $\dfrac{6,216}{8,904}$

2-40. $\dfrac{20,160}{22,080}$

2-5 Addition and Subtraction of Fractions. For the addition and subtraction of fractions we must remember the first law of addition and subtraction: *Only like quantities can be added or subtracted.* Two fractions are said to be *like* if they have the same denominator. Thus we can add $\frac{2}{9} + \frac{5}{9} = \frac{7}{9}$. In like manner, we can subtract $\frac{8}{11} - \frac{3}{11} = \frac{5}{11}$.

When the denominators are not alike, the fractions cannot be added directly. To attempt to add $\frac{3}{4}$ and $\frac{7}{10}$ would be similar to trying to add three quarters and seven dimes. In order to add unlike fractions, the fractions must be written as equivalent fractions having the same denominator.

2-6 Prime Factors. You will recall that a *factor* of a number is an exact divisor of that number. Thus factors of 18 are 1, 2, 3, 6, 9, 18.

A *prime factor* is a factor which is exactly divisible only by itself and 1. The prime factors of 18 are 1, 2, and 3. The other factors (6, 9, 18) of 18 are not prime because each is divisible, not only by 1 and itself, but also by 2 and/or 3.

To find the prime factors of a number one can start dividing the number by the smallest prime number 2 and continue dividing the consecutive quotients by 2 until he obtains a remainder not divisible by 2. He next will divide the last quotient (now a dividend) by 3. This process is repeated with increasing prime numbers as divisors until 1 is obtained as the final quotient.

EXAMPLE 2-1. Find the prime factors of 840.

Solution

$$
\begin{array}{r|l}
2 & 8\ 4\ 0 \\
\hline
2 & 4\ 2\ 0 \\
\hline
2 & 2\ 1\ 0 \\
\hline
3 & 1\ 0\ 5 \\
\hline
5 & 3\ 5 \\
\hline
7 & 7 \\
\hline
 & 1
\end{array}
$$

The number 840 can be expressed as the product of its prime factors: $840 = 2 \times 2 \times 2 \times 3 \times 5 \times 7$.

2-7   Least Common Multiple.   The smallest possible number that can be divided exactly by two or more numbers is called the *lowest common multiple* of those numbers (abbreviated LCM). Often the lowest common multiple can be found by inspection. When inspection fails to reveal the LCM, one can always find it by the following method:

1. Arrange the numbers in a column and express each number in prime factors.

2. Find the product of all the different prime factors, using each one the greatest number of times it appears in any one number. The product, thus found, is the least common multiple.

EXAMPLE 2-2. Find the LCM of 12, 15, 21.

Solution

$$12 = 2 \times 2 \times 3$$
$$15 = 3 \times 5$$
$$21 = 3 \times 7$$

The least common multiple is $2 \times 2 \times 3 \times 5 \times 7 = 420$.

EXAMPLE 2-3. Find the LCM of 21, 24, and 42.

Solution

$$21 = 3 \times 7$$
$$24 = 2 \times 2 \times 2 \times 3$$
$$42 = 2 \times 3 \times 7$$

The lowest common multiple is $2 \times 2 \times 2 \times 3 \times 7 = 168$.

2-8 Least Common Denominator. The *least common denominator* (abbreviated LCD) of two or more fractions is the lowest common multiple of the denominators of those fractions. When unlike fractions are added and subtracted, the fractions must first be changed to equivalent like fractions. This involves finding the least common denominators of those fractions.

EXAMPLE 2-4. Add $\frac{2}{3} + \frac{3}{4} + \frac{5}{6}$.

Solution. The LCD can be found, by inspection, to be 12.

$$\frac{2}{3} + \frac{3}{4} + \frac{5}{6} = \frac{8}{12} + \frac{9}{12} + \frac{10}{12}$$
$$= \frac{27}{12}$$
$$= 2\frac{3}{12} \text{ or } 2\frac{1}{4}$$

EXAMPLE 2-5. Simplify $\frac{7}{12} + \frac{11}{30} - \frac{9}{20}$.

Solution

$$12 = 2 \times 2 \times 3$$
$$30 = 2 \times 3 \times 5$$
$$20 = 2 \times 2 \times 5$$

The LCD is $2 \times 2 \times 3 \times 5$.

Then
$$\frac{7}{12} + \frac{11}{30} - \frac{9}{20} = \frac{35}{60} + \frac{22}{60} - \frac{27}{60}$$
$$= \frac{30}{60} \text{ or } \frac{1}{2}$$

EXAMPLE 2-6.   Simplify $5\frac{2}{3} + 3\frac{7}{12} - 2\frac{1}{4}$.

Solution

$$5\tfrac{2}{3} + 3\tfrac{7}{12} - 2\tfrac{1}{4} = \tfrac{17}{3} + \tfrac{43}{12} - \tfrac{9}{4}$$
$$= \tfrac{68}{12} + \tfrac{43}{12} - \tfrac{27}{12}$$
$$= \tfrac{84}{12} \text{ or } 7$$

EXAMPLE 2-7.   Simplify $8\frac{1}{7} - 2\frac{3}{5} + 4\frac{1}{4} - 6\frac{7}{15}$.

Solution

$$7 = 7$$
$$5 = 5$$
$$14 = 2 \times 7$$
$$15 = 3 \times 5$$

The LCD is $2 \times 3 \times 5 \times 7 = 210$.
Then

$$8\tfrac{1}{7} - 2\tfrac{3}{5} + 4\tfrac{1}{14} - 6\tfrac{7}{15} = \tfrac{57}{7} - \tfrac{13}{5} + \tfrac{57}{14} - \tfrac{97}{15}$$
$$= \frac{57 \cdot 2 \cdot 3 \cdot 5}{7 \cdot 2 \cdot 3 \cdot 5} - \frac{13 \cdot 2 \cdot 3 \cdot 7}{5 \cdot 2 \cdot 3 \cdot 7}$$
$$+ \frac{57 \cdot 3 \cdot 5}{14 \cdot 3 \cdot 5} - \frac{97 \cdot 2 \cdot 7}{15 \cdot 2 \cdot 7}$$
$$= \frac{1,710}{210} - \frac{546}{210} + \frac{855}{210} - \frac{1,358}{210}$$
$$= \tfrac{661}{210} \text{ or } 3\tfrac{31}{210}$$

EXAMPLE 2-8.   Add

$$9\tfrac{7}{8}$$
$$3\tfrac{11}{16}$$
$$5\tfrac{3}{4}$$

Solution.   This problem can be worked two ways.

$$
\begin{aligned}
9\tfrac{7}{8} &= 9\tfrac{14}{16}\\
3\tfrac{11}{16} &= 3\tfrac{11}{16}\\
5\tfrac{3}{4} &= 9\tfrac{12}{16}\\
\hline
17\tfrac{37}{16} &= 19\tfrac{5}{16}
\end{aligned}
$$

Alternate Solution

$$\tfrac{7}{8} + \tfrac{11}{16} + \tfrac{3}{4} = \tfrac{79}{8} + \tfrac{59}{16} + \tfrac{23}{4}$$
$$= \tfrac{158}{16} + \tfrac{59}{16} + \tfrac{92}{16}$$
$$= \tfrac{309}{16} \text{ or } 19\tfrac{5}{16}$$

EXAMPLE 2-9.   Subtract

$$58\tfrac{5}{16}$$
$$17\tfrac{7}{12}$$

Solution.   The least common denominator of the two fractions is 48.   In this problem we shall have to borrow 1 from 58 and change it to 48 48ths in order that the fractions can be subtracted.

$$58\tfrac{5}{16} = 58\tfrac{15}{48} = 57\tfrac{63}{48}$$
$$17\tfrac{7}{12} = 17\tfrac{28}{48} = 17\tfrac{28}{48}$$
$$40\tfrac{35}{48}$$

PROBLEMS

Find the prime factors in Probs. 2-41 to 2-50.

2-41. 36   **2-42.** 42   **2-43.** 120   **2-44.** 252
2-45. 450   **2-46.** 1,400   **2-47.** 693   **2-48.** 1,470
2-49. 2,600   **2-50.** 3,960

Find the LCM in Probs. 2-51 to 2-60

2-51. 4, 6, 15   **2-52.** 8, 9, 6   **2-53.** 16, 12, 15
2-54. 16, 18, 15   **2-55.** 16, 30, 75   **2-56.** 54, 45, 75
2-57. 14, 21, 35   **2-58.** 22, 21, 35   **2-59.** 56, 44, 42
2-60. 98, 50, 75

In Probs. 2-61 to 2-80 perform the indicated additions and subtractions.

2-61. $\tfrac{1}{3} + \tfrac{1}{3}$ **2-62.** $\tfrac{2}{5} + \tfrac{3}{10}$

2-63. $\frac{1}{3} + \frac{1}{4}$

2-64. $\frac{5}{6} - \frac{3}{6}$

2-65. $\frac{4}{5} - \frac{2}{10}$

2-66. $\frac{5}{6} - \frac{5}{8}$

2-67. $\frac{2}{7} + \frac{2}{3} + \frac{5}{7}$

2-68. $\frac{5}{8} + \frac{3}{4} + \frac{1}{2}$

2-69. $\frac{4}{4} + \frac{5}{8} - \frac{1}{6}$

2-70. $\frac{7}{10} - \frac{3}{20} + \frac{4}{5}$

2-71. $\frac{7}{15} + \frac{5}{6} - \frac{3}{4}$

2-72. $\frac{9}{16} + \frac{5}{18} - \frac{2}{15}$

2-73. $\frac{7}{54} + \frac{17}{45}$

2-74. $\frac{29}{45} - \frac{34}{75} + \frac{2}{15}$

2-75. $5\frac{5}{6} + 2\frac{1}{4} - 3\frac{7}{8}$

2-76. $4\frac{5}{16} + 6\frac{4}{21} + 8\frac{9}{35}$

2-77. $2\frac{7}{16} + 9\frac{5}{18} - 7\frac{4}{15}$

2-78. $87\frac{1}{2} + 33\frac{4}{15} - 26\frac{5}{6}$

2-79. $\frac{3}{98} + \frac{7}{50} + \frac{14}{75} - \frac{9}{30}$

2-80. $\frac{35}{56} - \frac{31}{44} - \frac{5}{42} + \frac{59}{77}$

2-81. Add: $9\frac{7}{9}$

$\qquad\quad 16\frac{2}{3}$

$\qquad\quad 13\frac{5}{6}$

2-82. Add: $208\frac{15}{16}$

$\qquad\qquad 1{,}593\frac{11}{30}$

$\qquad\qquad\; 845\frac{4}{21}$

2-83. Subtract: $28\frac{7}{8}$

$\qquad\qquad\quad 13\frac{2}{3}$

2-84. Subtract: $872\frac{11}{16}$

$\qquad\qquad\quad 254\frac{11}{12}$

2-85. Subtract: $39\frac{13}{54}$

$\qquad\qquad\quad 24\frac{17}{45}$

2-86. Subtract: $118\frac{9}{56}$

$\qquad\qquad\quad 79\frac{17}{44}$

2-87. $23\frac{5}{6}$ is how much greater than $15\frac{3}{4}$?

2-88. How much greater is $53\frac{5}{6}$ than $46\frac{7}{15}$?

2-89. What is the difference between $37\frac{7}{54}$ and $26\frac{19}{45}$?

2-90. A 15-ft board has cut from it lengths of $2\frac{3}{4}$, $1\frac{5}{6}$, $4\frac{1}{12}$, and $5\frac{1}{2}$ ft. How much of the board is left if the width of each saw cut is neglected?

2-91. A salesgirl on one day sold from one bolt of dry goods the following lengths of fabric: $4\frac{1}{2}$, $5\frac{2}{3}$, $12\frac{5}{8}$, 8, $18\frac{1}{2}$ yards (yd). How many yards of the material did she sell?

2-92. How many feet of molding are required to go around a room $18\frac{3}{4}$ ft wide and $35\frac{2}{3}$ ft long?

2-93. Three months ago Mr. Panagos weighed $220\frac{1}{2}$ lb. Today he weighs $186\frac{3}{4}$ lb. How many pounds did he lose in the 3 months?

2-94. In preparing an 11 by 15-in. sheet in the drawing class, pupils were instructed to draw border lines 1 in. from the left edge and $\frac{3}{8}$ in. from the other three edges of the sheet. What will be the dimensions between the border lines?

2-95. Determine the length of the bolt shown.

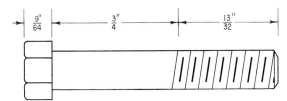

Problem 2-95

2-96. Determine the length *x*.

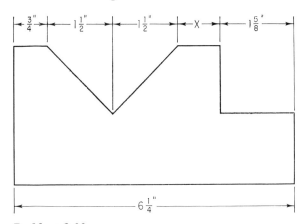

Problem 2-96

2-97. Determine the length of the radius labeled *x*.

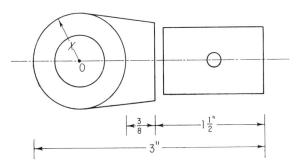

Problem 2-97

2-98. Determine the dimension x.

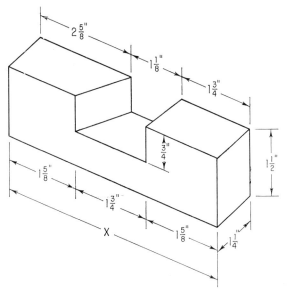

Problem 2-98

2-9 Multiplication of Fractions. By definition, multiplication is a short cut for adding equal quantities. To multiply 4 by $\frac{3}{8}$ means to add four $\frac{3}{8}$s. Thus,

$$4 \times \tfrac{3}{8} = \tfrac{3}{8} + \tfrac{3}{8} + \tfrac{3}{8} + \tfrac{3}{8} = \tfrac{12}{8} = \tfrac{3}{2}$$

It can be seen that we get the same result by multiplying 4 by 3 and dividing the product by 8.

▶ *Rule.* To multiply a number by a fraction, multiply the numerator of the fraction by the number and divide the resulting product by the denominator of the fraction.

To multiply a fraction by a whole number we apply the commutative law for multiplication. The law states that $\frac{3}{8} \times 4 = 4 \times \frac{3}{8} = \frac{3}{2}$. $\frac{3}{8} \times 4$ can be read "$\frac{3}{8}$ of 4." It will be noted that the product of an integer and a proper fraction is always smaller than the given integer. This is because in the product we are finding a fractional part of the integer.

The product of any two fractions can be illustrated by a simple drawing (see Fig. 2-4). Consider the problem of multiplying

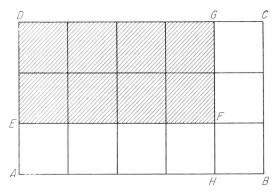

Fig. 2-4

$\frac{2}{3}$ by $\frac{4}{5}$. Let a rectangle *ABCD* be partitioned into five equal parts by vertical lines. The area of *AHGD* is $\frac{4}{5}$ the area of the rectangle. Next divide *AHGD* into thirds by horizontal lines. Then the area *DEFG* is $\frac{2}{3}$ the area *AHGD* (or $\frac{2}{3}$ of $\frac{4}{5}$ of area *ABCD*). It can be seen that *DEFG* is composed of 8 of the 15 rectangles that make up *ABCD*. Then area *DEFG* = $\frac{8}{15}$ area *ABCD* or $\frac{2}{3} \times \frac{4}{5} = \frac{8}{15}$.

▶ *Rule.* The product of fractions is a fraction whose numerator is the product of the numerators and whose denominator is the product of the denominators.

EXAMPLES

1. $\frac{7}{8} \times \frac{5}{12} = \frac{35}{96}$
2. $\frac{5}{3} \times \frac{7}{9} = \frac{35}{27} = 1\frac{8}{27}$

2-10   Canceling.   The product of two fractions should be reduced to lowest terms whenever possible.   This process can often be shortened by applying the fundamental principle of fractions before multiplying the numerators and the denominators.   For example, in finding the product of $\frac{8}{15}$ and $\frac{7}{12}$, we can divide both the numerator and the denominator by 4 before multiplying the numerators and the denominators.   Thus, we could write

$$\frac{8}{15} \times \frac{7}{12} = \frac{\overset{2}{\cancel{8}} \times 7}{15 \times \underset{3}{\cancel{12}}} = \frac{14}{45}$$

instead of writing

$$\frac{8}{15} \times \frac{7}{12} = \frac{8 \times 7}{15 \times 12} = \frac{56}{180} = \frac{14}{45}$$

As a still shorter form, we could solve the problem as

$$\frac{\overset{2}{\cancel{8}}}{15} \times \frac{7}{\underset{3}{\cancel{12}}} = \frac{14}{45}$$

This procedure is called *canceling*.   It is especially helpful in determining the product of several fractions.

EXAMPLES

1. $\frac{5}{13} \times \frac{7}{15} \times \frac{11}{14} = \frac{5}{13} \times \frac{7}{15} \times \frac{11}{14}$
   $= \frac{11}{78}$

2. $3\frac{1}{5} \times 7\frac{3}{4} \times 2\frac{1}{12} = \frac{16}{5} \times \frac{31}{4} \times \frac{25}{12}$
   $= \frac{155}{3}$ or $51\frac{2}{3}$

The student is cautioned not to make the following type common mistake.

$$\frac{\overset{1}{\cancel{2}} + 3}{5 + \underset{1}{\cancel{2}}} \overset{?}{=} \frac{4}{6} \qquad\qquad \frac{\overset{2}{\cancel{4}} + \overset{1}{\cancel{5}}}{\underset{2}{\cancel{10}} + \underset{3}{\cancel{6}}} \overset{?}{=} \frac{3}{5}$$

A quick check will reveal that the first fraction should be

reduced to $\frac{5}{7}$ (not $\frac{4}{6}$) while the second fraction should be reduced to $\frac{9}{16}$ (not $\frac{3}{5}$). In the first instance one was subtracted from both the numerator and the denominator. In the second, $2 + 4$ or 6 was subtracted from the numerator and $8 + 3$ from the denominator. This is not permissible.

PROBLEMS

Find the following products and reduce to lowest terms:

2-99. $\frac{5}{6} \times \frac{3}{5}$ **2-100.** $\frac{2}{3} \times \frac{5}{6}$ **2-101.** $\frac{7}{8} \times \frac{5}{12}$

2-102. $\frac{2}{3} \times \frac{5}{7}$ **2-103.** $\frac{7}{9} \times \frac{3}{4}$ **2-104.** $\frac{3}{4} \times 6$

2-105. $12 \times \frac{2}{3}$ **2-106.** $21 \times \frac{3}{7}$ **2-107.** $\frac{2}{3} \times \frac{8}{9}$

2-108. $\frac{4}{5} \times \frac{2}{3} \times \frac{3}{8}$ **2-109.** $\frac{18}{25} \times \frac{5}{9} \times \frac{3}{4}$ **2-110.** $\frac{9}{8} \times \frac{2}{3} \times \frac{12}{7}$

2-111. $\frac{12}{5} \times \frac{5}{16} \times \frac{4}{3}$ **2-112.** $\frac{7}{9} \times \frac{2}{5} \times \frac{3}{8}$

2-113. $\frac{16}{45} \times \frac{47}{66} \times \frac{90}{164} \times \frac{92}{141}$ **2-114.** $\frac{4}{5} \times \frac{11}{14} \times \frac{25}{48} \times \frac{16}{55}$

2-115. $12 \times 1\frac{5}{6}$ **2-116.** $30 \times 2\frac{9}{16}$

2-117. $1\frac{1}{5} \times 2\frac{1}{2}$ **2-118.** $4\frac{4}{5} \times 2\frac{1}{2}$

2-119. $7\frac{1}{3} \times 2\frac{4}{7}$ **2-120.** $5\frac{3}{4} \times 2\frac{6}{7}$

2-121. $2\frac{3}{4} \times 3\frac{3}{7} \times 5\frac{3}{5}$ **2-122.** $6\frac{1}{4} \times 12\frac{2}{5} \times 8\frac{2}{3}$

2-123. If 20 pieces of work can be machined in 8 hr, how many hours will it take to machine 12 pieces of work?

2-124. Pump A can fill a reservoir in 12 hr and pump B can fill it in 8 hr. What fractional part of the full reservoir will result if pump A operates 2 hr and pump B 3 hr?

2-11 Division of Fractions. The process of division of fractions follows easily from multiplication and the fundamental principle of fractions.

A fraction or mixed number divided by an integer can be interpreted as *partition*. Consider the problem $\frac{4}{5} \div 2$. We learned in Sec. 1-7 that dividing by 2 is to find the size of each of two equal parts into which a quantity can be partitioned. Since $\frac{2}{5} + \frac{2}{5} = \frac{4}{5}$, we know that $\frac{4}{5} \div 2 = \frac{2}{5}$. To divide a number by 2 is to take one-half of the number, to divide a number by 3 is to take one-third of the number, and so on. Thus, $\frac{4}{5} \div 2 = \frac{1}{2} \times \frac{4}{5} = \frac{2}{5}$ and $\frac{4}{5} \div 3 = \frac{1}{3} \times \frac{4}{5} = \frac{4}{15}$. It will be noted that, when a given fraction is divided by a number larger than 1, a number smaller than the given fraction will result.

An integer divided by a fraction or mixed number can be interpreted as *measurement*. For example, $4 \div \frac{1}{3}$ can mean how many times $\frac{1}{3}$ is contained in 4. We know that each unit has 3 thirds. Then 4 units must have 4×3 or 12 thirds. This can be written: $4 \div \frac{1}{3} = 4 \times \frac{3}{1} = 12$. Here we notice that, when a given integer is divided by a proper fraction, the quotient will always be larger than the given fraction.

Consider the problem $\frac{2}{3} \div \frac{3}{4}$. A possible instance in which such a problem might develop could be: "A recipe calls for $\frac{3}{4}$ ton of cement. If $\frac{2}{3}$ ton of cement is available, how much of the recipe can be made?" We know that $\frac{2}{3} \div \frac{3}{4}$ can be written $\frac{\frac{2}{3}}{\frac{3}{4}}$. Such a fraction, in which either or both terms are themselves fractions, is called a *complex fraction*. If we apply the fundamental principle of fractions to multiply both terms of the complex fraction by $\frac{4}{3}$, our complex fraction will reduce to an equivalent simple fraction. Thus, we have

$$\frac{2}{3} \div \frac{3}{4} = \frac{\frac{2}{3}}{\frac{3}{4}} = \frac{\frac{2}{3} \times \frac{4}{3}}{\frac{3}{4} \times \frac{4}{3}} = \frac{8}{9}$$

2-12 Reciprocals and Division of Fractions. Two numbers are said to be reciprocals if their product is 1. For example, the reciprocal of 2 is $\frac{1}{2}$, $\frac{1}{3}$ and 3 are reciprocals, $\frac{3}{4}$ and $\frac{4}{3}$ are reciprocals. It will be noted that the reciprocal of an integer is a unit fraction and the reciprocal of a unit fraction is an integer. If N is a number, then N and $1/N$ are reciprocals. The reciprocal of a fraction is often called the *inverted* fraction. It should be clear that any integer N can be expressed as the improper fraction $N/1$.

From the three illustrations (of Sec. 2-11) of divisions of fractions we can deduce the following generalization.

▶ To divide by a fraction, invert the fraction and multiply.

Since the division of a fraction by a fraction is a purely mechanical operation, the student sometimes makes the mistake of inverting the wrong fraction. The pupil should always check his answer to see if it is sensible. For example, we know that $\frac{3}{5} \div \frac{8}{9} = \frac{27}{40}$ is reasonable since if $\frac{8}{9}$ is larger than $\frac{3}{5}$, the quotient must be less than 1. If, on the other hand, we inverted the $\frac{3}{5}$ and multiplied to get the answer $\frac{40}{27}$, we should realize that the answer is not reasonable.

EXAMPLES

1. $\dfrac{18}{25} \div 4 = \dfrac{\overset{9}{\cancel{18}}}{25} \times \dfrac{1}{\underset{2}{\cancel{4}}} = \dfrac{9}{50}$

2. $27 \div \dfrac{3}{7} = \overset{9}{\cancel{27}} \times \dfrac{7}{\underset{1}{\cancel{3}}} = 63$

3. $\dfrac{8}{17} \div \dfrac{16}{51} = \dfrac{\overset{1}{\cancel{8}}}{\underset{1}{\cancel{17}}} \times \dfrac{\overset{3}{\cancel{51}}}{\underset{2}{\cancel{16}}} = \dfrac{3}{2} = 1\dfrac{1}{2}$

4. $\dfrac{8}{17} \div 1\dfrac{5}{51} \times \dfrac{8}{17} \times \dfrac{56}{51} = \dfrac{\overset{1}{\cancel{8}}}{\underset{1}{\cancel{17}}} \times \dfrac{\overset{3}{\cancel{51}}}{\underset{7}{\cancel{56}}} = \dfrac{3}{7}$

5. $2\dfrac{14}{15} \div 8\dfrac{2}{9} = \dfrac{44}{15} \div \dfrac{74}{9} = \dfrac{\overset{22}{\cancel{44}}}{\underset{5}{\cancel{15}}} \times \dfrac{\overset{3}{\cancel{9}}}{\underset{37}{\cancel{74}}} = \dfrac{66}{185}$

PROBLEMS

Divide and leave the answer in lowest terms.

2-125. $\frac{6}{7} \div 3$ **2-126.** $\frac{15}{17} \div 5$ **2-127.** $4 \div \frac{3}{8}$

2-128. $24 \div \frac{12}{35}$ **2-129.** $4 \div 3\frac{1}{2}$ **2-130.** $17 \div 2\frac{1}{3}$

2-131. $2\frac{7}{9} \div 3$ **2-132.** $13\frac{2}{3} \div 7$ **2-133.** $\frac{3}{7} \div \frac{4}{5}$

2-134. $\frac{9}{11} \div \frac{15}{33}$ **2-135.** $\frac{12}{25} \div \frac{8}{15}$ **2-136.** $\frac{49}{240} \div \frac{14}{30}$

2-137. $7\frac{1}{2} \div 5\frac{1}{4}$ **2-138.** $5\frac{2}{3} \div 4\frac{1}{7}$ **2-139.** $26\frac{4}{7} \div 3\frac{5}{6}$

2-140. $17\frac{2}{3} \div 34\frac{3}{4}$

2-141. $\dfrac{8}{\frac{2}{3}}$

2-142. $\dfrac{17}{\frac{3}{4}}$

2-143. $\dfrac{\frac{11}{12}}{2}$

2-144. $\dfrac{\frac{16}{17}}{8}$

2-145. $\dfrac{\frac{7}{8}}{\frac{4}{3}}$

2-146. $\dfrac{\frac{15}{64}}{\frac{45}{8}}$

2-147. $\dfrac{\frac{27}{32}}{2\frac{1}{4}}$

2-148. $\dfrac{\frac{25}{2}}{2\frac{2}{3}}$

2-149. $\dfrac{12\frac{1}{4}}{\frac{7}{30}}$

2-150. $\dfrac{13\frac{4}{5}}{\frac{9}{20}}$

2-151. $\dfrac{7\frac{5}{12}}{3\frac{5}{8}}$

2-152. $\dfrac{1\frac{5}{23}}{1\frac{5}{64}}$

2-153. $\dfrac{8}{3} \times \dfrac{15}{14} \div \dfrac{4}{7}$

2-154. $\dfrac{8}{3} \div \dfrac{15}{14} \times \dfrac{4}{7}$

2-155. $\dfrac{8}{3} \div \dfrac{4}{7} \times \dfrac{15}{4}$

2-156. $\dfrac{8}{3} \times \dfrac{4}{7} \div \dfrac{15}{4}$

2-157. $\dfrac{\frac{2}{3} \div \frac{3}{4}}{\frac{4}{5} \div \frac{5}{6}}$

2-158. $\dfrac{\frac{16}{21} \div \frac{2}{7}}{\frac{3}{5} \div \frac{12}{35}}$

2-159. $\dfrac{\frac{2}{3} + \frac{3}{4}}{\frac{4}{5} + \frac{5}{6}}$

2-160. $\dfrac{\frac{8}{15} + \frac{1}{3}}{\frac{11}{12} - \frac{3}{4}}$

2-161. A barrel holds $31\frac{1}{2}$ gal. How many barrels of oil are contained in an oil tanker that holds 34,000 gal?

2-162. In building a brick wall it was found that the average height of the brick and mortar was $2\frac{7}{8}$ in. How many layers of brick and mortar will be required to build a brick wall $7\frac{2}{3}$ ft high?

2-163. It is desired to cut from a 24- by 45-in. sheet of aluminum smaller rectangular pieces whose dimensions are $2\frac{2}{3}$ by $3\frac{3}{4}$ in. How many pieces can be cut from the sheet?

2-164. How many pieces of aluminum whose dimensions are $2\frac{3}{4} \times 3\frac{2}{3}$ in. can be cut from the sheet of Prob. 39? How much waste material will be left over?

2-165. A boy buys pencils at 3 for 10 cents. How many must he sell at 5 for 20 cents in order to make a profit of $1?

CHAPTER 3

Decimal Fractions

3-1 Extension of the Number System. Decimals. We have discussed the structure of our number system which uses only 10 different symbols. The real significance of the system lies in the place-value concept. Each digit has not only its own value but also a place value, depending upon its position in the sequence of symbols which represent the number. For example, the number 3,184 means $3(1,000) + 1(100) + 8(10) + 4(1)$. Thus the 3 represents three thousands, the 1 represents one hundred, the 8 represents eight tens, and the 4 represents four units. The set of such numbers is called the *decimal system* because 10 symbols are used to represent all numbers.

It is interesting to note that until 400 years ago the system allowed only for an unlimited number of digits to the left of the units digit but stopped with the units digit on the right. Not until the sixteenth century is there any record of attempts to extend the system with digits to the right of the unit digit. Credit for such an extension of the system is usually given to the Belgian mathematician Simon Stevin. Stevin published his ideas in 1585. He reasoned that, if each place in the number system has a value ten times the value of the next place to the right, then, conversely, each place must have a value one-tenth the next place to the left. When the place-value concept was extended to the right of the units place, the usefulness of our system was greatly increased.

With the extension of the number system it became necessary

to find some means of determining the value of each digit in a given number. This was done by using a symbol as a separatrix between the unit and a part of the unit. Various symbols have been used. We are most familiar with the dot (.) placed immediately to the right of the units digit.

Many European countries, e.g., Germany, France, Italy, Belgium, and the Scandinavian countries, use a comma as the separatrix. In England a dot is used, but it is placed in the middle of the line of writing. Thus π is approximated in England as 3 · 1416.

In England our decimal point is used to stand for multiplication. Thus, in England 3 . 1416 = 3 × 1416.

In the Scandinavian countries it is customary to print the fractional part in smaller print than the integral part. In America we often write \$86^{25} for \$86.25 to lessen the chance of forgery by altering the position of the decimal point.

3-2 Reading and Writing Decimal Fractions. While the decimal separates the fractional part from the integral part of a number, the value of a digit in a given number is determined by the number of spaces it is to the left or right of the unit place. Figure 3-1 illustrates the relationship between the corresponding values of digits on opposite sides of the units digit. The tens

Ten thousands	Thousands	Hundreds	Tens	Units		Tenths	Hundredths	Thousandths	Ten-thousandths	Hundred-thousandths
2	6	8	3	4	.	1	7	9	3	8

Fig 3-1

place is one place to the left of the units place, the tenths place is one place to the right of the units place, and so on.

It should be clear that such a number as 35.486 represents
3 tens + 5 units + 4 tenths + 8 hundredths + 6 thousandths.

$$35.486 = 3(10) + 5(1) + 4(\tfrac{1}{10}) + 8(\tfrac{1}{100}) + 6(\tfrac{1}{1,000})$$
$$= 35 + \tfrac{4}{10} + \tfrac{8}{100} + \tfrac{6}{1,000}$$
$$= 35 + \tfrac{400}{1,000} + \tfrac{80}{1,000} + \tfrac{6}{1,000}$$
$$= 35\tfrac{486}{1,000}$$

A fraction whose denominator is a multiple of 10 is called a
decimal fraction. A decimal fraction containing no whole part,
such as 0.125, is called a *pure decimal*. It is always good practice
to place a zero in the units place when writing a pure decimal.
This aids in reading the number and in preventing the decimal's
being overlooked.

A decimal fraction that contains a whole-number part, such as
28.35, is a *mixed decimal*. A whole number, such as 749, is
understood to have a decimal point to the right of the units place
(i.e., 749.).

In reading mixed decimal fractions, we read the whole-number
part as usual and the decimal part as if it were a whole number
and attach to it the place value of the last digit on the right.
The word "and" is used only for the decimal point.

EXAMPLES

1. 53.94 is read "fifty-three *and* ninety-four hundredths."

2. 2065.378 is read "two thousand, sixty-five *and* three
hundred seventy-eight thousandths."

3. 84.006 is read "eighty-four *and* six thousandths."

4. 0.000573 is read "five hundred seventy-three millionths."
Note that the word "and" is omitted in reading pure fractions.

5. 0.700 is read "seven hundred thousandths." 0.00007 is
read "seven hundred-thousandths."
Note the use of the hyphen in distinguishing the two numbers.

3-3 Exact and Approximate Numbers. In computing,
one must distinguish between an exact and an approximate

number. *Counting numbers are exact;* that is, a one-to-one correspondence is set up between the objects that are counted and the numbers used in counting them. If the number of students in a class were counted to be 32, the number would be an exact number. When we say that a book contains 386 pages, we mean exactly 386—no more and no less. We know we are dealing with exact numbers when we say that 250 dimes are equivalent in value to 25 dollars.

In measuring, one uses numbers in a different way from in counting. Suppose we are asked to measure the sides of a room. If one uses a foot rule graduated into hundredths of a foot, he might obtain, for example, the following measurements: 40.37, 25.13, 40.36, and 25.12 ft. These numbers would not be exact but would be *approximate.* Each dimension is found to *the nearest hundredth of a foot.* In this instance we would know that the actual first dimension would not differ from the measured value by more than $\frac{1}{2}$ of 0.01 ft. This number is often written 40.37 ± 0.005 ft to show that 0.005 ft is the greatest *possible* error in measurement.

All numbers which are measurements are approximate numbers. Numbers other than measurements are also approximations. For example, we often use 3.1416 as the approximate value for π, the ratio of the circumference of a circle to its diameter. Again, we might use 1.414 as the approximate value for $\sqrt{2}$.

In using a number such as 57,000 it is not clear if this number is accurate to the thousands, hundreds, tens, or units. Thus, when we state that the distance from the earth to the sun is 93,000,000 miles, the degree of accuracy in this measurement is not clear. It might be off by $\frac{1}{2}(1,000,000)$ miles, $\frac{1}{2}(10,000)$ miles, $\frac{1}{2}$ mile, and so on. When the degree of accuracy is critical, a *scientific notation* form is used. Thus, 9.3×10^7 miles would mean that the number is accurate to two *significant figures,* i.e., to the nearest 0.1×10^7 or 1,000,000 miles; 9.300×10^7 miles would mean that the number is accurate to the nearest 0.001×10^7 or 10,000 miles. In this book we shall assume that a number such as 93,000,000 will imply accuracy to the nearest 1,000,000, 37,400 will imply accuracy to the nearest 100, and so on.

It should be clear that the size of a number has nothing to do with the accuracy of that number. Thus, while 8,634,000 is a million million times as large as 0.0008634, they both have the same degree of accuracy. Each is accurate to four significant figures, or stated another way, each is accurate to one part in 8,634.

3-4 Zero and Significant Figures. It is important in solving problems to consider the accuracy of data and the consequent accuracy of solutions derived from such data. The accuracy of a computational solution can be no greater than the data from which it is derived. One method of indicating degrees of accuracy is the use of significant figures or significant digits as shown in the previous examples.

It is important to understand what is the meaning of significant figures. Let us give examples from which we can deduce certain rules concerning significant figures.

EXAMPLES

63,000 is (usually) correct to *two* significant digits.

0.0063 is correct to *two* significant digits.

6.3×10^4 is correct to *two* significant digits.

5.8715 is correct to *five* significant digits.

587.15 is correct to *five* significant digits.

6040 is correct to *three* significant digits.

0.6040 is correct to *four* significant digits.

60.40 is correct to *four* significant digits.

0.00006040 is correct to *four* significant digits.

We can summarize the notion of significant figures by the following:

1. Non-zero digits are always significant.
2. Zeros at the end of a whole number may or may not be

significant. Usually they serve only as place holders and are not significant.

3. Zeros at the beginning of a pure decimal are not significant but serve only as place holders.

4. Zeros between non-zero digits are significant.

5. Zeros occurring at the end of a decimal fraction are significant.

3-5 Rounding Numbers. Solutions to problems frequently are carried to more significant figures than the data from which they are derived. This practice not only is a waste of both time and energy but also is not justifiable in terms of its implied accuracy. Thus, for example, if we were asked to find the area of a circle whose radius was measured to be 8.4 ft, we would be inaccurate in solving the problem thus: $A = \pi R^2 = 3.1416 (8.4 \text{ ft})^2 = 221.671296$ ft. If the original data are given to two significant figures, the answer can be expected to be accurate to only two significant figures. Our computed area would be more realistic if it were determined to be 200 ft^2.

Much time can be saved, without loss of accuracy, by *rounding off* numbers. A number is rounded off by dropping one or more digits at its right end. The digits are replaced by zeros when it is necessary in order to keep the decimal point in its proper place.

Consider the following examples of rounded numbers:

Examples

3.14159 rounded to five digits is 3.1416.
3.14159 rounded to three digits is 3.14.
6.15 rounded to two digits is 6.2.
6.25 rounded to two digits is 6.2.
6.35 rounded to two digits is 6.4.
6.37482 rounded to three digits is 6.37.
6.37582 rounded to three digits is 6.38.

The method for rounding numbers can be given by the following rules.

1. If the digit to be dropped is less than 5, no change is made in the part retained.

2. If the digit to be dropped is more than 5, the digit on its immediate left is increased by 1.

3. If the digit to be dropped is 5 and is also the last significant digit of the number, round the number so its rightmost digit will be an even digit. If the digit to the left of the one to be dropped is already even, make no change to that digit; if it is odd, raise the digit to its left to the next even digit.

4. If several digits are dropped from a number and the left-hand digit of these digits is less than 5, the digit on the left of the dropped digits should not be changed. If the left-hand digit of those to be dropped is 5 or larger, the digit to the left of the dropped digits should be increased by 1.

It should be apparent that, in rounding off any set of decimals of type 3 above, in about half of the numbers the digits to the left of the dropped digit will be *decreased* to an even number while the remaining half will be *increased* to an even number. This is done to avoid a cumulative increase (or decrease) in a series of rounding off of numbers in a given problem solution.

PROBLEMS

3-1. Write in decimal form:

    (*a*) Six hundred forty-two thousandths.

    (*b*) Fourteen and one hundred eight thousandths.

    (*c*) Eighteen and four thousandths.

    (*d*) Fifty-six thousandths.

    (*e*) Eighty-seven and six hundred five ten-thousandths.

    (*f*) Two thousand two and two hundred thousandths.

    (*g*) $8\frac{3}{10}$

    (*h*) $47\frac{13}{1000}$

    (*i*) $\frac{7}{10} + \frac{3}{100}$

(j) $\frac{9}{10} + \frac{4}{100} + \frac{5}{1,000} + \frac{1}{10,000}$

(k) $4 + \frac{8}{10} + \frac{3}{1,000} + \frac{9}{10,000}$

3-2. Write in words:

  (a) 0.385
  (b) 0.207
  (c) 0.00436
  (d) 0.68
  (e) 0.1738
  (f) 42.027
  (g) 4,500.0017
  (h) 298,060.0304

3-3. Arrange the following set of numbers according to size, from the largest to the smallest: 0.01083, 0.1083, 1.083, 1.803, 0.01803, 0.10380, 0.0108, 1.08.

3-4. In the following, tell which numbers are exact and which are approximate:

  (a) Water freezes at 32°F.
  (b) Tom is 6 ft 3 in. tall.
  (c) Mrs. Jones purchased a dozen eggs and 3 lb of beans.
  (d) The moon is 240,000 miles from the earth.
  (e) Atmospheric pressure at sea level is 14.7 lb/in.^{2}
  (f) There are 1,728 in.^{3} in a cubic foot.
  (g) Iron will melt at 1535°C.
  (h) Dry air by volume is 12% oxygen.
  (i) Bill ran the 100-yd dash in 9.4 seconds (sec).
  (j) $\sqrt{5} = 2.236$.
  (k) Three cans of coffee cost $2.49.
  (l) The 25 acres of land in 1963 cost $75,000.

3-5. In each of the following pairs of numbers indicate which, if any, has the greater degree of accuracy:

  (a) 27,300, 20,370
  (b) 3,620, 0.362

    (*c*) 0.001053, 5,027

    (*d*) 92,350, 0.0004118

    (*e*) 20,063, 4.15 × 10³

    (*f*) 8007, 23.59

3-6. Between what two numbers do each of the following measurements lie? (NOTE: 3.57 lies between 3.565 and 3.575).

    (*a*) 87.24 ft

    (*b*) 0.309 in.

    (*c*) 12.4 yd

    (*d*) 85,000 gal

    (*e*) 0.0001037 centimeter (cm)

3-7. Round off the following numbers to the nearest hundredths, the nearest tenths, and the nearest thousandths:

    (*a*) 0.28634

    (*b*) 3.1416

    (*c*) 1.0732

    (*d*) 8.55555

    (*e*) 27,8350

    (*f*) 0.9005

3-8. Round off the following to the indicated accuracy:

    (*a*) 87,176   to the nearest hundred

    (*b*) 4,645 ft   to the nearest 10 ft

    (*c*) 20,390 bottles   to the nearest 1,000 bottles

    (*d*) 3,015 trees   to the nearest 10 trees

    (*e*) 99,291   to the nearest 100 gal

    (*f*) 183,279,000 people   to the nearest million people

3-6 Changing a Common Fraction to a Decimal Fraction. To convert a common fraction to an equivalent decimal fraction we need merely to divide the numerator by the denominator. To obtain the answer to the desired significant digits may require placing a decimal after the dividend and adding more zeros. For example, to change $\frac{4}{7}$ to a decimal fraction accurate to ten-thousandths, we divide as follows:

$$
\begin{array}{r}
0\;.\;5\,7\,1\,4^{\,+} \\
7\,\overline{)\,4\;.\;0\,0\,0\,0} \\
3\,5\,5 \\ \hline
5\,0 \\
4\,9 \\ \hline
1\,0 \\
7 \\ \hline
3\,0 \\
2\,8 \\ \hline
2
\end{array}
$$

Thus $\frac{4}{7} = 0.5714^{+}$. The $+$ is sometimes used to indicate that the answer is a little more than 0.5714. The number 0.3827^{-} would indicate a number closer to 0.3827 than to either 0.3826 or 0.3828 but less than 0.3827.

3-7   Changing a Decimal Fraction to a Common Fraction.   Occasionally it becomes necessary to change a decimal fraction to an equivalent common fraction. If we know how to read decimal fractions, we should have little trouble writing the equivalent common fractions.

EXAMPLES

1. 0.0384 is read "three hundred eighty-four ten thousandths."
   Hence $0.0384 = \frac{384}{10,000} = \frac{24}{625}$.
2. 13.275 is read "13 and 275 thousandths."
   Hence $13.275 = 13 + \frac{275}{10,00} = 13 + \frac{11}{40} = \frac{531}{40}$.

3-8   Addition and Subtraction of Decimal Fractions. We have observed that only items of the same kind can be added or subtracted. So it is in adding decimal fractions we can add only tenths to tenths, hundredths to hundredths, and so on. This should pose no problem in adding decimal fractions if we arrange the numbers in columns with corresponding decimal places in the same column.

EXAMPLE 3-1. Find the sum of 11.384, 5.06, 0.8, 4.107.

Solution

$$
\begin{array}{rcr}
1\,1\,.\,3\,8\,4 & & 1\,1\,.\,3\,8\,4 \\
5\,.\,0\,6 & & 5\,.\,0\,6\,0 \\
0\,.\,8 & \text{or} & 0\,.\,8\,0\,0 \\
4\,.\,1\,0\,7 & & 4\,.\,1\,0\,7 \\
\hline
2\,1\,.\,3\,5\,1 & & 2\,1\,.\,3\,5\,1
\end{array}
$$

Some people prefer to add the zeros, as in the second example, as an aid in keeping their columns straight. Subtraction of decimals is performed in like manner.

It should be apparent that the addition of decimal fractions is often considerably easier than the addition of equivalent common fractions. The same problem above expressed in common fractions would be:

$$\text{Add } 11\tfrac{49}{125} + 5\tfrac{3}{50} + \tfrac{4}{5} + 4\tfrac{107}{1,000}$$

PROBLEMS

Change the following to decimal fractions (accurate to four decimal places):

3-9. $\frac{3}{4}$	**3-10.** $\frac{3}{20}$	**3-11.** $\frac{5}{8}$	**3-12.** $\frac{7}{16}$
3-13. $\frac{9}{32}$	**3-14.** $\frac{13}{20}$	**3-15.** $\frac{35}{64}$	**3-16.** $\frac{57}{75}$
3-17. $\frac{4}{9}$	**3-18.** $\frac{9}{40}$	**3-19.** $\frac{3}{11}$	**3-20.** $\frac{19}{7}$

Convert to common fractions (reduce to lowest terms):

3-21. 0.375	**3-22.** 0.14	**3-23.** 4.125	**3-24.** 0.0625
3-25. 0.128	**3-26.** 0.6875	**3-27.** 0.71875	**3-28.** 0.96875
3-29. 8.4375	**3-30.** 3.5625		

Add each of the following sets of numbers:

3-31. 6.8, 0.354, 2.76, 8.08, 1.001
3-32. 3.76, 0.461, 2.46, 40.03, 12.5
3-33. 8.003, 250.01, 24.61, 8.703, 181.3

3-34. 6.01, 8.333, 2.0729, 0.0424, 3.8
3-35. 10.02, 2.112, 0.3224, 0.0433, 0.0054

Subtract:

3-36. 8.374 from 12.019
3-37. 283.0417 from 318.295
3-38. 824 − 0.307

Combine each set to a single term:

3-39. 18.07 + 2.534 − 7.006 − 3.1
3-40. 0.00394 + 2.51 + 0.509 − 2.5704
3-41. 13 − 0.03 + 5.1 − 8.201
3-42. 283.45 − 50.505 − 110.9 + 3.7921
3-43. 0.63 + 8.471 − 27.8 − 0.059 + 34.038

3-9 Multiplication of Decimal Fractions. We can arrive at the rule for multiplying decimal fractions inductively by considering some sample problems. Consider the problem of finding the product 3.4×2.76. We might write $3.4 \times 2.76 = \frac{34}{10} \times \frac{276}{100} = \frac{9,384}{1,000} = 9.384$. In like manner, $0.28 \times 0.319 = \frac{28}{100} \times \frac{319}{1,000} = \frac{8932}{100,000} = 0.08932$. Note that the number of zeros in the denominator of the product of the common fractions is equal to the sum of the zeros in the denominators of the factors. Hence, to find the product of two decimal fractions, multiply the numbers together as though they were whole numbers and then put the decimal point as many places from the right in the answer as the sum of the number of decimal places in the factors.

Our problems can, then, be solved as

$$
\begin{array}{r}
2\,.\,7\,6 \\
3\,.\,4 \\
\hline
1\,1\,0\,4 \\
8\,2\,8 \\
\hline
9.3\,8\,4
\end{array}
\qquad
\begin{array}{r}
0\,.\,3\,1\,9 \\
0\,.\,2\,8 \\
\hline
2\,5\,5\,2 \\
6\,3\,8 \\
\hline
0\,.\,0\,8\,9\,3\,2
\end{array}
$$

3-10 Division of Decimal Fractions. To divide a decimal by a decimal we first apply the fundamental principle of fractions to reduce the problem to the quotient of two integers.   Let us illustrate with an example.

$$81.357 \div 0.26 = \frac{81.357}{0.26} = \frac{8135.7}{26} = 312.9^+$$

It will be noted that the dividend and divisor (numerator and denominator) were each multiplied by 100.   This resulted in moving the decimal point the same number of places to the right in both the dividend and the divisor.   The symbol $\wedge$, called a caret, is often used to indicate the new locations of the decimals in the division.   The solution form appears below,

```
              3 1 2 . 9                        0 . 1 5 3
    0 . 2 6 | 8 1 . 3 5 7          4 1 . 5 | 6 . 3 8 2 9
           ∧           ∧                 ∧     ∧
          7 8                           4   1 5
          ─────                         ─────────
          3  3                          2   2 3 2
          2  6                          2   0 7 5
          ─────                         ─────────
             7 5                          1 5 7 9
             5 2                          1 2 4 5
            ─────                        ─────────
            2 3 7                          3 3 4
            2 3 4
            ─────
              3
```

Frequently the quotient of two decimal fractions cannot be expressed as a simple decimal fraction without a remainder.   In practice it is customary to carry the division out to the desired number of significant digits.   Then, if the remainder is less than half the divisor, it is dropped, but if the remainder is greater than half the divisor, the quotient is increased by one digit in the last place of the quotient.

EXAMPLE 3-2.   Divide 0.083 by 2.46, and round off the quotient to the nearest thousandth.

Solution

$$
\begin{array}{r}
0.0337 \\
2.46\overline{)0.083000} \\
738 \\
\hline
920 \\
738 \\
\hline
1820 \\
1722 \\
\hline
\end{array}
$$

Rounding off to the nearest thousandth, the quotient is 0.034.

PROBLEMS

Multiply the following:

3-44. 0.375×10

3-45. 12.354×100

3-46. $4.962 \times 1,000$

3-47. $1.00504 \times 10,000$

3-48. 37.8×25.4

3-49. 6.007×2.12

3-50. 803.2×1.014

3-51. 49.15×0.03426

3-52. 246.1358×0.00555

3-53. 30.303×0.030303

3-54. $(0.305)(0.21)(8.37)$

3-55. $(2.76)(0.345)(0.0108)$

Divide the following:

3-56. $0.07\overline{)0.83}$ to the nearest hundredth

3-57. $0.35\overline{)0.0264}$ to the nearest thousandth

3-58. $0.26\overline{)87}$ to the nearest hundred

3-59. $9.03\overline{)4.53921}$ to the nearest hundredth

3-60. $2.234\overline{)891.273941}$ to the nearest thousandth

3-61. $70.05\overline{)6235.2909}$ to the nearest thousandth

3-62. $0.0136\overline{)0.000059}$ to the nearest thousandth

3-63. $0.00237\overline{)5.218499}$ to the nearest thousand

3-64. A shaft should have a diameter of $1\frac{5}{8}$ in. It was measured to be 1.704 in. How much too large was it?

3-65. What is the area of the figure?

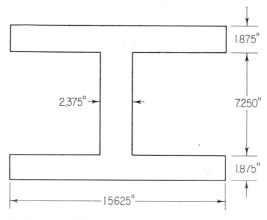

Problem 3-65

3-66. A dealer buys 640 gal of paint for $4.86 per gallon and sells it for $1.75 per quart. How much is his profit?

3-11 Computation with Approximate Data. The result of any computation which uses one or more approximate numbers must likewise be an approximate number. The accuracy of the computed number will depend upon the accuracy of each number involved in the calculation. The result will be no more accurate than the least accurate number used in the calculations.

In computing with approximate numbers one must also consider the purpose of the answer to the computation. Thus, if one were interested in calculating the volume of a silo for storing corn, he would be foolish to measure the diameter and height of the silo accurate to 0.001 in. On the other hand, many precision pieces of equipment must be measured to tolerances of 0.00001 in. However, most technical calculations involve measured data with degrees of accuracy that can be handled with a good 10-in. slide rule. In calculating with approximate numbers it is well to eliminate all calculations which do not affect the final result.

3-12 Addition and Subtraction of Approximate Numbers. Before we give a rule for adding and subtracting approximate numbers, let us consider the problem of adding the approximate numbers 2.354, 1.08, and 5.7. Let us tabulate the least possible values, the greatest possible values of the numbers and their sums and then the computed sum of the numbers, as follows:

Least possible value	Greatest possible value	Measured value
2 . 3 5 3 5	2 . 3 5 4 5	2 . 3 5 4
1 . 0 7 5	1 . 0 8 5	1 . 0 8
5 . 6 5	5 . 7 5	5 . 7
9 . 0 7 8 5	9 . 1 8 9 5	9 . 1 3 4

It will be noted that our sum could range from 9.0785 to 9.1895. Each of the three answers has the same value only when rounded off to two places (or fewer). Thus, we can be certain that our answer is accurate to only two places. Hence, our answer should be 9.1.

Let us next carry through the addition of the same numbers taken to one more place accuracy than the least accurate of the original numbers.

$$\begin{array}{r} 2.35 \\ 1.08 \\ \underline{5.7} \\ 9.13 \end{array}$$

Again our total will be 9.1 accurate to two places. Our working rule then will be:

▶ *Rule.* In adding or subtracting approximate numbers
1. Round off each number to one more place than the least accurate of the given numbers.
2. Round off the sum or difference of these numbers to the same number of places as the term having the least accuracy.

EXAMPLE 3-3.   Add 75.3592, 254.08, 30.291, 8.6.

Solution

$$
\begin{array}{r}
75.36 \\
254.08 \\
30.29 \\
8.6 \\
\hline
368.33
\end{array}
$$

The answer should be 368.3.

EXAMPLE 3-4. Subtract: 28.56 − 13.4072.

Solution

$$
\begin{array}{r}
28.56 \\
13.407 \\
\hline
15.153
\end{array}
$$

The answer should be 15.15.

3-13 Multiplication and Division of Approximate Numbers. Suppose the floor area of a room is to be computed from its measured dimensions of 24.7 and 15.8 ft. Considering the range of values possible for the dimensions of the room, we compute

1. The smallest possible area = 24.65 ft $\times$ 15.75 ft = 388.2375 ft².

2. The largest possible area = 24.75 ft $\times$ 15.85 ft = 392.2875 ft².

3. The computed area = 24.7 ft $\times$ 15.8 ft = 390.26 ft².

It should be clear that we can be certain that the area must lie between 388.2375 and 392.2875 ft². The three areas do not have the same whole-number part, much less the same decimal part. However, the value 3.90×10^2 is about in the middle of the range of possible values. It also has the same number of significant figures as does each measured dimension.

▶ *Rule.* To find the product or quotient of two approximate numbers

1. Round off each number to not more than one more significant place than the least accurate of the numbers.

2. Round off the product or quotient to the same number of significant digits contained in the least accurate of the numbers used.

PROBLEMS

In Probs. 3-67 to 3-74 determine the least possible and the greatest possible values for the answer. Then give the most reasonable answer.

3-67. Add 4.15, 8.762, 0.03, 1.2.
3-68. Add 0.0043, 0.105, 0.82, 0.059.
3-69. Subtract 87.05 − 23.147.
3-70. Subtract 0.09253 − 0.0416.
3-71. Multiply 2.7 × 5.4.
3-72. Multiply 1.53 × 2.64.
3-73. Divide 8.9 by 5.1.
3-74. Divide 27.6 by 3.04.

In Probs. 3-75 to 3-87 all numbers are approximate (unless stated otherwise). Using the working rules for computations with approximate numbers, perform the indicated operations.

3-75. Add 215.3 + 3.086 + 7.21 + 89.
3-76. Add 10.503 + 2.43 + 8.0769 + 33.76.
3-77. Add 649.11 + 22.212 + 98 + 76.3.
3-78. Add $2.34 \times 10^3 + 1.659 \times 10^2 + 5.69 \times 10^2$.
3-79. Subtract 8.7 − 0.24921.
3-80. Subtract 63.452 − 0.089092.
3-81. Subtract $(2.47 \times 10^6) − (8.36 \times 10^5)$.
3-82. Multiply 314.6 × 2.7.
3-83. Multiply 0.039254 × 5.61.
3-84. Multiply 0.351762 × 82 (consider 82 is an exact number).
3-85. Divide 25.3 by 6.47.
3-86. Divide 3749.62 by 268.53.
3-87. Divide 803.4 by 56 (consider 56 as an exact number).

CHAPTER 4

Percent

4-1 The Meaning of Percent. In our study thus far we have learned that fractions such as $\frac{67}{100}$ and 0.67 are two ways of expressing the same thing. They mean, in this instance, 67 parts out of 100 equal parts or 67 out of a group of 100. We shall now study a third way, called percent, of writing the same thing.

The term *percent* comes from the Latin *per centum,* meaning "by the hundred." Thus, 67 percent means 67 out of each hundred. The symbol % stands for the word "percent." Any fraction having 100 as a denominator is a percent, whether it is written as a common fraction, as a decimal fraction, or with the percent sign. It is interesting to note that the symbol % contains two zeros. One might consider the zeros to stand for the zeros in 100.

The word percent can be used for any fraction having 100 as a denominator, including improper fractions, such as 325 percent, 1,200 percent, and so on.

The arithmetic dealing with percent is sometimes called *percentage.* However, the terms *percentage* and *percent* are often used interchangeably. Percentages are used extensively in many walks of life. Local, county, state, and Federal taxes are collected on a percentage basis. Percentage increase or decrease is used in expressing death rates, birth rates, population trends, school enrollments, assessed valuations, costs of living, sales records, employment and unemployment conditions, and so on.

Perhaps one of the greatest advantages of using percents in

preference to common and decimal of fractions is the ease of comparing sizes of things expressed as percents. Common fractions cannot be compared for size unless they have been converted to equivalent fractions with a common denominator. Percents always have the same denominator. For example, if you were given a choice between investing in Company A which will return a profit of $\frac{16}{25}$ of your investment each year and Company B which will return $\frac{13}{20}$ of your investment each year, you probably would have to think twice before deciding which will give you the greater profit. On the other hand, if you were told that Company A will return 64 percent and Company B will return 65 percent of your investment each year, your decision would be easy.

The classroom teacher often converts test scores to percents because of the ease of comparing the scores.

A glance at the circular graph of Fig. 4-1 and the percentages

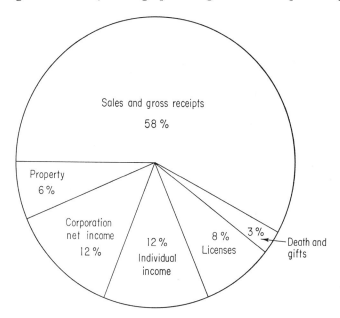

Fig. 4-1

given provides a ready means of comparison of the major sources of tax collections in the state of California in 1961.

4-2 Changing Percents to Decimal Fractions. The advantage of the use of percent lies in the simple way it can be used to describe situations which occur often enough to be common. However, any computations with percent involve first changing the percent to a common fraction or to a decimal fraction. Therefore, it is essential to know how to determine these equivalences.

Since percent is simply a kind of fraction, we need only apply what we have already learned about fractions to make our conversions. We have already considered converting common fractions to decimal fractions and vice versa.

From the definition of percent, we know that

$$7 \text{ percent} = \tfrac{7}{100} = 0.07$$

or that $62\frac{1}{2}$ percent $= \dfrac{62\frac{1}{2}}{100} = \dfrac{125}{200} = 0.62\frac{1}{2}$ or 0.625.

▶ *Rule.* To reduce a percent to a decimal fraction

1. Rewrite the given number, omitting the % sign.
2. Move the decimal point two places to the left.

EXAMPLES

$$6\% = 0.06$$
$$75\% = 0.75$$
$$140\% = 1.40$$
$$5.6\% = 0.056$$
$$13\tfrac{3}{4}\% = 0.13\tfrac{3}{4} = 0.1375$$
$$\tfrac{3}{4}\% = 0.00\tfrac{3}{4} = 0.0075$$

4-3 Changing a Decimal Fraction to a Percent. To change a decimal fraction to an equivalent percent we need only to reverse the procedure of the last paragraph.

▶ *Rule.* To reduce a decimal fraction to a percent

1. Copy the given number.
2. Move the decimal point two places to the right.
3. Annex the percent sign, %.

EXAMPLES

$$0.09 = 9\%$$
$$0.375 = 37.5\%$$
$$5.70 = 570\%$$
$$234.27 = 23{,}427\%$$

4-4 Changing a Percent to a Common Fraction. If the student will remember that the word "percent" means hundredths, he should have no difficulty in accepting the following rule.

▶ *Rule.* To change a percent to a common fraction

1. Make a fraction by writing the given number as the numerator and the number 100 as the denominator.
2. Reduce to lowest terms.

EXAMPLES

$$3\% = \tfrac{3}{100}$$
$$42\% = \tfrac{42}{100} = \tfrac{21}{50}$$
$$5\tfrac{1}{2}\% = \frac{5\tfrac{1}{2}}{100} = \frac{11}{200}$$
$$62.5\% = \tfrac{62.5}{100} = \tfrac{625}{1000} = \tfrac{5}{8}$$
$$750\% = \tfrac{750}{100} = \tfrac{15}{2}$$

4-5 Changing a Common Fraction to a Percent. Since we know how to change a common fraction to a decimal fraction and a decimal fraction to a percent, we can combine the two processes to get the following rule.

▶ *Rule.* To change a common fraction to a percent

1. Change the common fraction to decimal by dividing the numerator by the denominator, finding the quotient to two decimal places.
2. Rewrite the quotient, omitting the decimal point.
3. Annex the percent sign, %.

EXAMPLES

$$\frac{2}{5} = 0.40 = 40\%$$
$$\frac{7}{8} = 0.87\frac{1}{2} = 87\frac{1}{2}\%$$
$$\frac{18}{25} = 0.72 = 72\%$$
$$\frac{37}{4} = 9.25 = 925\%$$
$$5\frac{1}{3} = 5.33\frac{1}{3} = 533\frac{1}{3}\%$$

PROBLEMS

Change each from a percent to a decimal fraction:

4-1. 11%	**4-2.** 60%	**4-3.** 8.4%	**4-4.** 135%
4-5. $137\frac{1}{2}\%$	**4-6.** $87\frac{1}{2}\%$	**4-7.** $\frac{1}{4}\%$	**4-8.** 52.13%
4-9. 0.4%	**4-10.** 0.04%	**4-11.** 0.007%	**4-12.** $\frac{9}{16}\%$
4-13. 374.5%	**4-14.** $0.5\frac{3}{4}\%$	**4-15.** $0.06\frac{1}{4}\%$	

Change each to a percent:

4-16. 0.08	**4-17.** 0.009	**4-18.** $0.83\frac{1}{3}$	**4-19.** $0.2\frac{1}{2}$
4-20. 3	**4-21.** 0.0004	**4-22.** 0.235	**4-23.** 7.6
4-24. $0.6\frac{1}{4}$	**4-25.** 12	**4-26.** 0.3079	**4-27.** $0.08004\frac{1}{2}$
4-28. $1\frac{3}{8}$	**4-29.** 283	**4-30.** 72.9	**4-31.** $\frac{7}{12}$
4-32. $\frac{4}{5}$	**4-33.** $\frac{5}{16}$	**4-34.** $\frac{7}{32}$	**4-35.** $\frac{9}{64}$
4-36. $\frac{6}{7}$	**4-37.** $\frac{13}{20}$	**4-38.** $5\frac{3}{10}$	**4-39.** $7\frac{11}{12}$
4-40. $\frac{13}{1,000}$	**4-41.** $2\frac{5}{16}$	**4-42.** $\frac{74}{25}$	**4-43.** $\frac{89}{50}$
4-44. $\frac{33}{16}$	**4-45.** $\frac{185}{8}$		

Change to common fractions or mixed numbers:

4-46. 36%	**4-47.** 125%	**4-48.** 44%	**4-49.** 548%
4-50. 75%	**4-51.** 1,500%	**4-52.** $12\frac{1}{2}\%$	**4-53.** $87\frac{1}{2}\%$

4-54. $83\frac{1}{3}\%$ **4-55.** $41\frac{1}{4}\%$ **4-56.** $3\frac{2}{7}\%$ **4-57.** $47\frac{3}{4}\%$
4-58. $\frac{1}{5}\%$ **4-59.** $\frac{2}{3}\%$ **4-60.** $\frac{4}{9}\%$

4-6 Determining a Percent of a Number. There are three common types of problems involving percentage. The first can be illustrated by the question, "What is 25 percent of 60?" A fractional part of 60 is to be determined. The fraction has a denominator of 100. The answer to the question can be found as follows: 25 percent of $60 = \frac{25}{100} \times 60 = 15$.

▶ *Rule.* To determine a specified percent of a number

1. Change the percent to a decimal or common fraction.
2. Multiply the given number by this fraction.

In the example, 25 percent of $60 = 15$, the 25 percent is called the *rate*, the 60 is called the *base*, and the 15 is called the *percentage* of the problem. The problem, then can be expressed

$$\text{Rate} \times \text{base} = \text{percentage} \qquad (4\text{-}1)$$

If any two of the three quantities are known, the third can be calculated. By selecting different pairs of known values, the three types of percentage problems are obtained. The above gives values for the rate and the base and requests the percentage.

EXAMPLE 4-1.   Find $37\frac{1}{2}\%$ of $1,200.

Solution

$$37\frac{1}{2}\% \text{ of } \$1,200 =$$
$$0.375 \times \$1,200 = \$450$$

EXAMPLE 4-2.   Find $6\frac{1}{3}\%$ of 240.

Solution

$$6\frac{1}{3}\% \text{ of } 240 =$$
$$\frac{6\frac{1}{3}}{100} \times 240 =$$
$$\frac{19}{300} \times 240 = 15\frac{1}{5}$$

4-7 Determining the Percent One Number Is of Another. Frequently a question of the type "What percent of 75 is 15?" is asked. In this case the base and the percentage are known and the rate is to be determined. The relationship of these quantities can be written as a "multiplier statement": Rate × 75 = 15. Division is the converse of multiplication. Consequently the "multiplication statement" can be converted to an equivalent "division statement." Thus,

$$\text{rate} = \tfrac{15}{75} = \tfrac{1}{5} = 0.20 = 20 \text{ percent}$$

As a general statement, if rate × base = percentage, then

$$\text{Rate} = \frac{\text{percentage}}{\text{base}}$$

▶ *Rule.* To determine the percent one number is of another

1. Form a fraction with the percentage the numerator and the base the denominator.
2. Change the fraction to a percent.

EXAMPLE 4-3. 33 is what percent of 55?

Solution

$$\text{Percentage} = 33$$
$$\text{Base} = 5$$
$$\text{Rate} = \tfrac{33}{55} = \tfrac{3}{5} = 0.60 = 60\%$$

EXAMPLE 4-4. 11 is what percent of 40?

Solution

$$\text{Rate} = \tfrac{11}{40} = 0.275 = 27.5\%$$

4-8 Determining a Number When a Specified Percent Is Known. Consider the question, "Eight per cent of what number is 56?" In this case the percentage (56) and the rate

(8 percent) are known and the base is to be calculated.   Using the relationship among the three numbers, we get

$$8 \text{ percent} \times \text{base} = 56$$

If division is treated as the converse of multiplication, the base can be computed as follows: Base $= \dfrac{56}{8\%} = \dfrac{56}{0.08} = 700.$

$$\text{Base} = \frac{\text{percentage}}{\text{rate}}$$

▶ *Rule.*   To determine a number when a percent of it is known

1. Form a fraction with the percentage as numerator and rate as denominator.
2. Convert the rate to a decimal fraction or a common fraction.
3. Determine the quotient.

EXAMPLE 4-5.   50% of what number is 80?

Solution
$$\begin{aligned}
\text{Percentage} &= 80 \\
\text{Rate} &= 50\% \\
\text{Base} &= \frac{80}{50\%} = \frac{80}{0.50} = 160
\end{aligned}$$

EXAMPLE 4-6. $\frac{3}{16}\%$ of what number is 12?

Solution
$$\text{Base} = \frac{12}{\dfrac{\frac{3}{16}}{100}} = \frac{12}{\frac{3}{16} \times \frac{1}{100}} = \frac{12}{\frac{3}{1{,}600}}$$

$$= \frac{(12)(1{,}600)}{3} = 6{,}400$$

PROBLEMS

4-61. Determine 8% of 400.

4-62. Determine 72% of 25.

4-63. 20% of 48 is what number?

4-64. What number is 12% of 360?

4-65. 250% of \$1,800 is how much?

4-66. 60 is what percent of 150?

4-67. If 40% of 284 is N, what is N?

4-68. 36 is what percent of 48?

4-69. 15% of what number is 120?

4-70. What percent of 70 is 210?

4-71. 32 is what percent of 960?

4-72. Determine a number such that 40% of it is 14.

4-73. Determine a number such that 74% of it is 145.

4-74. Eighty-six and thirty-five hundredths is 45% of what number?

4-75. Two hundred sixty-four and three hundred eighty-seven thousandths is 25% of what number?

4-76. 18.4 is what percent of 368?

4-77. 13.2 is what percent of 6.6?

4-78. If $12\frac{1}{2}\%$ of a number is 108, what is the number?

4-79. If $37\frac{1}{2}\%$ of a number is 441, what is the number?

4-80. $137\frac{1}{2}\%$ of \$18.30 is how much?

4-81. 0.8% of 423,450 is how much?

4-82. 222 is $16\frac{1}{4}\%$ of what number?

4-83. $16\frac{2}{3}\%$ of what number is 72?

4-84. 54% of what number is 0.0345?

4-85. If $5\frac{3}{4}\%$ of a given number is 0.184, what is the number?

4-86. If $13\frac{3}{8}\%$ of a given number is 0.0928, what is the number?

4-87. \$168 is $33\frac{1}{3}\%$ of what cost?

4-88. $83\frac{1}{3}\%$ of 426 is how much?

4-89. If $37\frac{1}{2}\%$ of a number is 46, what is the number?

4-90. 960 is 125% of what number?

4-91. Determine 23.16% of 0.0392.

4-92. Determine a number such that 284% of it is 356.

4-93. $87\frac{1}{2}\%$ of what weight equals 13 lb?

4-94. What percent of a foot is an inch?

4-95. What percent of an inch is a foot?

4-96. Which is larger: 6% of 308 or 7% of 289? How much larger?

4-97. 4,500% of 15 is how much?

4-98. 262% of what number is 0.308?

4-99. What percent of 833 is 175?

4-9 Applications of Percent. Percents arise in numerous situations encountered in business, engineering, and technology. The use of percentage (or percent) is very common in newspapers and magazines. The radio and television media assume of listeners an understanding of percentage and similar commonly used mathematical concepts.

The greatest difficulty in solving problems in percentage seems to come from the inability to determine the "percent of what" of the situation. Several examples of the more common uses of percentages will now be given.

4-10 Sales Tax. Many cities and states levy a sales tax, which is based on a percent of the sales price.

EXAMPLE 4-7. The retail sales tax in California is 4%. Mr. Smith purchased a metal lathe, priced $535, and a three-jaw chuck, priced $52.50. What was the amount of the sales tax he had to pay to the state?

Solution

$$\text{Total sales} = \$535 + \$52.50$$
$$= \$587.50$$

Then

$$\text{Sales tax} = 4\% \text{ of } \$587.50$$
$$= 0.04 \times \$587.50$$
$$= \$23.50$$

4-11 Discount. The regular or full price of an article is called the *list price*. Sometimes articles are sold below the list price. For example, an article may be marked or priced at $75 but sold for $60. The difference between the list price and the *sales* or *net price* is called the *discount*. In this example the sale price is $60 and the discount is $15. The discount is often quoted as a percent of the list price and is called the *discount rate*. Thus, the discount rate in this situation would be $\frac{15}{75} = \frac{1}{5} = 20$ percent.

EXAMPLE 4-8. If a set of four tires originally priced at $132.80 is discounted 15% in a state where the sales tax rate is $3\frac{1}{2}\%$, what is the total cost of the four tires?

Solution A. The discount rate is based on the list price.

$$
\begin{aligned}
\text{Discount} &= 15\% \text{ of } \$132.80 \\
&= 0.15 \times \$132.80 \\
&= \$19.92 \\
\text{Sale price} &= \$132.80 - \$19.92 \\
&= \$112.88 \\
\text{Sale tax} &= 3\tfrac{1}{2}\% \text{ of } \$112.88 \\
&= 0.035 \times \$112.88 \\
&= \$3.95 \\
\text{Purchase price} &= \$112.88 + \$3.95 \\
&= \$116.83
\end{aligned}
$$

Solution B. Since the list price is reduced by 15%, the sale price will be 85% of the list price.

$$
\begin{aligned}
\text{Sales price} &= 85\% \text{ of } \$132.80 \\
&= 0.85 \times 132.80 \\
&= \$112.88 \\
\text{Purchase price} &= \$112.88 + 0.035 \times \$112.88 \\
&= \$116.83
\end{aligned}
$$

4-12 Commission. Salesmen are often paid a "flat salary" augmented by a sum of money, called a *commission*, based on the total sale value of the goods they sell. The commission rate is frequently given as a percent of the sale price.

EXAMPLE 4-9. A salesman received $645.25 in commissions for selling $12,905 worth of cars. Under what commission rate was he working?

Solution

$$\text{Commission rate} \times \text{total sales} = \text{commission}$$

or

$$\text{Commission rate} = \frac{\text{commission}}{\text{total sales}}$$

$$= \frac{\$645.25}{\$12,905.00}$$

$$= \frac{1}{20}$$

$$= 5\%$$

4-13 Profit and Loss. If an article cost a merchant $10 and he sold it for $12, his profit would be $12 − $10 or $2. That is,

$$\text{Profit} = \text{selling price} - \text{cost}$$

or

$$\text{Selling price} = \text{cost} + \text{profit}$$

and

$$\text{Cost} = \text{selling price} - \text{profit}$$

The profit can also be expressed as (1) a percent of the cost or (2) a percent of the selling price. In the preceding example, the profit on the cost would be $\frac{2}{10} = 0.20 = 20$ percent. The profit based on the selling price would be $\frac{2}{12} = \frac{1}{6} = 0.16\frac{2}{3} = 16\frac{2}{3}$ percent. While both methods are used, the more common practice is to base the profit on the selling price.

In the problems that follow, it will be assumed that the percent profit is based upon the selling price.

EXAMPLE 4-10. What must be the selling price on a tractor which costs the merchant $8,400 for him to realize a profit of 25% on the sale price?

Solution

$$25\% \text{ of the selling price } = \text{profit}$$
then
$$75\% \text{ of the selling price } = \text{cost}$$

As a multiplication statement,

$$0.75 \times \text{selling price } = \text{cost}$$

As an equivalent division statement,

$$\text{Selling price } = \frac{\text{cost}}{0.75} = \frac{\$8,400}{0.75}$$
$$= \$11,200$$

4-14 Efficiency. The efficiency of a machine is defined as its output divided by its input. Usefully the efficiency is expressed as a percent. It should be clear that both output and input must be expressed in the same units. Thus,

$$\text{Efficiency, in}\% = \frac{\text{output}}{\text{input}} \times 100$$

Since it is impossible to get out of any machine as much as is put into it, the efficiency must always be less than 100 percent.

Example 4-11. An electric motor receives an input of 7,500 watts and delivers 7.5 horsepower (hp) output. What is the efficiency of the motor? (Note: 1 hp is equivalent to 746 watts.)

Solution. In order to use the defining equation for efficiency, the output and input must be expressed in the same units.

$$\text{Output} = 7.5 \text{ hp}$$
$$= 7.5 \times 746 \text{ watts}$$
Then
$$\text{Efficiency} = \frac{7.5 \times 746 \text{ watts}}{7,500 \text{ watts}} \times 100$$
$$= 74.6\%$$

4-15 Simple Interest. When a person borrows money from a bank, he must pay an *interest* for the use of that money. The money borrowed is called the *principal*. The sum of the principal and the interest is called the *amount*. These quantities are related by the formula

Interest = principal $\times$ rate per year $\times$ time in years

EXAMPLE 4-12. Mr. Ryan borrowed $12,000 at 6% simple interest for 3 years. How much interest did he owe at the end of 3 years? What amount was due at the end of 3 years?

Solution

$$
\begin{aligned}
\text{Interest} &= \text{principal} \times \text{rate} \times \text{time} \\
&= \$12,\!000 \times \tfrac{6}{100} \times 3 \\
&= \$2,\!160 \\
\text{Amount} &= \text{principal} + \text{interest} \\
&= \$12,\!000 + \$2,\!160 \\
&= \$14,\!160
\end{aligned}
$$

PROBLEMS

4-100. A gun listed at $129.50 was sold for $99.95. What was the percent of discount (to the nearest whole number)?

4-101. If the sales tax is 3%, what tax must be paid on a purchase of $135.95?

4-102. Two years ago Mr. Owens had a salary of $7,200. Last year he was given a 10% cut in salary. This year his salary was increased 10%. What is his present salary?

4-103. Paul Turner is paid a salary of $2,500 a year plus a commission of 5% on his sales. What must be the amount of his sales to guarantee him an annual salary of $7,500?

4-104. Goe's variety store buys a box of 24 candy bars for 75 cents and sells them for 5 cents each. What is the percent of profit when based upon the selling price?

4-105. A certain motor is rated 80% efficient. The output of the motor is 30 hp. What is the input of the motor in watts? (NOTE: 1 hp = 746 watts.)

4-106. A salesman earned $500 in commissions during the month of October. If his commission rate was 8%, what was the value of his sales?

4-107. Mr. Bishop purchased goods listed at $276.50. He was given a 20% discount for paying cash. The state taxed him 2% of the purchase price. What cash did he have to give for the goods?

4-108. If the sales tax on $579.95 is $20.30, what is the tax rate?

4-109. The sales tax on a jig saw is $0.62. The retail sales tax rate is $2\frac{1}{2}\%$. What is the price of the saw before tax? After tax?

4-110. An interior decorator receives 15% commission on all sales to his clients. One of his clients purchased the following merchandise at 5% off list price: broadloom carpet, list $1,500; draperies, list $1,200; chesterfield, list $450; lamps, list $125; fixtures, list $75. How much did the client pay for the merchandise? How much was the decorator's commission?

4-111. If lumber lists at $65 per 1,000 board feet and is offered at $57.20 per 1,000 board feet, what is the rate of discount?

4-112. A hi-fi set is listed at $459.95. The set is discounted 20% on a store-wide fire sale. What is the selling price?

4-113. What selling price must a merchant put on an article which costs him $27.50 if he is to realize a profit of 40% on the list price?

4-114. If a merchant wishes to realize a profit of $12 at a profit of 15% on the list price of an article, what must he list as the sale price of the article?

4-115. A man borrows $1,800 at 6% simple interest per year for 30 months. How much interest will he owe at the end of the 30 months? What is the total amount he will owe at that time?

4-116. A man bought a house listed at $24,000. He paid 25% down and gave a mortgage bearing 6% simple interest for the remainder. What was his annual interest on the loan?

4-117. An aluminum solder is made of the following metals by weight: 78% tin, 9% aluminum, 8% zinc, 5% cadmium. How many pounds each of aluminum, zinc, and cadmium must be added to 234 lb of tin in making the solder? How many pounds of solder can be made from this amount of metal?

4-118. A manufacturer produces an article for $5.60. He sells it at a profit of 20% on his sale price to a wholesaler. The wholesaler sells the article to a retailer at a profit of 25% on his sale price. The retailer sells the article to a consumer at a profit of 30% on his sale price. What does the consumer pay for the article?

4-119. A salesman is paid a salary of $2,500 a year plus a commission of 5% on his sales. What must be the amount of his sales if he is to receive a total salary of $8,500 per year?

4-120. The alloy Wood's metal used in overhead safety sprinkler systems has the following composition: bismuth, 50%; lead, 25%; tin, $12\frac{1}{2}$%; cadmium, $12\frac{1}{2}$%. How many pounds of the alloy can be made if only 50 lb of cadmium is available?

4-121. Mr. Brown owns a house worth $10,000. He sells it to Mr. Black at a 10% profit based on the worth of the house. Mr. Black sells the house back to Mr. Brown at a 10% loss. How much does Mr. Brown make on the deal?

4-122. A rise of 600 ft is required to get a railroad line over a mountain. The grade can be kept down by lengthening the track and curving it around the mountain peak. Find the additional length of track required to reduce the grade from 3 to 2%.

4-123. A man has $10,000 to invest. He invests $4,000 at 5% and $3,500 at 4%. At what rate must he invest the remainder to have a yearly income of $500 from his three investments?

CHAPTER 5

The Slide Rule

5-1 Uses of the Slide Rule. The slide rule is an instrument which is designed to save time and labor in the common mathematical processes of multiplication, division, raising to powers, taking roots, finding trigonometric and logarithmic functions, and combinations of these processes. Addition and subtraction are two processes for which the slide rule cannot be used.

Every technician should be able to use the slide rule in solving problems and checking his computations. Much valuable time can be saved and tedious work can often be avoided with the help of this instrument.

There are many sizes, types, and costs of slide rules, but they all operate on the theory and properties of logarithms. It is beyond the scope of this text to discuss the various types of rules and the theory on which they are based. We shall limit our discussion in this chapter to the use of the C, D, A, K, CF, DF, CI, and DI scales.

5-2 Reading the C and D Scales. Every slide rule has a C and a D scale. The C scale and the D scale are exactly alike in each of the various types of rule. Each of these scales is divided into nine parts by *primary* marks numbered from 1 on the extreme left through the numbers 2, 3, 4, 5, 6, 7, 8, 9, 1 (see Fig. 5-1). The distances between consecutive primary marks decrease toward the right.

The space between any two primary marks is divided into ten parts by nine shorter *secondary* marks. The distances between

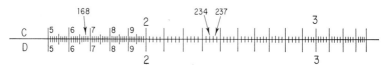

Fig. 5-1

consecutive secondary marks decrease toward the right. With the exception of the secondary marks between the 1 and 2 primary marks, numerals are not printed beside the smaller graduations.

The space between each secondary graduation at the left end of the rule (from primary graduation mark 1 to primary graduation 2) is separated into ten parts by nine tertiary marks. Between primary graduations 2 and 4 each secondary space is divided into five spaces. Between primary graduation 4 and the right graduation 1 each secondary space is subdivided into two spaces. None of the tertiary marks are identified by number on the rule.

To find 168 on the D scale, look for the left primary division 1 (see Fig. 5-2), then for the secondary division numbered 6, and

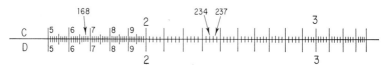

Fig. 5-2

then for the eighth tertiary division to the right of the secondary division 6 (this subdivision is not numbered). Similarly, 234 is found between primary division marks 2 and 3, between secondary graduation marks 3 and 4, and two tertiary marks to the right of the secondary mark 3. Note the space between two consecutive marks represents 2 units. The number 237 would be found in the same manner as for 234, except that the 7 digit would be located halfway between the third and fourth tertiary marks to the right of the secondary mark 3.

The student should note that, between the left primary number 1 and the primary number 2, the space between any two consecutive tertiary marks represents a unit in the third place; between 2 and 4, the space between two consecutive marks represents 2 units in the third place; while at the right of 4 each space between consecutive tertiary marks represents 5 units in the third place.

On the D scale in Fig. 5-3, the student will find some sample settings. He should read the numbers associated with the marks

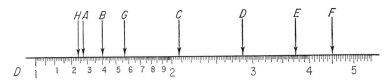

Fig. 5-3

lettered A, B, C, . . . , and check his readings with the following:
A 127, B 140, C 207, D 285, E 374, F 450, G 1565, H 1237.

5-3   Location of the Decimal Point.   The C and D scales on a slide rule give only the sequence of significant digits of a number. The position of the decimal is completely ignored in the scales. When a number is to be located on the D scale, the first significant digit is located by using the primary marks; the second digit is located by using the secondary graduations; the third digit is located by using the tertiary graduations. For example, mark A in Fig. 5-3 could represent 0.0127, 0.127, 1.27, 12.7, 127, 1270, 12,700, etc. The context of the problem will determine for the operator the location of the decimal point.

When the slide rule is used for performing operations such as multiplication and division, the sequence of significant digits in the solution is obtained without regard to the location of the decimal point. The location of the decimal can usually be obtained by "rounding off" numbers and mentally approximating the answer.

For example, if the slide rule is used to multiply 7.83 by 2.59,

the sequence of digits obtained in the answer by the rule will be
203.   It will be noted that the answer is approximately

$$8 \times 2.5 = 20$$

Thus, the answer will be 20.3.

5-4   Parts of the Slide Rule.   The slide rule has three
main components (see Fig. 5-4): the stock, the slide, and the
indicator.

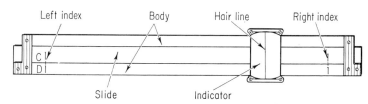

Fig. 5-4

The *stock* (or body) is the frame of the rule and consists of an
upper and lower rectangular bar usually held together by means
of metal or plastic strips at the ends.

The middle sliding part of the rule is called the *slide*.   The
edges of the slide have upper and lower tongues which fit grooves
on the inner edges of the bars of the stock.

The transparent runner which slides along the face of the rule is
referred to as the *indicator* (or cursor).   The indicator has an
engraved vertical hairline on each side.   This hairline serves as a
perpendicular for use in aligning numbers on two scales which
are to be used together.

The primary number 1 on the left end of either the C or D scale
is called the *left index* of that scale.   The primary number 1 on
the other end of the scale is called the *right index* of that scale.

5-5   Multiplication.   The following examples illustrate the
method of multiplying by using the C and D scales.

EXAMPLE 5-1.   Multiply 2×3.

Solution. Set the left index of the C scale on 2 of the D scale. Then push the indicator until the hairline is over the 3 on the C scale. Below the hairline on the D scale read the answer 6. This would be the procedure to find 200 × 30, 0.002 × 0.0003, etc.

EXAMPLE 5-2.   Multiply 15.76 × 4.28.
Solution. To find the product, first disregard the decimal point and proceed as in the above example to get the sequence of digits 675. To locate the decimal point, approximate the answer by noting that 16 × 4 = 64. Hence, the answer is 67.5.

EXAMPLE 5-3.   Multiply 0.0372 × 65.8.
Solution. Disregard temporarily the decimal points in the factors. If we proceed to solve this problem as we did the previous two, we shall not be able to read the answer on the D scale opposite 658 on the C scale. We must modify our procedure as follows:

Place the right index of the C scale on 658 of the D scale. Push the indicator until the hairline is over 372 on the C scale. Read 245 under the hairline on the D scale. Note that

$$0.04 \times 60 = 2.4$$

Hence, the answer will be 2.45.

▶ *Rule.* To find the product of two numbers, over one of the factors marked on the D scale set the index of the C scale. Locate the mark on the C scale whose sequence of digits is the same as those of the second factor. Directly below it on the D scale, read the sequence of digits in the answer. When the product falls outside the limit of the D scale, the wrong index of the C scale is being used. In this event "interchange the indexes" of the C scale and proceed as before (see Fig. 5-5).

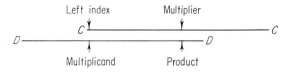

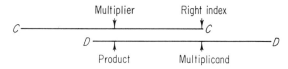

Fig. 5-5

PROBLEMS

Perform the indicated operations:

5-1. 2.4 × 3.2	**5-2.** 1.87 × 5.5
5-3. 1.264 × 4.39	**5-4.** 4.56 × 63.8
5-5. 3.82 × 724	**5-6.** 886 × 43.2
5-7. 204 × 806	**5-8.** 1.846 × 0.00639
5-9. 955 × 453	**5-10.** 10.95 × 84.7
5-11. 71.3 × 756	**5-12.** 48,200 × 0.00013
5-13. 0.01016 × 1,008	**5-14.** 207 × 0.0306
5-15. 630 × 0.0000201	**5-16.** 0.492 × 0.00274
5-17. 0.003 × 708	**5-18.** 917,000 × 0.000372
5-19. 0.01947 × 259	**5-20.** 4.76 × 80.3

5-6 Division. The operation of division is the inverse of multiplication. Thus in dividing two numbers with a slide rule, we need only reverse the steps given in Sec. 5-5 for multiplication. Consider again the problem 2 × 3, given in Example 5-1. Reversing the steps of the process to find 6 ÷ 3, we first set the 3 of the C scale opposite the 6 of the D scale. The quotient 2 is found on the D scale opposite the left index of the C scale.

▶ *Rule.* To divide two numbers, set the divisor on the C scale opposite the dividend on the D scale. The quotient is read on the D scale under the index of the C scale (see Fig. 5-6).

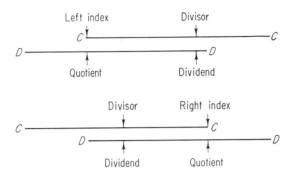

Fig. 5-6

EXAMPLE 5-4. Divide $2860 \div 34.7$.

Solution. Move the indicator until the hairline is over 286 of the D scale. Move the slide until 347 of the C scale is under the hairline. The quotient is read on the D scale opposite the right index of the C scale. The sequence of digits in the quotient will be 824. Since $2,900 \div 30 = 90$ (approx.), our quotient will be 82.4.

PROBLEMS

Perform the indicated operations:

5-21. $8.34 \div 2.76$ **5-22.** $91.1 \div 42.7$
5-23. $37.5 \div 0.0444$ **5-24.** $0.668 \div 47.3$
5-25. $0.00397 \div 0.0551$ **5-26.** $0.01462 \div 7.89$
5-27. $80,200 \div 93.6$ **5-28.** $192.8 \div 13.76$
5-29. $71.30 \div 0.01774$ **5-30.** $1.037 \div 100.6$
5-31. $10.05 \div 37.0$ **5-32.** $82,900 \div 35.7$
5-33. $94,900 \div 725$ **5-34.** $8.73 \div 26,700$
5-35. $1.530 \div 0.351$ **5-36.** $693 \div 0.0257$

5-37. 0.01852 ÷ 0.000839   **5-38.** 0.00357 ÷ 0.361
5-39. 40.4 ÷ 718   **5-40.** 1.607 ÷ 83.5

5-7   Combined Multiplication and Division.   Sometimes the product of three or more numbers is required in solutions to problems.   Other times problems call for combinations of multiplication and division.   The slide rule is extremely applicable for these computations.

EXAMPLE 5-5.   Multiply 27.49 × 13.65 × 5.80.

Solution.   Estimate the product as 25 × 10 × 6 = 1,500. The true product should be in the neighborhood of 1,500. Remembering that only three significant figures can be placed on the C and D scales for numbers whose first significant digit is not 1, we "round off" 27.49 to 27.5.   The 13.65 can be read on the scales, as can 5.80.

Set the left index of the C scale on 275 of the D scale.   Push the indicator until the hairline is over 1365 on the C scale.   (Note that the sequence of digits for this partial product is 375.)   Next move the slide until the right index of the C scale is under the hairline (opposite 375 of the D scale).   Push the indicator until the hairline is over 58 of the C scale.   Below the hairline read the sequence of digits 218 on the D scale.   The answer for the product is 2,180.

EXAMPLE 5-6.   Evaluate $\dfrac{81.72 \times 5.34}{62.91}$

Solution.   Estimate the answer to be $\dfrac{80 \times 5}{60} = 7$ (approx.).

Let us first divide 817 by 629 as follows: Move the hairline over 817 on the D scale.   Under the hairline set 629 of the C scale. (Note that the sequence of digits in the partial quotient is 1299.) Next move the indicator until the hairline is over 534 of the C scale.   The reading under the hairline on the D scale has 694 as the sequence of digits.   The answer then should be 6.94.

PROBLEMS

5-41. $\dfrac{709 \times 1.124}{0.672}$

5-42. $\dfrac{326 \times 5.318}{386}$

5-43. $\dfrac{87.3 \times 2.47}{64.5 \times 12.89}$

5-44. $\dfrac{4,290 \times 7.93}{348 \times 817}$

5-45. $\dfrac{0.00264}{0.0854 \times 0.27}$

5-46. $\dfrac{0.0001148}{0.00275 \times 0.0854}$

5-47. $2,641 \times 0.00385 \times 0.01916$

5-48. $2.37 \times 81.4 \times 0.00886$

5-49. $0.0000420 \times 805 \times 9.04$

5-50. $63,600 \times 2120 \times 639$

5-51. $\dfrac{78.4 \times 9.04 \times 1,326}{21.7 \times 8.26 \times 7,030}$

5-52. $\dfrac{0.00610 \times 0.0184 \times 67.3}{0.0627 \times 0.810 \times 0.1004}$

5-53. $\dfrac{23.74 \times 821 \times 0.00608}{83.6 \times 77.70}$

5-54. $\dfrac{92.87 \times 0.001523 \times 0.07376}{44.05 \times 28.80}$

5-55. $\dfrac{0.00381 \times 0.000847 \times 0.01166}{0.274 \times 0.00929 \times 0.00001115}$

5-56. $\dfrac{0.0650 \times 0.6868 \times 55.5}{94,700 \times 30,004}$

5-57. $\dfrac{37.2 \times 11.86 \times 995 \times 263}{234 \times 869 \times 9.87}$

5-58. $\dfrac{0.0762 \times 0.1714 \times 0.417 \times 0.975}{472 \times 0.819}$

5-59. $\dfrac{0.000389 \times 0.01258}{27.0 \times 0.00182 \times 0.2748}$

5-60. $\dfrac{8.26 \times 0.0918}{2.14 \times 8.54 \times 918 \times 619}$

5-8 The CF and DF Scales. The CF (on the slide) and DF (on the body) scales are identical in graduation with the C and D scales.   However, the CF and DF scales are folded in such a way as to place the indexes near the middle and π at the end positions.   Because of the position of the graduations, they are called the *folded* scales.

The chief use of the folded scales is to avoid the necessity of resetting the indexes of the slide.   It does not increase the capability of the rule, but it does often minimize the number of manipulations in multiplying and dividing.   A glance at Fig. 5-7 will

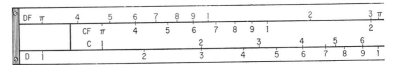

Fig. 5-7

show that, if for any setting of the slide, a number N of the C scale is opposite a number M on the D scale, then that same number N on the CF scale will be opposite the same second number M on the DF scale.   Note, for example, that the following ordered pairs can be found on either the C and D scales or on the CF and DF scales:

C or CF	1	2	3	4	5	6
D or DF	1.5	3	4.5	6	7.5	9

Thus, any process which will match two numbers on the C and D scales will at the same time match the same two numbers on the CF and DF scales.   This property of the rule is used to shorten the processes of multiplication and division.

EXAMPLE 5-7.   Multiply 4.82 × 5.37.

Solution.   If we set the left index of the C scale opposite 4.82 of the D scale and then try to move the hairline over 5.37 of the C scale, we shall realize that this is impossible.   However, we can move the hairline over 5.37 of the CF scale and read the product under the hairline on the DF scale. This saves having to interchange indexes. The product will be 25.9.

EXAMPLE 5-8. Using the folded scales, find $21.6 \div 7.75$.

Solution. Set the hairline over 216 of the DF scale. Under the hairline set 775 of the CF scale. Read the answer on the DF scale opposite the index of the CF scale. The answer will be 2.79. Note the same answer can be read on the D scale opposite the left index of the C scale.

EXAMPLE 5-9. Find the value of $\dfrac{3.50 \times 96.6}{2.12 \times 57.8}$.

Solution. There are many procedures that can be used here. One method follows. Set the hairline over 350 of the D scale. Under the hairline set 212 of the C scale. Next move the hairline over 966 of the CF scale. Then move the slide until 578 of the CF scale is under the hairline. The sequence of digits in the final answer is found on the DF (or D) scale opposite the index of the CF (or C) scale. The answer is 2.76.

PROBLEMS

Perform the indicated operations:

5-61. 2.83×7.54 **5-62.** 37.4×95.1

5-63. 80.4×27.7 **5-64.** 5.50×0.0376

5-65. 0.00839×62.4 **5-66.** $17.76 \div 4.53$

5-67. $0.0315 \div 0.00784$ **5-68.** $0.000300 \div 0.001056$

5-69. $\dfrac{11.37 \times 1.563}{2.74}$ **5-70.** $\dfrac{89.7}{54.4 \times 42.2}$

5-71. $\dfrac{0.0879 \times 2.63}{0.425 \times 1.115}$ **5-72.** $\dfrac{31.7 \times 45.5}{99.2 \times 11.7}$

5-73. $\dfrac{0.358}{0.472 \times 0.1106}$ **5-74.** $\dfrac{253}{42.1 \times 5.09}$

5-75. $\dfrac{2.85 \times 0.904 \times 1.550}{4.39 \times 8.71}$

5-76. $\dfrac{0.1154 \times 0.00246 \times 0.833}{0.276 \times 0.000559}$

5-77. $\dfrac{29.3 \times 1.156 \times 37.4}{843}$ **5-78.** $\dfrac{0.0393 \times 0.929 \times 0.238}{0.707}$

5-79. $\dfrac{224}{1.35 \times 24.6 \times 7.89}$ **5-80.** $\dfrac{0.00385}{0.198 \times 0.276 \times 0.345}$

5-9 The CI, DI, CIF Scales. The reciprocal of a number N is 1 divided by the number. Thus $\frac{1}{4}$ is the reciprocal of 4; $\frac{3}{5}$ is the reciprocal of $\frac{5}{3}$.

The CI, CIF, and DIF scales are graduated like the C, CF, and DF scales but in the reverse direction so that the numbers on the scales increase from right to left. These scales are called the *reciprocal* or inverted scales. The CI and CIF scales usually appear on the same (front) face, while the DIF scale appears on the other face of the rule. The scales are printed with red numbers to facilitate recognition.

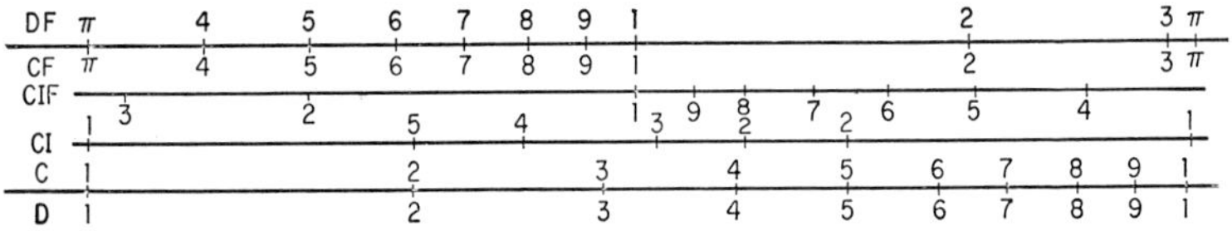

Fig. 5-8

Figure 5-8 illustrates the relationship between a scale and its inverted counterpart. It will be noted that, if the hairline is set above any number on the C, D or CF scale, the hairline will also be above the reciprocal of that number on the corresponding inverted scale. Note, for example, the following ordered pairs:

CI,CIF, DI	1	0.5 $(=\frac{1}{2})$	0.4 $(=1/2.5)$	0.25 $(=\frac{1}{4})$	0.2 $(=\frac{1}{5})$	0.125 $(=\frac{1}{8})$
C, CF, D	1	2	2.5	4	5	8

The CI, CIF, and DIF scales are of considerable value in solving problems that involve continued products.

The student should recognize that the C and D scales are the best to use in performing division, since the answer never falls outside the limits of the D scale. In like manner, he will find that the CI and DI scales are best for multiplication.

EXAMPLE 5-10. Multiply 5 × 4.

Solution. To multiply 5 × 4, we consider the equivalent expressions $5 \times \dfrac{1}{\frac{1}{4}} = 5 \times \dfrac{1}{0.25} = \dfrac{5}{0.25}$. The problem reduces to one of dividing 5 by the reciprocal of 4. The reciprocal of 4 can be found on the C scale opposite 4 of the CI scale. The C and D scales are then used to divide. Procedure: First, move the hairline over 5 on the D scale. Then set the 4 of the CI scale under the hairline. The product (=20) is read on the D scale opposite the left index of the C scale.

EXAMPLE 5-11. Find the product 2.54 × 3.68 × 11.70 × 5.05 × 4.29.

Solution. Consider the equivalent expression

$$2.54 \times 3.68 \times 11.70 \times 5.05 \times 4.29 = 2.54 \times \frac{1}{\frac{1}{3.68}}$$
$$\times 11.70 \times \frac{1}{\frac{1}{5.05}} \times 4.29$$

Procedure. Opposite 254 of the D scale set 368 of the CI scale. Move the hairline over 117 of the C scale. Then move the slide until 505 of the CI scale is under the hairline. Finally, move the hairline over 429 of the C scale. The sequence of digits in the answer will be found under the hairline on the D scale. The answer is 2,370.

EXAMPLE 5-12. Find the product 2.39 × 0.1875 × 2.16 × 0.840.

Solution. Opposite 239 of the D scale set 1875 of the CI scale. Since 216 is beyond the D scale, move the hairline over 216 of the CF scale. Next move the slide until 840 of the CIF scale is set under the hairline. The answer, namely, 0.813, is on the DF (or D) scale opposite the index of the CF (or C) scale.

PROBLEMS

Multiply:

5-81. $9.18 \times 3.25 \times 1.456$
5-82. $7.35 \times 0.492 \times 0.364$
5-83. $0.001184 \times 5.25 \times 7.66$
5-84. $851 \times 0.00534 \times 0.906$
5-85. $0.01083 \times 50.2 \times 27.4$
5-86. $8.27 \times 59,100 \times 0.000373$
5-87. $2.14 \times 5.90 \times 1.104 \times 3.77$
5-88. $0.499 \times 0.888 \times 663 \times 78.5$
5-89. $0.00504 \times 40.5 \times 39.6 \times 2.74$
5-90. $80.70 \times 91,200 \times 0.000503 \times 0.0212$
5-91. $27.1 \times 1.349 \times 3.57 \times 6.14 \times 87.2$
5-92. $2.83 \times 0.001159 \times 0.938 \times 2.57 \times 5.67$
5-93. $0.0000404 \times 68,000 \times 0.1090 \times 28.4 \times 7.44$
5-94. $27.2 \times 53.9 \times 0.0804 \times 0.358 \times 22.4$
5-95. $383 \times 49.2 \times 5.71 \times 0.625 \times 0.00744$
5-96. $0.208 \times 7.21 \times 5.46 \times 4.33 \times 0.000779$
5-97. $5.32 \times 8.391 \times 1.467 \times 118.0 \times 0.2357$
5-98. $60.7 \times 3.92 \times 4,550 \times 0.01986 \times 7.358$
5-99. $42.5 \times 8.06 \times 0.1783 \times 3.33 \times 0.00212 \times 0.0663$
5-100. $0.2761 \times 0.4352 \times 0.008947 \times 50.25 \times 6.139 \times 11.98$

5-10 Powers and Roots. The solutions to many technical problems involve multiplying a number by itself several times. Mathematicians use a convenient bit of symbolism to indicate this process. For example:

$$2 \times 2 \times 2 \times 2 = 2^4$$
$$3 \times 3 \times 3 \times 3 \times 3 = 3^5$$
$$4 \times 4 = 4^2$$
$$10 \times 10 \times 10 = 10^3$$
$$5^3 = 125$$
$$5^1 = 5$$
$$7^1 = 7$$

The number in small type on the upper right of a second number is called an *exponent*. The exponent indicates how many times a second number, called the *base*, is to be used as a factor in repeated multiplication. When no exponent is written, it is understood to imply 1. The numbers 2, 2^2, 2^3, 2^4, . . . are called *powers of* 2. The numbers 3, 3^2, 3^3, 3^4, . . . are *powers of* 3. Thus,

2 or 2^1 is read "two to the first power" or simply "two."

2^2 is read "two to the second power" or "two squared."

2^{10} is read "two to the tenth power."

7^{16} is read "seven to the sixteenth power."

The inverse of raising to a power is called *extracting the root*. When a number is equivalent to the product of two or more equal factors, the root of the number is one of its equal factors. For example, the two equal factors of 16 are 4 and 4 ($4 \times 4 = 16$). Therefore, 4 is a root of 16. In like manner, 2, 2, 2, are the three equal factors of 8. Therefore, 2 is a root of 8.

When a number has two equal factors, either one is called the *square root* of the number. Thus, 4 is the square root of 16.

When there are three equal factors, any of the factors is called the *cube root* of that number. Thus, 2 is the cube root of 8. Likewise, 3 is the fourth root of 81, and so on.

The symbol used for indicating the square root of a number is $\sqrt{}$. The symbol $\sqrt[3]{}$ is used to indicate the cube root; $\sqrt[4]{}$ is used for the fourth root; $\sqrt[5]{}$ for the fifth root; and so on. The symbol $\sqrt{}$ is called the *radical sign*. The small number at the upper left corner is called the *index*. If no index is shown, it is understood to be 2. Thus, $\sqrt{16} = 4$, $\sqrt[3]{8} = 2$, $\sqrt[4]{81} = 3$, $\sqrt[5]{32} = 2$, and so on.

In this book we shall be primarily interested in extracting square roots and cube roots.

5-11 Comparing Numbers. Besides the symbols for numbers and operations of addition, subtraction, multiplication, and division, there are symbols that tell how two numbers are related to each other. We have already been using the symbol for equality. For example, we may write $3 + 5 = 8$ to indicate that

3 + 5 and 8 are names for the same number.   In like manner, we write $\frac{4}{6} = \frac{2}{3}$ and $\frac{1}{4} = 0.25$ to indicate equivalence of numbers.

There are three more symbols in common use to indicate relative sizes of two numbers.   They are $\neq$, $>$, $<$.

> $\neq$ means "is not equal to."
> $>$ means "is greater than."
> $<$ means "is less than."

EXAMPLES

1. $5 \neq 9 \qquad 5 < 9 \qquad 9 > 5$
2. $5 \cdot 3 \neq 53 \qquad 5 \cdot 3 > 4 \cdot 3 \qquad 5 \cdot 3 < 16$
3. $1 + 1 > 1 \times 1 \qquad 1 \div 1 < 1 + 1$
4. $5^3 \neq 3^5 \qquad 5^3 < 3^5$
5. $\sqrt{\frac{8}{2}} \neq \frac{1}{2}\sqrt{8} \qquad \sqrt{1,000} < 10\sqrt{100}$

PROBLEMS

Find the numerical values of the following:

5-101. 2^3	**5-102.** $(1^2)(2^2)(3^2)$
5-103. 5^2	**5-104.** $(\frac{1}{2})^3$
5-105. $(\frac{2}{3})^3$	**5-106.** $(\frac{1}{2})^2(2^2)$
5-107. $1^2 + 2^2 + 3^2$	**5-108.** $\sqrt[3]{64}$
5-109. $\sqrt{\frac{4}{9}}$	**5-110.** $\sqrt[3]{\frac{8}{27}}$

In Probs. 5-111 to 5-130 indicate which statements are true and which are false.

5-111. $3 \cdot 4 = 7$	**5-112.** $3 \cdot 4 > 7$
5-113. $3 \cdot 4 \neq 12$	**5-114.** $10^2 = 2^{10}$
5-115. $3 + 3 \neq 3 \cdot 3$	**5-116.** $2 + 3 \neq 2 \cdot 3$
5-117. $2 \cdot 18 > 2^5$	**5-118.** $2 + 2 \neq 2 \cdot 2$
5-119. $2^6 < 8^2$	**5-120.** $5 \cdot 0 = 1$
5-121. $\frac{0}{7} \neq 0$	**5-122.** $0 + 0 > 0$
5-123. $0 < (0 + 0)$	**5-124.** $0 \cdot 0 = 0$
5-125. $3 + 2 \cdot 5 < (3 + 2)(5)$	
5-126. $16 - 6 \div 3 \neq 16 - (6 \div 3)$	

5-127. $\sqrt{4} \cdot \sqrt{16} = \sqrt{4 \cdot 16}$ **5-128.** $834 \cdot 835 < 835^2$
5-129. $\sqrt[3]{27} > \sqrt{25}$ **5-130.** $3{,}176 = 3.176 \times 10^3$

In Probs. 5-131 to 5-150 are pairs of numbers. Indicate, by using the symbols $=$, $>$, $<$, the correct relationship between the numbers of each pair.

5-131. $1{,}019$, $1{,}109$ **5-132.** 3^2, 2^3
5-133. 0.5, 0.4 **5-134.** 15^2, 225
5-135. $\sqrt{196}$, 16 **5-136.** 8^2, $8 \cdot 2$
5-137. $\sqrt{0.25}$, 0.05 **5-138.** $\sqrt[3]{0.001}$, $\sqrt[4]{0.0016}$
5-139. $-2(8 - 13)$, 10 **5-140.** $\sqrt{\frac{9}{4}}$, $\sqrt{\frac{4}{9}}$
5-141. $9 \cdot 9 \div 9$, $9 \div 9 \cdot 9$ **5-142.** 7^2, 14
5-143. $16 - 6 \cdot 2$, $16 - 2 \cdot 6$ **5-144.** $8(7 - 2)$, $4(14 - 4)$
5-145. $2 \times 7 \times 5$, $5 \times 2 \times 7$ **5-146.** $2^3 \times 2^2$, 2^5
5-147. $\dfrac{\sqrt{16}}{\sqrt{4}}$, $\sqrt{\dfrac{16}{4}}$ **5-148.** $\sqrt[3]{8} \cdot \sqrt[3]{1{,}000}$, $\sqrt[3]{8{,}000}$
5-149. $8^3 \times 9^2$, $9^3 \times 8^2$ **5-150.** 0.00459, 4.59×10^3

5-12 Squares and Square Roots. Tables are available for finding the squares and square roots of numbers. Consider the following taken from such a table:

(a)	(b)	(c)	(d)
$2^2 = 4$	$11^2 = 121$	$237^2 = 56169$	$0.2^2 = 0.04$
$5^2 = 25$	$48^2 = 2304$	$392^2 = 153664$	$0.5^2 = 0.25$
$8^2 = 64$	$79^2 = 6241$	$581^2 = 337561$	$0.8^2 = 0.64$

(e)	(f)	(g)
$0.11^2 = 0.0121$	$0.237^2 = 0.056169$	$2.3^2 = 5.29$
$0.48^2 = 0.2304$	$0.392^2 = 0.153664$	$2.37^2 = 5.6169$
$0.79^2 = 0.6241$	$0.581^2 = 0.337561$	$23.7^2 = 561.69$

It will be noted in the above that the square of a single-digit number is a one- or two-digit number, the square of a two-digit number is a three- or four-digit number, the square of a three-digit number is a five- or six-digit number, and so on.

If we were to find the square roots of the numbers to the right of the equality signs in the examples just given, we would get the numbers on the left of the equality signs. We would get, for example:

(a) $\sqrt{\widehat{25}} = 5$ (b) $\sqrt{2{,}\widehat{30}\widehat{4}} = 48$

(c) $\sqrt{\widehat{5}\,\widehat{61}\widehat{69}} = 237$ (d) $\sqrt{0.\widehat{04}} = 0.2$

(e) $\sqrt{0.\widehat{01}\widehat{21}} = 0.11$ (f) $\sqrt{0.\widehat{15}\widehat{36}\widehat{64}} = 0.392$

(g) $\sqrt{\widehat{5}.\widehat{61}\widehat{69}} = 2.37$

We shall now consider illustrative examples of finding square roots by arithmetical processes.

EXAMPLE 5-13. Find the square root of 288,369.

Solution

$\widehat{2\,8}\,\widehat{8\,3}\,\widehat{6\,9}$ 1. Mark off the number in blocks of two, starting at the right, as shown.

$\dfrac{5}{\widehat{2\,8}\,\widehat{8\,3}\,\widehat{6\,9}}$
$\underline{2\,5}$
3

2. Find the largest number whose square is equal to or less than the first block, in this case 28. Write that number (5) directly over the first block. Then subtract the square of that number from the first block ($28 - 25 = 3$).

$\dfrac{5\ ?}{\widehat{2\,8}\,\widehat{8\,3}\,\widehat{6\,9}}$
$\underline{2\,5}$
$1\,0\ ?\ |\ \ 3\,8\,3$

3. Bring down the next block (83) and annex to the difference (3) to form a new dividend. Multiply the first digit of the root by 2 and place the product (10) to the left of the new dividend (383). The 10 becomes a *trial divisor*. Next ask

yourself "What is the largest number (marked ?) that can be placed to the right of 10 and also above the second block of the given number such that the product of the two numbers will be equal to or less than the new dividend (383)?" The number is 3.

$$
\begin{array}{r}
5\ \ 3 \\
\overline{2\ \widehat{8\ 8}\ \widehat{3\ 6\ 9}} \\
2\ 5 \\
1\ 0\ 3\ |\ \ \overline{3\ 8\ 3} \\
3\ 0\ 9 \\
\overline{7\ 4}
\end{array}
$$

4. Place the product of these numbers $(3 \times 103 = 309)$ under the new dividend. Subtract to get a remainder of 74.

$$
\begin{array}{r}
5\ \ 3\ \ ? \\
\overline{2\ \widehat{8\ 8}\ \widehat{3\ 6\ 9}} \\
2\ 5 \\
1\ 0\ 3\ |\ \ \overline{3\ 8\ 3} \\
3\ 0\ 9 \\
1\ 0\ 6\ ?\ |\ \ \overline{7\ 4\ 6\ 9}
\end{array}
$$

5. Bring down the third block (69) and annex to the difference (74) to get 7469. Multiply the first two figures of the square root (53) by 2 and place the product to the left of the second new dividend. This number (106) becomes our new trial divisor.

$$
\begin{array}{r}
5\ \ 3\ \ 7 \\
\overline{2\ \widehat{8\ 8}\ \widehat{3\ 6\ 9}} \\
2\ 5 \\
1\ 0\ 3\ |\ \ \overline{3\ 8\ 3} \\
3\ 0\ 9 \\
1\ 0\ 6\ 7\ |\ \ \overline{7\ 4\ 6\ 9} \\
7\ 4\ 6\ 9
\end{array}
$$

6. Again ask, in step 5, what is the largest number that can be placed to the right of the new trial divisor and above the third block of the given number such that the product of the two numbers will be equal to or less than the new dividend (7469)? This number is 7. Place the product under the new dividend and subtract. In this case there is no remainder. Therefore, our result will be $\sqrt{288{,}369} = 537$.

EXAMPLE 5-14.   Find the square root of 85,849.

Solution.   The solution to this problem is similar to the solution of Example 5-13.   However, as we mark off blocks starting from the right, the last block will have only one digit.   We shall proceed as we did in the previous example.   The solution follows.

$$
\begin{array}{r}
2 \quad 9 \quad 3 \\
\overline{8\,5\,8\,4\,9} \\
4 \\
\hline
4\,9\ |\ \overline{4\,5\,8} \\
4\,4\,1 \\
\hline
5\,8\,3\ |\quad 1\,7\,4\,9 \\
1\,7\,4\,9 \\
\hline
\end{array}
$$

Thus, $\sqrt{85,849} = 293$.

EXAMPLE 5-15.   Find the square root of 559.621.

Solution.   The solution will be the same as in the previous two examples.   It will be noted that the blocks are marked from the decimal point, going both to the left and to the right, and that adding a cipher to the given number does not alter the size of the number.

$$
\begin{array}{r}
2 \quad 3 \ . \ 6 \quad 5 \quad 2 \\
\overline{5\,5\,9\,.\,4\,2\,1\,0\,0\,0} \\
4 \\
\hline
4\,3\ |\ \overline{1\,5\,9} \\
1\,2\,9 \\
\hline
4\,6\,6\ |\quad 3\,0\,4\,2 \\
2\,7\,9\,6 \\
\hline
4\,7\,2\,5\ |\quad 2\,4\,6\,1\,0 \\
2\,3\,6\,2\,5 \\
\hline
4\,7\,3\,0\,2\ |\quad 9\,8\,5\,0\,0 \\
9\,5\,6\,0\,4 \\
\hline
\end{array}
$$

Thus, $\sqrt{559.421} = 23.65$ (accurate to four significant digits).

EXAMPLE 5-16.   Find the square root of 0.064839.

Solution.   Starting at the decimal, we mark off blocks of two in both directions from the decimal point.   We then proceed as in the previous examples.

```
            0 . 2   5   4   6
          ‾‾‾‾‾‾‾‾‾‾‾‾‾‾‾‾‾‾‾‾‾
            0 . 0 6 4 8 3 9 0 0
                4
      4 5 |     2 4 8
              2 2 5
    5 0 4 |     2 3 3 9
              2 0 1 6
    5 0 8 6 |     3 2 3 0 0
              3 0 5 1 6
```

The answer will be closer to 0.255 than to 0.254.   Thus, accurate to three significant digits, our answer will be $\sqrt{0.064839}$ = 0.255.

PROBLEMS

Extract the square roots of the following.   If the answer is not exact, determine the answer accurate to three significant digits.

5-151. 841	**5-152.** 2,916	**5-153.** 21,904
5-154. 74,529	**5-155.** 184,041	**5-156.** 337,561
5-157. 516,961	**5-158.** 649,636	**5-159.** 9,486.76
5-160. 83.7225	**5-161.** 0.770884	**5-162.** 0.585225
5-163. 0.00378225	**5-164.** 0.094864	**5-165.** 0.00085849
5-166. 25.7083	**5-167.** 149,739	**5-168.** 407,059
5-169. 0.326083	**5-170.** 0.00233209	

5-13   Slide-rule Solutions for Squares and Square Roots.
A study of the A and B scales of a slide rule will reveal that they are double scales.   Each scale is divided into two identical parts.

The A and B scales are comparable to the C and D scales placed end to end and then compressed to the length of one C or D scale. Hence, the A and B scales each have three indexes: a left index, a center index, and a right index.

Multiplication and division can be performed with the A and B scales in the same manner as is done with the C and D scales. The accuracy of the solutions using the A and B scales, however, will not be so high as might be obtained with the C and D scales, since the A and B scales are each half the length of the C and D scales.

The A and B scales are used primarily to square numbers and to extract square roots. It will be noted that, if the left indexes of the A, B, C, and D scales are aligned, any number on the A (or B) scale is the square of the number on the D (or C) scale opposite it (see Fig. 5-9). This affords a ready method for finding the squares and square roots of numbers.

EXAMPLE 5-17. Find the square of 2.38.
Solution. Move the hairline over the 238 of the D scale. The answer (= 5.66) is on the A scale under the hairline. The answer could also be obtained in similar manner using the C and B scales.

EXAMPLE 5-18. Find the square root of 546.
Solution. In this problem we reverse the procedure of the previous example. However, there are two identical sets of markings on the A (and B) scale. We shall follow the rule: Mark off the number into blocks of two, starting from the decimal, and if there is only one significant digit in the block farthest to the left, use the left half of the A (or B) scale; if the farthest left block contains two significant digits, use the right half of the A (or B) scale. In this instance we shall move the hairline over 546 of the left half of the A (or B) scale and read the answer under the hairline on the D (or C) scale. The result will be $\sqrt{546} = 23.4$.

EXAMPLE 5-19.   Find the square root of 0.00817.

Solution.   Mark off the digits in blocks of two from the decimal point.   The first block containing at least one significant digit has two of them.   Hence, use the right half of the A (or B) scale. The result will be $\sqrt{0.008170} = 0.0904$.

EXAMPLE 5-20.   Evaluate $\dfrac{0.274 \times 635 \times \sqrt{2,490} \times \sqrt{5.37}}{756 \times \sqrt{1,338}}$.

Solution

Multiply 0.274 by 635:	Place hairline over 274 on the D scale and draw 635 on the CI scale under the hairline.
Multiply by $\sqrt{2,490}$:	Push the hairline to 2,490 of right half of the B scale.
Divide by 756:	Draw 756 of C scale under the hairline.
Multiply by $\sqrt{5.37}$:	Move the hairline to 537 of the left half of the B scale.
Divide by $\sqrt{1,338}$:	Draw 1,338 of the right half of the B scale under the hairline.
Read the answer:	Opposite the right index of the C scale read the significant digits in the answer. The answer is 0.728.

PROBLEMS

Using a slide rule, find the squares of the numbers in Probs. 5-171 to 5-180.

5-171. 2.3   **5-172.** 5.4   **5-173.** 8.7

5-174. 0.609   **5-175.** 42.6   **5-176.** 30.8

5-177. 278   **5-178.** 0.542   **5-179.** 0.0853

5-180. 0.0725

Using the slide rule, find the square roots of the numbers in Probs. 5-181 to 5-190.

5-181. 56   **5-182.** 7.8   **5-183.** 258

5-184. 600   **5-185.** 827   **5-186.** 3,840

5-187. 45,900   **5-188.** 0.0537   **5-189.** 0.1157

5-190. 0.00495

Evaluate the following:

5-191. $24 \sqrt{5.27}$ **5-192.** $3.58 \sqrt{20.6}$

5-193. $\sqrt{38.5} \div 2.54$ **5-194.** $\sqrt{377} \div 8.09$

5-195. $0.834 \div \sqrt{0.0527}$ **5-196.** $83.1 \div \sqrt{5,840}$

5-197. $\dfrac{\sqrt{60.8}}{4.37 \times \sqrt{5.20}}$ **5-198.** $\dfrac{53.4}{8.72 \times \sqrt{12.36}}$

5-199. $28.9 \times 1.053 \sqrt{70,800}$ **5-200.** $\dfrac{7.39 \sqrt{6.45}}{\sqrt{0.846}}$

5-14 Slide-rule Solutions for Cubes and Cube Roots.
The K scale is used to cube a number and to extract cube roots.
Examination of the K scale (see Fig. 5-9) will reveal that it is a

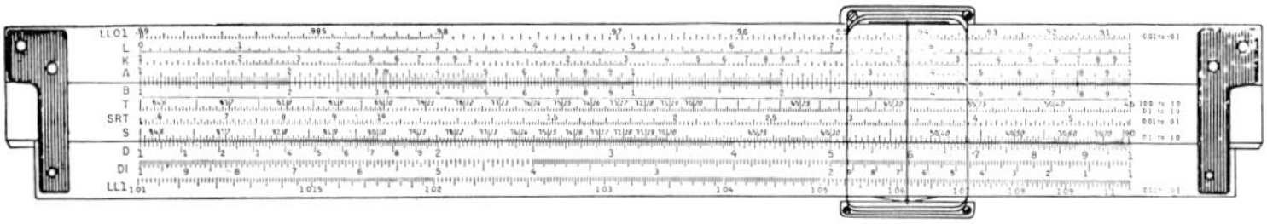

Fig. 5-9

triple scale. It is divided into three identical parts and can be
compared with three C (or D) scales placed end to end and then
compressed to the length of one C (or D) scale. The K scale has
four indexes which partition it into three identical sections.

If the left indexes of the C, D, and K scales are aligned, any
number on the K scale is the cube of the number on the D (or C)
scale opposite it. Thus, to raise any number to the third power,
the hairline is set over that number on the D scale (or on the C
scale if the K scale is on the slide) and the cube is read directly
under the hairline on the K scale.

To extract the cube root of a number, the hairline is set over the number on the proper section of the K scale. The cube root is read under the hairline on the D scale (or C scale if the K scale is on the slide).

The rule for selecting the proper section of the K scale is similar to that used in computing square roots: Mark off the digits in the number in blocks of three from the decimal point—in both directions. If the first block at the left of the number contains one significant digit, use the left third of the scale. If the first block contains two significant digits, use the middle third of the scale. If the first block contains three significant digits, use the right third of the K scale.

The student should verify the following cube roots on his slide rule.

$$\sqrt[3]{3,860} = 15.7 \qquad \sqrt[3]{0.003860} = 0.157$$
$$\sqrt[3]{38,600} = 33.8 \qquad \sqrt[3]{0.038600} = 0.338$$
$$\sqrt[3]{386,000} = 72.8 \qquad \sqrt[3]{0.386} = 0.728$$

PROBLEMS

Find the cubes of the numbers in Probs. 5-201 to 5-210.

5-201. 2.8   **5-202.** 5.3   **5-203.** 0.62
5-204. 1.44   **5-205.** 0.384   **5-206.** 0.857
5-207. 83.2   **5-208.** 74.5   **5-209.** 0.0884
5-210. 0.0736

Find the cube roots of the numbers in Probs. 5-211 to 5-220.

5-211. 7.59   **5-212.** 28.3   **5-213.** 573
5-214. 84.9   **5-215.** 0.680   **5-216.** 0.347
5-217. 0.0359   **5-218.** 0.00859   **5-219.** 87,200
5-220. 184,600

Evaluate:

5-221. $4.2 \sqrt[3]{9.27}$

5-222. $25.7 \sqrt[3]{30.5}$

5-223. $\sqrt[3]{58.6} \div 2.28$

5-224. $\sqrt[3]{0.256} \div 0.0347$

5-225. $\sqrt[3]{0.0459} \div 0.808$

5-226. $\sqrt[3]{0.00852} \div 0.1593$

5-227. $3.26 \times 5.49 \sqrt[3]{0.0803}$

5-228. $\dfrac{\sqrt[3]{2,850}}{\sqrt{57}}$

5-229. $\dfrac{\sqrt{487}}{\sqrt[3]{52,800}}$

5-230. $\dfrac{5.02 \sqrt[3]{0.0836}}{\sqrt{0.651}}$

CHAPTER 6

Measurement and Dimensional Relations

6-1 Measurement. When man started to measure, industrial and technological progress began. With the precision measuring instruments of today it is possible to manufacture parts and subassemblies for complex machines in a locality where raw materials, power, and skilled labor are readily available and assemble the finished product thousands of miles away, months or years later if need be, with full assurance of perfect fit.

Before a quantity can be measured, a *unit of measurement* must be selected. The magnitude of the unit of measurement is quite arbitrary. Consequently, there exist various units of measurements that have been developed throughout the history of civilization.

6-2 Fundamental Units of Measurements. All measurements are relative in the sense that they are comparisons with some standard unit of measurement. Actually there are only three *fundamental units* of measurement. They are *length*, *mass*, and *time*. Other well-known measures are called derived *units*, since they can each be expressed in terms of the fundamental units. For examples, the unit of *area* (e.g., the square yard) is a product of a length times a length; the unit of *velocity* (e.g., miles per hour) is obtained by dividing a length unit by a time unit; the unit of *density* (e.g., pounds per cubic inch) is

99

derived by dividing a mass unit by the cube of a length unit; and so on.

6-3 The English System of Measurements. The standard unit of length used in English-speaking countries is the *yard*. In Great Britain the yard is legally defined as the distance between two ruled lines scratched on a bronze metal bar while it is at a temperature of 62°F. The metal bar is kept at the British Exchequer. In the United States the standard yard is defined as $\frac{3,600}{3,937}$ meter. In the United States the *foot* is a more commonly used unit. Other units of length are the *inch* and the *mile*.

Mass is defined as the quantity of matter contained in a body and is distinguished from *weight*, which is measured by the pull of gravity on the body. Numerically, mass and weight are equal at sea level. Both mass and weight measurements in the English system are based upon the *pound* as the basic unit. The *ounce*, the *grain*, and the *ton* are also units of mass and weight in the United States and the British Commonwealth of Nations.

The unit of time in the English system is the *second*. It is defined as $\frac{1}{86,400} = \left(\dfrac{1}{24 \text{ hr/day} \times 60 \text{ min/hr} \times 60 \text{ sec/min}} \right)$ of the mean solar day.

6-4 The Metric System of Measurements. All industrial countries except the United States and Britain use the *metric system* of measurements. The standard units in the metric system are the *meter*, the *gram*, and the *liter*.

The *meter* is defined as the distance between the centers of two lines ruled on a platinum-iridium bar stored at the International Bureau of Weights and Measures at Sèvres, France, while it is kept at a temperature of 0°C. Other common units of length are the *millimeter*, the *centimeter*, the *kilometer*, and the *micron*.

The metric system is a decimal system. Because of the ease of working with a system based upon the number 10, scientists throughout the world use the metric system of measurement.

Table 6-1. Units of Measurements

English System

Units of Length	*Units of Mass or Weight*
1 yard = the standard	1 pound = the standard
12 inches (in.) = 1 foot (ft)	16 ounces (oz) = 1 pound (lb)
3 feet = 1 yard (yd)	100 pounds = 1 hundredweight
$16\frac{1}{2}$ feet = 1 rod	2,000 pounds = 1 short ton
5,280 feet = 1 mile	2,240 pounds = 1 long ton

Units of Area

144 square inches (in.²) = 1 square foot (ft²)
9 square feet = 1 square yard (yd²)
160 square rods = 1 acre
640 acres = 1 square mile

Units of Volume

1,728 cubic inches (in.³) = 1 cubic foot (ft³)
27 cubic feet = 1 cubic yard (yd³)

Dry Measure	*Liquid Measure*
2 pints = 1 quart (qt)	2 gills = 1 cup
8 quarts = 1 peck (pk)	2 cups = 1 pint
4 pecks = 1 bushel (bu)	2 pints = 1 quart (qt)
	4 quarts = 1 gallon (gal)
	$31\frac{1}{2}$ gallons = 1 barrel (bbl)
	231 cubic inches = 1 gallon

Metric System

Units of Length	*Units of Mass or Weight*
1 meter (m) = the standard	1 kilogram (kg) = the standard
1 decimeter = 0.1 meter	1 gram (g) = 0.001 kilogram
1 centimeter (cm) = 0.01 meter	1 centigram = 0.01 gram
1 millimeter (mm) = 0.001 meter	1 milligram (mg) = 0.001 gram
1 micron = 0.000001 meter	
1 kilometer (km) = 1,000 meters	

Liquid Measures

1 milliliter (ml) = 0.001 liter
1,000 liters = 1 kiloliter

Even in the United States the metric system is the recognized measuring system of science.

The standard unit of mass in the metric system is the *kilogram*. It is defined as the mass of 1,000 cubic centimeters of water at 4°C. The volume of 1,000 cubic centimeters is called the *liter*. Subdivision of the kilogram are the *gram*, the *centigram*, and the *milligram*.

The unit of time in the metric system, as in the English system, is the *second*.

6-5 Table of Weights and Measures. Table 6-1 lists some of the more common units of weights and measures and gives the accepted abbreviation for each.

6-6 Conversion Tables. Numbers which express units of measurement are called *denominate numbers*. In using denominate numbers, it is sometimes necessary to change from one unit of measurement to an equivalent unit. Such change of units within a given system of measurement is called a *reduction*. If the change of units is from one system of measurement to another, it is called a *conversion*. The following table gives some approximate relations between the two systems.

Table 6-2. English and Metric Equivalents

Measures of Length

1 inch = 2.54 centimeters
1 foot = 30.48 centimeters
1 meter = 39.37 inches
1 mile = 1.609 kilometers
1 kilometer = 0.621 mile

Measures of Area

1 square inch = 6.452 square centimeters

1 square meter = 10.76 square feet

Measures of Volume

1 cubic inch = 16.39 cubic centimeters
1 cubic foot = 28.32 liters
1 pint (liquid) = 473.2 cubic centimeters
1 liter = 1.056 quarts

Measures of Weight

1 pound = 453.6 grams
1 ounce = 28.35 grams
1 kilogram = 2.205 pounds

6-7 Dimensional Analysis. In representing a physical quantity mathematically it is necessary to use a combination of a number to describe the magnitude and a name to indicate the unit in which the quantity is measured. Thus 3 ft, 3 hr, and

3 lb describe the same number of different entities—units of length, time, and weight (or mass), respectively. In like manner, 3 in., 3 ft, and 3 miles denote the same number of different units of the same entity—that of length.

Frequently, it becomes necessary to change a given quantity from one unit of measurement to a different unit. For example, it is impossible to add 2 ft, 8 in., and 3 yd until each quantity is expressed in terms of a common unit. Thus,

$$2 \text{ ft} + 8 \text{ in.} + 3 \text{ yd} = 2 \text{ ft} + \tfrac{2}{3} \text{ ft} + 9 \text{ ft} = 11\tfrac{2}{3} \text{ ft}$$

The changing of a unit to an equivalent unit involves a quite simple operation. For example, if it is desired to convert 750 m to miles and it is known that 1 m is equivalent to 100 cm, 2.54 cm is equivalent to 1 in., 12 in. is equivalent to 1 ft, and 5,280 ft is equivalent to 1 mile, we could use the following procedure:

$$750 \text{ m} = 750 \text{ m} \left(\frac{100 \text{ cm}}{1 \text{ m}} \right) \left(\frac{1 \text{ in.}}{2.54 \text{ cm}} \right) \left(\frac{1 \text{ ft}}{12 \text{ in.}} \right) \left(\frac{1 \text{ mile}}{5,280 \text{ ft}} \right)$$
$$= 0.466 \text{ mile}$$

It will be noted that the four fractions in parentheses each equal unity, since the measured values of the numerators are equivalent to the measured value of the corresponding denominators. Essentially, then, we have multiplied 750 by (1) (1) (1) (1). Each of the units on the right side of the equality sign cancels out except the miles unit.

EXAMPLE 6-1. Reduce 60 mph to feet per second.

Solution

$$60 \text{ mph} = 60 \text{ mph} \times \frac{5,280 \text{ ft}}{1 \text{ mile}} \times \frac{1 \text{ hr}}{60 \text{ min}} \times \frac{1 \text{ min}}{60 \text{ sec}}$$
$$= 88 \frac{\text{ft}}{\text{sec}}$$

EXAMPLE 6-2. Convert 0.0875 ton/ft³ to kilograms per cubic meter.

Solution.   Using Table 6-2 we solve as follows:

$$0.0875 \frac{\text{ton}}{\text{ft}^3} = 0.0875 \frac{\text{ton}}{\text{ft}^3} \left(\frac{2{,}000 \text{ lb}}{1 \text{ ton}}\right)\left(\frac{453.6 \text{ g}}{1 \text{ lb}}\right)$$
$$\left(\frac{1 \text{ kg}}{1{,}000 \text{ g}}\right)\left(\frac{1 \text{ ft}}{30.48 \text{ cm}} \times \frac{100 \text{ cm}}{1 \text{ m}}\right)^3$$
$$= 2.80 \times 10^3 \frac{\text{kg}}{m^3}$$

PROBLEMS

In Probs. 6-1 to 6-32, reduce:

6-1. 28.3 cm to meters
6-2. 84,072 cm to kilometers
6-3. 0.00593 cm to millimeters
6-4. 90,536 mg to kilograms
6-5. 873.2 cg to grams
6-6. 45.09 kg to grams
6-7. 6,115 ml to liters
6-8. 0.00531 kl to liters
6-9. 87.5 yd to inches
6-10. 3,584 yd to miles
6-11. 2.87 miles to feet
6-12. 28.7 oz to pounds
6-13. 2,879 lb to short tons
6-14. 8.75 short tons to long tons
6-15. 29.3 pecks to bushels
6-16. 3.46 gal to pints
6-17. 8 cups to cubic inches
6-18. 83.9 cm² to square meters
6-19. 5.93 cm² to square decimeters
6-20. 5.41 m³ to cubic centimeters
6-21. 83,500 ml³ to cubic meters
6-22. 8.45 yd² to square feet
6-23. $\frac{3}{8}$ ft² to square inches
6-24. 8 square miles to acres

6-25. 5 cubic rods to cubic yards

6-26. 80 cm per second to meters per minute

6-27. 4 microns per second to meters per hour

6-28. 25 kg/m² to grams per square centimeter

6-29. 875 g/cm³ to kilograms per cubic meter

6-30. 20 tons (short) per hour to pounds per second

6-31. 70 lb/ft³ to ounces per cubic inch

6-32. 14.7 lb/in.² to short tons per square yard

In Probs. 6-33 to 6-45 perform the conversions, using a slide rule when necessary. Leave answers accurate to three significant figures.

6-33. 1,250 in. to meters

6-34. 875 gal to liters

6-35. 2.47 kg. to pounds

6-36. 3.59 km to miles

6-37. 60.5 ft/sec to centimeters per minute

6-38. 19.3 ft³/hr to cubic centimeters per second

6-39. 0.00522 kg/cm² to pounds per square inch

6-40. 0.0808 km/min to inches per second

6-41. 1.83 short tons per cubic yard to grams per cubic centimeter

6-42. 3.54 oz/in.² to grams per square centimeter

6-43. 25.7 lb/in.² to milligrams per square millimeter

6-44. 0.352 in.³/oz to cubic centimeters per gram

6-45. 525 mph to kilometers per minute

6-46. If 8 bars of iron 6 ft long, 3 in. broad, and 1.5 in. thick weigh 735 lb, what will be the weight of 5 bars of the same material if each is 9 ft long, 4 in. broad, and 2.4 in. thick?

6-47. A skilled craftsman can roll a pound of aluminum into foil so thin that it will make a sheet 6 ft wide and 90 ft long. How thick will this sheet be if aluminum has a density of 168 lb/ft³? Leave answer in inches.

6-48. If 10 machines can produce 4,800 castings in 20 days working 8 hr a day, how many days will be required for 15 machines working 6 hr a day to produce 4,320 castings?

CHAPTER **7**

Signed Numbers

7-1 Positive and Negative Numbers. Many concepts in our daily lives have their opposites. For example, we use the opposites glad and sad, bitter and sweet, hard and soft, pretty and ugly, fast and slow, etc. This dual notion also exists in mathematical concepts. Consider the opposites $8 earned and $8 spent, 5° above zero versus 5° below zero, 25 miles east and 25 miles west, 10 lb gain versus 10 lb loss, etc.

Mathematicians often represent these ideas symbolically by the use of a plus (+) or a minus (−) sign. He may represent

Eight dollars earned as +$8
Eight dollars spent as −$8
Five degrees above zero as +5°
Five degrees below zero as −5°
Twenty-five miles east as +25 miles
Twenty-five miles west as −25 miles

and so on.

Numbers preceded by a plus sign are called *positive* numbers. They are greater than zero. Numbers preceded by a minus sign are called *negative* numbers. They are less than zero. Positive and negative numbers taken together are called *signed* numbers. Zero is neither positive nor negative. If no sign is written before a number, the number is understood to be positive.

The *absolute value* of a number is the numerical value of the number and is always positive. The absolute value of +5 is 5;

106

the absolute value of −5 is 5. The absolute-value symbol is designated by two vertical bars. Thus, $|+5| = 5$, $|−5| = 5$, $|−3| = 3$, etc. Thus $|n| = n$ if n is positive and $|n| = −n$ if n is negative.

7-2 The Number Scale. A graduated horizontal (or vertical) line is useful in visualizing the relative sizes of signed numbers (Fig. 7-1). We can select any arbitrary point on the line,

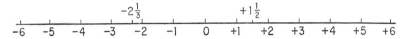

Fig. 7-1

called the *origin*, and label it 0. Then using any convenient unit of length, we can mark off equally spaced points to the right (or above) and left (or below) of the origin. The points to the right (or up) we designate as positive numbers, and those to the left (or down) as negative. Note, again, that the origin 0 is neither positive nor negative. It should be noted that there is a one-to-one correspondence between the magnitude of a number and its distance from the origin. That is, $+4$ is twice as far from the origin as is $+2$; $−3$ is three times as far from the origin as is $+1$ and is also on opposite sides of the origin along the number scale. Therefore it should be clear that, while the point on the number scale is labeled with a number, the distance this point is from the origin actually determines the number.

We know that $+5$ is greater than $+3$ and that $+6$ is greater than $+5$. Note on the horizontal scale that $+5$ is on the right of $+3$ and that $+6$ is to the right of $+5$. It should be apparent that, if we are dealing with positive number points, the larger of two numbers will lie on the right of the smaller number. In the same way, we can say that, given two points representing negative numbers on a horizontal scale, the larger number point is to the right of the smaller number point. For example, the point representing $−2$ is to the right of the point representing $−3$.

7-3 Symbols of Inequality. The symbols $>$ and $<$ are commonly used for the words "greater than" and "less than," respectively. Thus, $5 > 3$, $2 > 0$, $-3 < 0$, $-4 < -1$, $-2 < 0 < 1$, etc. If N is used to stand for a number and $N > 0$, we know that N is a positive number. Similarly, if $N < 0$, then N is a negative number.

7-4 Addition of Signed Numbers. Let us consider the addition of signed numbers. One way of illustrating addition of signed numbers is to use the idea of gain and loss. Consider the four additions

	$+\$5$ (gain)	$-\$5$ (loss)	$+\$5$ (gain)	$-\$5$ (loss)
	$+\$2$ (gain)	$-\$2$ (loss)	$-\$2$ (loss)	$+\$2$ (gain)
Sum:	$+\$7$ (gain)	$-\$7$ (loss)	$+\$3$ (gain)	$-\$3$ (loss)

These examples suggest the following rule for addition of signed numbers:

▶ *Rule.* To add two numbers with like signs, find the sum of their absolute values and prefix the common sign to the sum.

▶ *Rule.* To add two numbers with unlike signs, find the difference between their absolute values and prefix the sign of the number having the greater absolute value to the difference.

7-5 Dual Use of Plus and Minus Signs. In previous chapters in this book we have used the $+$ and $-$ signs to indicate addition and subtraction. That is, they were used as *signs of operation*, telling what mathematical operation is to be performed.

In this chapter we have shown that these signs are also used to indicate opposites, positive and negative numbers. In these cases they are used as *signs of quality* and indicate the *kind* of number, such as $+5$, -3, -2, $+1$.

This dual meaning often causes confusion for the beginning student. With practice, however, the confusion should disappear.

EXAMPLE 7-1. The following are equivalent forms.

(a)	$+5$	$5 + 3$	$= 8$
	$+3$	$(+5) + (+3) = +8$	
Sum:	$+8$	$5 + (+3)$	$= 8$

(b)	-5	$(-5) + (-3) = -8$
	-3	
Sum:	-8	

(c)	-5	$-5 + 3$	$= -2$
	$+3$	$(-5) + (+3) = (-2)$	
Sum:	-2	$(-5) + 3$	$= -2$

(d)	$+5$	$(+5) + (-3) = 2$
	-3	$5 - 3$	$= 2$
	$+2$	$5 + (-3)$	$= 2$

PROBLEMS

Which number in each pair is the smaller?

7-1. 3, 7   **7-2.** $-3, -6$ **7-3.** 2, 0   **7-4.** $-1, 0$
7-5. $-15, -25$ **7-6.** 0, -7 **7-7.** $-5, -3$ **7-8.** $-6, 0$
7-9 to **7-12.** Use the symbol $>$ to compare the pairs in Probs. 7-1 to 7-4.
7-13 to **7-16.** Use the symbol $<$ to compare the pairs in Probs. 7-5 to 7-8.

What is the numerical value of each of the following?

7-17. $|-5|$ **7-18.** $|-3|$
7-19. $|-2|^3$ **7-20.** $|-3|^2$

Add each of the following:

7-21. $+13$	**7-22.** -24	**7-23.** -15	**7-24.** $+36$
$+35$	$+65$	-12	-14

7-25.	0	**7-26.**	-15	**7-27.**	47	**7-28.**	-86
	-13		0		-47		10

7-29.	15	**7-30.**	-2	**7-31.**	$+47$	**7-32.**	11
	$-\ 5$		-7		-35		34
	-10		$\cdot\ 5$		-23		-79

7-33.	2	**7-34.**	49	**7-35.**	-23	**7-36.**	15
	-3		-16		-38		-26
	-8		-32		-17		$+34$
	4		-11		$+88$		$-\ 8$

7-37. $(+18) + (+12)$ **7-38.** $(-23) + (-15)$

7-39. $(-71) + (+26)$ **7-40.** $(+59) + (-85)$

7-41. $(8) + (-43)$ **7-42.** $(+2) + (+7) + (-3)$

7-43. $(-16) + (+4) + (-18) + (-3)$

7-44. $87 + (-25) + 6 + (-35)$

7-45. $(+75 - 23) + (-34 - 11)$

7-46. $(+8.5 - 1.3) + (-2.7 - 3.0)$

7-47. $(+5.8) + (-8.6) + (-7.3) + (9.2)$

7-48. $(+\frac{2}{3}) + (-\frac{1}{4}) + (-\frac{1}{6}) + (-\frac{1}{2})$

7-49. $(\frac{3}{4} - \frac{2}{3}) + (-\frac{7}{12} + \frac{1}{2})$

7-50. $(-6\frac{3}{5}) + (-2\frac{2}{3}) + (5\frac{1}{2}) + (8\frac{5}{6})$

7-6 Subtraction of Signed Numbers. Subtraction is a process inverse to that of addition. To subtract a number b from a number a we must find the number c which when added to b gives a. Thus $a - b = c$, if, and only if, $c + b = a$.

Suppose in buying a tube of glue costing 67 cents you gave the clerk a one dollar bill. In all probability, in giving you your change, the clerk will give you three pennies, a nickel, and a quarter while saying "67 cents, 70 cents, 75 cents, a dollar." The clerk by so doing will have subtracted 67 from 100 by counting what must be added to 67 to get 100.

Consider the following examples:

EXAMPLE 7-2. Subtract 5 from 3.

Solution. Our problem can be written

Minuend   +3
Subtrahend +5   or $(+3) - (+5) = [?]$
Difference   [?]

To find the answer we try to determine the number which when placed in the [ ] will solve an equivalent addition problem:

[?]
+5   or $[?] + (+5) = (+3)$
Sum: +3

The missing number is -2, because $[-2] + (+5) = (+3)$. Therefore, $(+3) - (+5) = -2$
or $3 - 5 = -2$

EXAMPLE 7-3. Subtract $+6$ from -3.

Solution. We must ask ourselves, "What number must be added to $+6$ to get -3?"

$$(-3) - (+6) = [?] \qquad \text{or} \qquad [?] + (+6) = -3$$

Since we know that $[-9] + (+6) = -3$, we get

$$(-3) - (+6) = -9$$

EXAMPLE 7-4. Subtract -34 from -18.

Solution. The problem is $(-18) - (-34) = [?]$. We rewrite the problem: $[?] + (-34) = -18$. Since the sum of $+16$ and -34 is -18, we get

$$(-18) - (-34) = +16$$

The foregoing illustrative examples lead to the following:

▶ *Rule.* To subtract two signed numbers, change the sign of the subtrahend. Then add the changed subtrahend to the minuend.

By the use of the above rule, the three illustrative examples just studied could be solved as follows:

(7-2) $+3$ $\qquad\qquad (+3) - (5) =$
$\qquad\quad \underline{-5}$ $\qquad$ or $\qquad (+3) + (-5) = -2$
Sum: $\overline{-2}$
(7-3) $\quad (-3) - (+6) =$
$\qquad\qquad (-3) + (-6) = -9$
or $\qquad\qquad\qquad 3 - 6 = -9$
(7-4) $(-18) - (-34) =$
$\qquad\qquad (-18) + (+34) = +16$
or $\qquad\qquad -18 + 34 = 16$

EXAMPLE 7-5. Combine to a single number $(+34) - (-16) - (+25) + (-43) - (-61)$.

Solution

$$(+34) - (-16) - (+25) + (-43) - (-61) =$$
$$(+34) + (+16) + (-25) + (-43) + (+61) =$$
$$34 + 16 - 25 - 43 + 61 =$$
$$(111) + (-68) = 43$$

EXAMPLE 7-6. If x is a number, find the value of x which makes $x - (-2) = -6$ a true statement.

Solution

$$x - (-2) = -6$$
$$x + (+2) = -6$$

We are asked, "What number added to $+2$ gives -6?" The answer should be recognized to be -8.

PROBLEMS

Subtract the bottom number from the top number:

7-51. $+8$ $\qquad$ **7-52.** -7 $\qquad$ **7-53.** $+12$ $\qquad$ **7-54.** -64
$\qquad \underline{-5}$ $\qquad\qquad\quad \underline{-3}$ $\qquad\qquad\quad\ \underline{+18}$ $\qquad\qquad\quad\ \underline{+37}$

7-55.   0   **7-56.**   0   **7-57.** 83   **7-58.** -39
     -18 -25 417 -107

Subtract the top number from the bottom number:

7-59.   13   **7-60.** 27   **7-61.** -83 **7-62.**   0
    -46 23 -107 -2

7-63. 78   **7-64.**   103   **7-65.**   6.32   **7-66.** -1.07
    87   -230 -5.79 -4.35

Find each of the following differences:

7-67. $(-8) - (+5)$ **7-68.** $(2) - (7)$
7-69. $(+11) - (-11)$ **7-70.** $(-14) - (-16)$
7-71. $(0) - (-39)$ **7-72.** $(-37) - (+26)$
7-73. $(-1) - (+18)$ **7-74.** $(23) - (-64)$
7-75. $(-87) - (0)$

Find the value of the letter which makes each equation a true statement:

7-76. $x - 7 = 5$ **7-77.** $y - (-3) = -6$
7-78. $z - (-4) = 0$ **7-79.** $(11) - x = -12$

Combine each of the following into a single number:

7-80. $(-12) - (-10) - (+8) + (+24)$
7-81. $(-36) + (15) - 10 - 28$
7-82. $-36 + 15 - 10 - 28 + 7$
7-83. $(+24) - (-12) - (+12) + (-12)$
7-84. $(-2) - (+3) + (-4) - (-5) + (-6)$
7-85. $(-1.72) - (-3.04) + (+2.97) + (-5.40) - (+0.09)$
7-86. $(0.05) + (-0.03) - (-8.09) + (+9.06) - (+5.35)$

7-7 Multiplication of Signed Numbers. You will recall that we defined multiplication as a repeated addition. With this definition we can find the product of any two numbers. Thus, $3(-4) = -4 - 4 - 4 = -12$ and $2(-5) = -5 - 5 = -10$.

Consider the product $-4(3)$.   Applying the commutative law for multiplication (see Sec. 1-6), we know that *the product of two numbers with unlike signs is a negative number.*

Now consider the product of two numbers with like signs.   We already realize that the product of two positive numbers is a positive number; e.g., $(+3)(+4) = +12$.   Recalling the distributive property of multiplication (see Sec. 1-6), we can determine a rule for multiplying two negative numbers.   Let us find the product of -4 and -5.   First look at

$$(-4)[(5) + (-5)] = -4[0] = 0$$

By the distributive law,

$$(-4)[(5) + (-5)] = (-4)(5) + (-4)(-5)$$
or
$$-4(0) = -20 + (-4)(-5)$$
and
$$0 = -20 + (-4(-5)$$

This tells us that $(-4)(-5)$ is a number which added to -20 gives 0.   There is only one such number.   That number is $+20$. Therefore it must be true that

$$(-4)(-5) = +20$$

We can now state that *the product of two numbers with like signs is a positive number.*

The associative property of grouping factors can be extended to find the product of three or more signed numbers.   Thus,

$$(-3)(-4)(-5) = -3[(-4)(-5)]$$
$$= -3[20]$$
$$= -60$$
and
$$(-2)(-3)(-4)(-5) = [(-2)(-3)][(-4)(-5)]$$
$$= [+6][+20]$$
$$= +120$$

It should now be clear that the product of two or more signed numbers is positive if there is an even number of negative factors and is negative if there is an odd number of negative factors.

7-8 Division of Signed Numbers. In Chap. 1 it was pointed out that division is the inverse of multiplication. Hence the rules for division of signed numbers will follow those for multiplication. For example, we have shown that $(-4)(+3) = -12$. It then must follow that $\frac{-12}{3} = -4$ and $\frac{-12}{-4} = +3$. We are now ready to state the following general rule:

▶ *Rule.* The product or quotient of two numbers with like signs is a positive number. The product or quotient of two numbers with unlike signs is a negative number.

PROBLEMS

Perform the indicated operations:

7-87. $(+6)(-5)$ **7-88.** $(-3)(+7)$ **7-89.** $(-7)(-9)$

7-90. $10(-2)$ **7-91.** $(-2)^2$ **7-92.** $(-2)^3$

7-93. $(-\frac{1}{2})^2$ **7-94.** $(-\frac{1}{2})^3$ **7-95.** $(-\frac{2}{3})^2$

7-96. $(-\frac{2}{3})^3$ **7-97.** $(-1)(-4)(+5)$

7-98. $(-2)(+3)(-4)$ **7-99.** $(-7)(+\frac{1}{2})(+8)$

7-100. $(-12)(-2)(-3)$ **7-101.** $(-\frac{5}{7})(+\frac{14}{15})(+\frac{9}{8})$

7-102. $(-1)(-1)(-2)(-2)$ **7-103.** $(-5)(-2)(+4)(+3)$

7-104. $(7)(-1)(-3)(-2)$ **7-105.** $(8)(-\frac{1}{4})(-\frac{1}{2})(-5)$

7-106. $-8(-14 + 10)$ **7-107.** $-6(27 - 15)$

7-108. $\dfrac{-84}{-12}$ **7-109.** $\dfrac{210}{-14}$

7-110. $(-16) \div (12)$

7-111. $(19) \div (-4)$ **7-112.** $\dfrac{(-5)(-2)}{(+4)(+15)}$

7-113. $\dfrac{(7)(-12)}{(-1)(-14)}$ **7-114.** $\dfrac{(-1)(-24)(+7)}{(-3)(-14)}$

7-115. $\dfrac{(-8)(+5)(-3)}{(-6)}$ **7-116.** $(-4)^3 \div (-2)^2$

7-117. $(-4)^2 \div (-2)^3$ **7-118.** $(-\frac{8}{27}) \div (\frac{4}{9}) \div (-\frac{2}{3})$

7-119. $(3\frac{1}{5}) \div (-1\frac{1}{6}) \times (\frac{4}{15})$

Place one of the following symbols $<$, $>$, $=$ between the pairs of quantities to make a true statement for each of the following

7-120. $(5 + 7)$?̲ $(9 - 3)$

7-121. $\frac{1}{3} + \frac{1}{4}$?̲ $\frac{1}{2}$

7-122. $(-4 + 7)^3$?̲ $(21 + 6)$

7-123. $\frac{3}{7} \div \frac{5}{6}$?̲ $\frac{7}{3} \times \frac{5}{6}$

7-124. $-7(-8 + 5)$?̲ $(-6 + 3)(-2 - 1)$

7-125. $3(5 - 7)^2$?̲ $(-1.3)^2$

7-126. $(8.537 - 7.294)$?̲ $\frac{3}{7} \div \frac{1}{3}$

CHAPTER 8

Elementary Algebra

8-1 Meaning of Algebra. Algebra is an extension of arithmetic in which letters are often used to represent numbers. For example, to find the area of a rectangle, we multiply the number of units in the length by the number of units in the width. If we let l represent the number of units in length, w the number of units in width, and A the units of area, we can write

$$A = l \cdot w \qquad \text{or} \qquad A = lw$$

In algebra, when two or more letters representing numbers are written next to each other with no operation symbol between them, it is understood to mean the product of the numbers represented by them. Thus we see that algebra generalizes arithmetic.

8-2 Literal Numbers. Any letter used to represent a number is called a *literal* number. The four fundamental processes, indicated by the symbols $+$, $-$, $\times$, $\div$, have the same meaning in algebra as they have in arithmetic. If a and b represent two numbers, $a + b$ represents their sum; $a - b$, their difference; $a \times b$, their product; $a \div b$, their quotient; $\sqrt{a}$ represents the square root of a; etc.

Since x is commonly used as a symbol for a number, it is not often used in algebra as a symbol for multiplication. To indicate the product of numbers represented by a and b, we write $(a)(b)$, $a \cdot b$, or simply ab.

117

Literal numbers often cannot be added, subtracted, multiplied, and divided the same way as arithmetic numbers. In arithmetic, if we want to find the sum of, for example, 6 and 2, we can express their sum by one symbol, namely, 8. If we want to add two numbers represented by x and y, we can only indicate the operation, i.e., $x + y$. In like manner, the difference, product, and quotient of the two numbers can be expressed by single numbers, 4, 12, and 3, respectively. The difference between x and y is expressed $x - y$. The product is xy. The quotient is x/y or $x \div y$.

In arithmetic, $8\frac{1}{3}$ means the sum of 8 and $\frac{1}{3}$, while in algebra, xy is used to indicate the product of two numbers represented by x and y. 54 means $5(10) + 4$. This differs from the algebraic meaning of, say, ab.

The raised dot should be avoided when decimals are present. The use of parentheses as a symbol for multiplication should then be used if needed for clarity's sake. For example, we should write $3(0.05)$ rather than $3 \cdot 0.05$.

8-3 Algebraic Terminology. The expression $3xy$ is used to indicate the product of 3 and numbers represented by x and y. The 3 is called the *numerical factor* and x and y are called the *literal factors* of the product. The numerical factor is called the *numerical coefficient* of the remaining literal factors. Thus, 3 is the numerical coefficient of xy; xy is the literal coefficient of 3; y is the coefficient of $3x$; etc. We usually do not write 1 as a coefficient. When the letter x is written to denote a number, it is understood to mean $1x$.

Any combination of arithmetic numbers, literal numbers, and symbols of operation, when written according to the rules of algebra, is called an *algebraic expression*. Thus $2a$, $5yz$, $3x + 4y$, $3h$ are algebraic expressions.

A *term* or *monomial* is an algebraic expression whose parts are not separated by a $+$ or a $-$ sign. An algebraic expression such as $3x + 4y$ is the sum of two terms. The difference of the terms would be expressed as $3x - 4y$ or $4y - 3x$.

An algebraic expression of two terms is called a *binomial*. An algebraic expression of three terms is called a *trinomial*. An algebraic expression of two or more terms is called a *polynomial*. Thus a trinomial is a polynomial of three terms.

Two terms which have the same literal factors are called *similar terms*. Thus, $2x$ and $5x$ are similar terms. Two terms that do not have the same literal factor are called *dissimilar terms*. Thus $5a$ and $7y$ are dissimilar terms.

A *power* of a quantity is the product obtained when that quantity is multiplied by itself a number of times. A short cut indicating this product is achieved by the use of exponents. An *exponent* is a number written to the right and a little above the quantity to indicate how many times the quantity is taken as a factor. Thus

$(5)(5)$ is written 5^2 and is the second power of 5.

$a \cdot a$ is written a^2 and is the second power of a.

$a \cdot a \cdot a$ is written a^3 and is the third power of a.

$a \cdot a \cdot a \cdot a$ is written a^4 and is the fourth power of a.

The number to which an exponent is affixed is called the *base*. In the previous examples 5 and a were bases.

a^2 is generally read "a squared."

a^3 is generally read "a cubed."

a^4 is generally read "a to the fourth power."

$6a^2b^3$ is read "six a squared b cubed."

$2a^2 + 3ab^2 - 4b^3$ is read "two a squared plus three ab squared minus four b cubed."

If the power of a quantity is not indicated, it is understood to be 1. Thus, we usually write x rather than x^1 and $5ab^2$ rather than $5a^1b^2$.

8-4   Evaluation of Algebraic Expressions.   A very important process in algebra is finding the numerical value of algebraic expressions when the numerical values of the literal factors are known. Whenever we evaluate an algebraic expression, we substitute numbers for letters. Hence, the process is often called *substitution*.

EXAMPLE 8-1. If $a = 1$, $b = 2$, $c = 3$, find the value of $2a - 3b + 5c$.

Solution

$$2a - 3b + 5c =$$
$$2(1) - 3(2) + 5(3) =$$
$$2 - 6 + 15 = 11$$

EXAMPLE 8-2. If $x = 2$, $y = -1$, $z = 3$, find the value of $3xy - 5yz - 7xz$.

Solution

$$3xy \quad - \quad 5yz \quad - \quad 7xz \quad =$$
$$3(2)(-1) - 5(-1)(3) - 7(2)(3) =$$
$$-6 \quad + \quad 15 \quad - \quad 42 \quad = -33$$

EXAMPLE 8-3. If $u = 2$, $v = 3$, $w = -1$, find the value of $3u^2 - 2uv + 4v^2w^3$.

Solution

$$3u^2 \quad - 2uv \quad + 4u^2w^3 \quad =$$
$$3(2)^2 - 2(2)(3) + 4(2)^2(-1)^3 =$$
$$12 \quad - \quad 12 \quad - \quad 16 \quad = -16$$

PROBLEMS

8-1. Given the algebraic expression $6x^2y + 5xyz + 9ab - 3x^2y$.

    (*a*) What is the third term?

    (*b*) What is the numerical coefficient of the first term?

    (*c*) What is the coefficient of x in the second term?

    (*d*) Which terms are similar?

Express the following as algebraic expressions:

8-2. The sum of 3, s, and t

8-3. Subtract x from y

8-4. The difference between a and b

8-5. 8 more than d

8-6. The product of 5 and y

8-7. 6 less than c

8-8. h increased by 1

8-9. y decreased by z

8-10. Four more than three times x

8-11. The sum of r and s divided by their product

8-12. The quotient of $15a$ divided by $13b$

8-13. The product of u and w divided by their sum

8-14. Six times the sum of x and y

8-15. The sum of r and s decreased by the sum of h and k

8-16. Eight times the difference between x and y

8-17. The product of $2x$ and $3y$

Evaluate the following if $x = 1$, $y = -1$, $z = 2$, $w = -2$, $k = 3$:

8-18. $x + y + z$ **8-19.** $5xy$ **8-20.** $\dfrac{x + y}{z}$

8-21. $3z - 2$ **8-22.** x^2y **8-23.** $5y^2z$

8-24. $3w^2 - 2yz$ **8-25.** $\dfrac{2w + 5k}{7}$ **8-26.** $\dfrac{2y - 5w}{4}$

8-27. $xy + yz + zw$ **8-28.** $3(y + z)$ **8-29.** $(x + z)^2$

8-30. $x(y + z)$ **8-31.** $5x^2y^2z^2$ **8-32.** $(2k - y)^2$

8-33. $(x + y)(z + k)$ **8-34.** $(x + z)(w + k)$ **8-35.** $x^2 - y^2$

8-36. $z^2 + k^2$ **8-37.** $5xk - 2yw$ **8-38.** $\dfrac{1}{x} - \dfrac{2}{y}$

8-39. $\dfrac{1}{x} + \dfrac{2}{y}$ **8-40.** $7k - (2x + 3z)$ **8-41.** $5k + 4(3y - 2z)$

8-5 Addition of Similar Terms. In Chap. 1 we added numbers by adding units to units, tens to tens, hundreds to hundreds, etc., and by adding tenths to tenths, hundredths to hundredths, etc. In adding fractions we added only like fractions. These were applications of the *first law of addition:* Only like quantities can be added. We now apply this law to obtain the rule:

▶ *Rule.* To add similar terms, add their numerical coefficients and multiply the sum by the common literal factor.

Example 8-4.   Add $5xy + 3xy + 4xy$

Solution

$$5xy + 3xy + 4xy = 12xy$$

Example 8-5.   Add $2h^2 + 7hk - 3hk^2$, $5h^2k + 6hk - 9hk^2$, $4h^2k - 5hk + 6hk^2$.

Solution

$$2h^2k + 7hk - 3hk^2$$
$$5h^2k + 6hk - 9hk^2$$
$$4h^2k - 5hk + 6hk^2$$

Sum:
$$11h^2k + 8hk - 6hk^2$$

Often in adding terms we can take advantage of two more properties of addition.   The *law of order:* addition is commutative; that is, $a + b = b + a$.   The *law of grouping:* addition is associative; that is, $a + b + c = (a + b) + c = a + (b + c) = (a + c) + b$.

Example 8-6.   Simplify $3x + 8x + 17x + 32x$.

Solution

$$3x + 8x + 17x + 32x =$$
$$3x + 17x + 8x + 32x =$$
$$20x + 40x = 60x$$

Example 8-7.   Simplify $5x^3 + 2x^2y - 3xy^2 + 4y^3 + 7xy^2 - 8x^2y + 2x^3 - 9y^3$.

Solution

$$5x^3 + 2x^2y - 3xy^2 + 4y^3 + 7xy^2 - 8x^2y + 2x^3 - 9y^3 =$$
$$(5x^3 + 2x^3) + (2x^2y - 8x^2y) + (-3xy^2 + 7xy^2) + (4y^3 - 9y^3) =$$
$$7x^3 - 6x^2y + 4xy^2 - 5y^3$$

8-6   Subtraction of Similar Terms.   Algebraic subtraction follows logically from arithmetic subtraction. You will recall that subtraction was defined as the inverse of addition. For example, we know that $8x - 5x = 3x$ because $3x + 5x = 8x$. This leads directly to the following rule.

▶ *Rule.* To subtract two similar terms, find the difference of the coefficients and multiply it by the common literal factor.

EXAMPLE   8-8.   Subtract $12a^2b - 5ab + 8ab^2$ from $6a^2b + 3ab - 4ab^2$.

Solution

$$6a^2b + 3ab - 4ab^2$$
$$12a^2b - 5ab + 8ab^2$$

Difference: $-6a^2b + 8ab - 12ab^2$

PROBLEMS

Add:

8-42. $4a$ **8-43.** $-5k$ **8-44.** $6xy$ **8-45.** $-3ab$
$\underline{3a}$ $\underline{+2k}$ $\underline{xy}$ $\underline{-5ab}$

8-46. $-11b^2c$ **8-47.** $8cd$ **8-48.** $-4xy^2$ **8-49.** bd
$\underline{+\ 3b^2c}$ $\underline{-3cd}$ $\underline{+3xy^2}$ $\underline{-7bd}$

8-50. $-5m^2n$ **8-51.** $6r^2t^2$ **8-52.** $-3x^2y^3$ **8-53.** $-b^3c^2$
$\underline{-2m^2n}$ $\underline{4r^2t^2}$ $-2x^2y^3$ $2b^3c^2$
x^2y^3 b^3c^2
$\underline{8x^2y^3}$ $\underline{4b^3c^2}$

8-54. uv^3 **8-55.** $9.1xy$ **8-56.** $2x^2 - 3xy + 7y^2$
$3uv^3$ $-2.6xy$ $x^2 + xy - 4y^2$
$-8uv^3$ $-5.3xy$ $\underline{5x^2 - 2xy - 5y^2}$
$\underline{2uv^3}$ $\underline{-4.1xy}$

8-57. $11a^3 - 5a^2b + 3ab^2$
$-5a^3 + 7a^2b \qquad\quad - 9b^3$
$\quad\;\; - 5a^2b - 4ab^2 + 7b^3$

8-58. Subtract $3x^2 - 2xy + 4y^2$ from $5x^2 - 3xy - 6y^2$.

8-59. Subtract $11r^2s^2 + 7rs - 5$ from $3r^2s^2 - 4rs + 8$.

8-60. From $8a^3 + b^3$ take away $2a^3 + 3a^2b - ab^2$.

8-61. From $5a^3 - 6ab + 2b^3$ take away $8a^3 - 4ab - b^3$.

Complete the following:

8-62. $7x + (?) = 11x$ **8-63.** $3a + (?) = -8a$

8-64. $24w = (?) + 36w$ **8-65.** $25k = 13k + (?)$

8-66. $13xy - (?) = 2xy$ **8-67.** $42rs - (?) = -25rs$

8-68. $18a^2b = (?) - 27a^2b$ **8-69.** $21lm = 25lm - (?)$

Combine the following:

8-70. $5x - 3x + 7x + 4x$

8-71. $11ab + 4ab - 10ab - 8ab$

8-72. $x - x^3 + 5x + 6x^3$

8-73. $2a - 3 + 11a + 5 - 4a$

8-74. $d^4 + d^2 + 2d^3 + d^2$

8-75. $5x^2y - 3xy + 5x + 6xy - x^2y$

8-76. $a^2b - b^3 - ab^2 + 2a^3 + 5ab^2 + 11a^2b$

8-77. $3a + b + 2a - 5c - b - 2c + 8a$

8-78. $x + 2x^2 - 5 + x^3 - 2x - 2x^2 + 2$

8-79. $(2x^2y - xy^2 + 7xy) + (xy^2 - 5x^2y + 8xy)$

8-80. $(8a^3 - 2a^2b + 4ab^2 - 6b^3) - (4a^3 - 3a^2b - 2ab^2 - b^3)$

8-81. $(5x^2 - y^2) - (6x^2 - 3y^2) - (8x^2 + 2y^2)$

8-7 Laws of Exponents. Algebraic multiplication is subject to the same laws as arithmetic multiplication (see Sec. 1-6), namely:

1. Multiplication is commutative; that is, $xy = yx$.

2. Multiplication is associative; that is, $xyz = (xy)z = x(yz)$.

3. Multiplication is distributive with respect to addition; that is, $x(y + z) = xy + xz$.

We shall now develop some laws for exponents for the product and quotient of two powers. Consider the following:

1. *Product of powers.*

$$x^6 \cdot x^2 = (x \cdot x \cdot x \cdot x \cdot x \cdot x)(x \cdot x) \qquad \text{by definition of exponent}$$
$$= x \cdot x \cdot x \cdot x \cdot x \cdot x \cdot x \cdot x \qquad \text{by the law of associativity}$$
$$= x^8 \qquad \text{by definition of exponent}$$

▶ *Rule.* The exponent of the product of powers with the same base is the sum of the exponents of the factors. In general

$$x^m \cdot x^n = x^{m+n}$$

2. *Quotient of powers.*

$$x^6 \div x^2 = \frac{x^6}{x^2}$$
$$= \frac{x \cdot x \cdot x \cdot x \cdot x \cdot x}{x \cdot x} \qquad \text{by definition of exponent}$$
$$= x \cdot x \cdot x \cdot x \qquad \text{by fundamental principle of fraction}$$
$$= x^4 \qquad \text{by definition of exponent}$$

▶ *Rule.* The exponent of the quotient of two powers with the same base is the difference of the exponents of the factors. In general,

$$x^m \div x^n = x^{m-n}$$

3. *Power of a power.*

$$(x^3)^2 = x^3 \cdot x^3 \qquad \text{by definition of exponent}$$
$$= x^6 \qquad \text{by Rule 1 above}$$

▶ *Rule.* The exponent of a power of a power is the product of the exponents of the powers. In general,

$$(x^m)^n = x^{mn}$$

4. *Power of a product.*

$$(xy)^2 = (xy)(xy) \qquad \text{by definition of exponent}$$
$$= x \cdot y \cdot x \cdot y \qquad \text{by meaning of } xy$$
$$= x \cdot x \cdot y \cdot y \qquad \text{by commuting the two middle factors}$$
$$= x^2 y^2 \qquad \text{by definition of exponent}$$

▶ *Rule.* To raise a product of two factors to a given power multiply the exponents of the factors by the exponent of the power to which the product is raised. In general,

$$(x^a y^b)^m = x^{am} y^{bm}$$

5. *Power of a quotient.*

$$\left(\frac{x^2}{y^3}\right)^2 = \frac{x^2}{y^3} \cdot \frac{x^2}{y^3} \qquad \text{by definition of exponent}$$

$$= \frac{x^2 \cdot x^2}{y^3 \cdot y^3} \qquad \text{by rule for finding product of fractions}$$

$$= \frac{x^4}{y^6} \qquad \text{by Rule 1 above}$$

▶ *Rule.* To raise a quotient of two quantities to a given power, multiply each of the exponents of the two quantities by the exponent of the power and divide. In general,

$$\left(\frac{x^a}{y^b}\right)^m = \frac{x^{am}}{y^{bm}}$$

8-8 Multiplication of Monomials. Consider the following problem in multiplication: $(-15x^2yz^3)(3xy^3z^4)$. To find the product, let us apply the laws of multiplication and the laws of exponents.

$$(-15x^2yz^3)(3xy^3z^4) = -15(x^2)(y)(z^3)(3)(x)(y^3)(z^4),$$
$$= -15(3)(x^2)(x)(y)(y^3)(z^3)(z^4)$$
$$= -45x^3y^4z^7$$

The solution to this problem illustrates the following rule.

▶ *Rule.* To find the product of two or monomials: (1) Determine the sign of the product by applying the rule for signs in multiplication; (2) multiply the numerical coefficients of the factors to get the numerical coefficient of the product; (3) multiply this coefficient (with proper sign) by the product of the literal factors.

8-9   Division of Monomials.   Consider the following problem in division: $(-15x^2yz^3) \div (3xy^3z^4)$. Here we apply the fundamental principle of fractions and the laws of exponents.

$$(-15x^2yz^3) \div (3xy^3z^4) = \frac{-15x^2yz^3}{3xy^3z^4}$$

$$= -\frac{5x}{y^2z}$$

▶ *Rule.* To find the quotient of two monomials: (1) Determine the sign of the quotient by applying the rules for signs in division; (2) divide the numerical coefficients to find the numerical coefficient of the quotient; (3) apply the fundamental principle of fractions to reduce the quotient of the literal factors to one involving the smallest positive exponents for each factor; (4) multiply this quotient by the numerical coefficient, with proper sign.

PROBLEMS

Simplify:

8-82. $8 \cdot 8 \cdot 8 \cdot 8 \cdot 8$

8-83. $x \cdot x \cdot y \cdot y \cdot y$

8-84. $a \cdot b \cdot b \cdot a \cdot a$

8-85. $(8a)(8a)(8a)(8a)(8a)$

8-86. $xy(2xy)$

8-87. $a^5 \cdot a^3$

8-88. $s \cdot s \cdot s \cdot s \cdot x \cdot x \cdot x \cdot y \cdot z \cdot z \cdot z$

8-89. $u^7 \cdot u \cdot u^4$

8-90. $5^3 \cdot 5^2$

8-91. $(3x)(4x)$

8-92. $(-5y)(3y)$

8-93. $(-4y^2)(5y^3)$

8-94. $(2ab)(3cd)$

8-95. $(-2rs)(3rt)(-4st)$

8-96. $(xy)(xyz)(-yz)$

8-97. $(-5ab^2c)(-2a^3c^2)(-3bc)$

8-98. $a \cdot a + b \cdot b$

8-99. $3x \cdot x \cdot x - x \cdot x \cdot x$

8-100. $k \cdot k \cdot k + k \cdot k$

8-101. $9z \cdot z \cdot z - 4z \cdot z$

8-102. $(rs)^3$

8-103. $(xz^2)^3$

8-104. $(2ab)^2$

8-105. $(-5x^2y^3)^2$

8-106. $(-3c^2d)^3$

8-107. $(-2xy^2z^3)^4$

8-108. $\dfrac{-12x^2y^3}{6xy}$

8-109. $\dfrac{-18ab^3c^2}{-3abc}$

8-110. $(-24r^2s^3t^7) \div (3rs^3t^4)$ **8-111.** $(-6x^3yz) \div (-6xyz)$

8-112. $(40c^5d^3e^4) \div (-5c^4d^3e^2)$

8-113. $(-48d^4km^2) \div (16d^3k^3m^3)$

8-114. $\dfrac{x^3 \cdot x^4}{x^2}$ **8-115.** $\dfrac{3^7 \cdot 3^2 \cdot 3^9}{3^5}$

8-116. $\dfrac{x^4y^2}{(xy)^2}$ **8-117.** $\dfrac{a^3(b^2)^4}{(ab^3)^2}$

8-118. $\dfrac{(-cD^3)^2}{(-c^2D)^3}$ **8-119.** $\dfrac{x^3(-y^2)^3}{(-xy)^3}$

8-120. $\dfrac{(-x^3)^2(y^2)}{x^2(-y)^2}$ **8-121.** $\left[\dfrac{a^2(-bc^4)^3}{b^4(-a^3c^5)^2}\right]^3$

8-10 Multiplication of a Polynomial by a Monomial.
When a polynomial is multiplied by a monomial, use is made of
the associative and distributive laws of addition.   Thus,

$$a(x + y + z) = a[(x + y) + z] \quad \text{by the associative law}$$
$$= a(x + y) + az \quad \text{by the distributive law}$$
$$= ax + ay + az \quad \text{by the distributive law}$$

▶ *Rule.* To multiply a polynomial by a monomial, multiply
each term of the polynomial by the monomial.

EXAMPLE 8-9.   Multiply $2x^2 - 5xy + 8y^2$ by $3xy^2$.

Solution

$$3xy^2(2x^2 - 5xy + 8y^2) = 3xy^2(2x^2) + (3xy^2)(-5xy)$$
$$+ (3xy^2)(8y^2)$$
$$= 6x^3y^2 - 15x^2y^3 + 24xy^4$$

8-11 Multiplication of a Polynomial by a Polynomial.
The distributive, commutative, and associative laws for addition
and multiplication can now be used to find the product of two
polynomials.   Consider the product of two binomials.   For
example,

$$(a + b)(x + y) = (a + b)x + (a + b)y \qquad \text{by the distributive law}$$

$$= x(a + b) + y(a + b) \qquad \text{by the commutative law}$$

$$= ax + bx + ay + by \qquad \text{by the distributive law}$$

$$= ax + ay + bx + by \qquad \text{by the associative law}$$

The above solution can be written in a vertical arrangement as follows:

$$
\begin{array}{l}
x + y \\
a + b \\
\hline
ax + ay \\
\qquad\quad + bx + by \\
\hline
ax + ay + bx + by
\end{array}
$$

It will be noted that four separate multiplications are required to obtain the product. The first step is to multiply each term of the multiplicand by the first term of the multiplier. Next each term of the multiplicand is multiplied by the second term of the multiplier. If there are more than two terms in the multiplier, the process is continued until each of the terms in the multiplicand is multiplied by each term in the multiplier. The partial products are then combined by addition. The sum of like terms is replaced by a single term.

EXAMPLE 8-10. Multiply $(x^2 + 2xy - 3y^2)$ by $(x + 5y)$.

Solution

$$
\begin{array}{l}
x^2 + 2xy - 3y^2 \\
x + 5y \\
\hline
x^3 + 2x^2y - 3xy^2 \\
\qquad\quad + 5x^2y + 10xy^2 - 15y^3 \\
\hline
x^3 + 7x^2y + 7xy^2 - 15y^3
\end{array}
$$

In multiplying polynomials, it is desirable to rearrange, if necessary, the terms of the multiplicand and multiplier in a descending order of powers of one of the letters. Consider the next example.

EXAMPLE 8-11. Multiply $(2x - 3x^2 - 8 + x^3)$ by $(4 + 5x)$.

Solution. Rearrange the terms in descending powers of x before multiplying.

$$
\begin{array}{l}
x^3 - 3x^2 + 2x - 8 \\
5x + 4 \\
\hline
5x^4 - 15x^3 + 10x^2 - 40x \\
\quad\;\; + 4x^3 - 12x^2 + 8x - 32 \\
\hline
5x^4 - 11x^3 - 2x^2 - 32x - 32
\end{array}
$$

PROBLEMS

Perform the indicated multiplications:

8-122. $2ab(a^2 - bc + c^2)$ **8-123.** $-5ab^2(3a^2 - ab + 4b^2)$

8-124. $3x^2y(x^2 - 2xy + 3y^2)$ **8-125.** $4k(k^3 - 2k^2 + 5k - 7)$

8-126. $6x^2(5x^2 - 2x + 3)$ **8-127.** $-3u^2v^2(u^3 - 4u^2v + 7v^2)$

8-128. $2x(x - y + 3)(5y)$ **8-129.** $3ab(a^2 - 2ab - b^2)$

8-130. $(x + 3)(x + 4)$ **8-131.** $(a + 5)(a - 3)$

8-132. $(y - 9)(y - 4)$ **8-133.** $(z + 7)(z - 11)$

8-134. $(2x + 3)(x - 4)$ **8-135.** $(3a - 5)(2a - 7)$

8-136. $(3 - 3y)(2 - y)$ **8-137.** $(7 + 2x)(2x - 7)$

8-138. $(3x^2 - y)(2x^2 + 3y)$ **8-139.** $(5m^2 - 2m)(3m^2 - 4m)$

8-140. $(a + 4b)(a^2 - 2ab + b^2)$

8-141. $(x - 2y)(2x^2 - 3xy + y^2)$

8-142. $(2k^2 - 3m^2)(3k^2 - km - 4m^2)$

8-143. $(x^2 - 5y^2)(x^2 - xy - 3y^2)$

8-144. $(x^2 - 2x - 3)(x^2 + x + 4)$

8-145. $(a^2 - 3a + 6)(a^2 + 2a - 5)$

8-146. $(x^2 + xy + y^2)(x^2 - xy + y^2)$

8-147. $(a^2 - ab - 2b^2)(2a^2 - ab + b^2)$

8-148. $(2x^2 - 3xy + 4y^2)(5x^2 - 6xy - y^2)$

8-149. $(3a^2 + ab - 2b^2)(2a^2 - ab + b^2)$

8-150. $(3x^2 - 5x + 2x^3 - 7)(2 + 3x)$

8-151. $(2x^2y - 3xy^2 + x^3 - y^3)(-7y + 4x)$

8-152. $(x + 2)(x - 3)(2x + 1)$

8-153. $(a - 6)(a - 2)(a + 1)$

8-154. $(2x - 1)(x + 2)(2x + 1)$

8-155. $(3a - 2)(a + 3)(a + 3)$

8-156. $(x - 2y)(2x - y)(x + y)$

8-157. $(2a - b)(a - 3b)(a + 5b)$

8-12 Division of a Polynomial by a Monomial.   Division is inverse to multiplication. To divide, then, we reverse the process of multiplication.

▶ *Rule.* To divide a polynomial by a monomial, divide each of the terms in the dividend by the divisor and add the results.

Example 8-12.   Divide $12ax^3y^3 - 8ax^2y^2 + 6axy$ by $2axy$.

Solution

$$\frac{12ax^3y^3 - 8ax^2y^2 + 6axy}{2axy} = 6x^2y^2 - 4xy + 3$$

8-13 Division of a Polynomial by a Polynomial.   The procedure for dividing one polynomial by another polynomial is similar to the process of long division of arithmetic. The procedure can best be shown by an example.

Example 8-13.   Divide $(x^3 + 6x^4 - 3x^2 - 19 - 8x)$ by $(2x - 3)$.

Solution.   To avoid confusion, the terms in the dividend and divisor should be arranged in descending powers of x. The complete steps of the solution follow.

$$3x^3 + 5x^2 + 6x + 5 + \frac{-4}{2x - 3}$$

$$2x - 3 \overline{\smash{\big)}\, 6x^4 + x^3 - 3x^2 - 8x - 19}$$

$$\underline{6x^4 - 9x^3}$$
$$10x^3 - 3x^2$$
$$\underline{10x^3 - 15x^2}$$
$$12x^2 - 8x$$
$$\underline{12x^2 - 18x}$$
$$10x - 19$$
$$\underline{10x - 15}$$
$$- 4$$

1. Divide $6x^4$ by $2x$ to get $3x^3$.

2. Place $3x^3$ as the first term in the quotient.

3. Multiply $(2x - 3)$ by $3x^3$ to get $6x^4 - 9x^3$. Place this quantity under the similar terms in the dividend.

4. Subtract similar terms to get a remainder of $10x^3$.

5. Bring down the next term, $-3x^2$, to get a new dividend, $10x^3 - 3x^2$.

6. Divide $10x^3$ by $2x$ to get $5x^2$.

7. Place $5x^2$ as the second term of the quotient.

8. Multiply $(2x - 3)$ by $5x^2$ to get $10x^3 - 15x^2$. Place this quantity under similar terms in the new dividend.

9. Subtract to get a remainder of $12x^2$.

10. Bring down the next term, $-8x$, to get a second new dividend.

11. Continue the process until the last remainder, -4, is of lower order than the first term of the divisor.

The solution, then, can be written:

$$\frac{6x^4 + x^3 - 3x^2 - 8x - 19}{2x - 3} = 3x^3 + 5x^2 + 6x + 5 + \frac{-4}{2x - 3}$$

PROBLEMS

Perform the indicated divisions:

8-158. $(12x^4 - 16x^3 - 8x + 4) \div 4$

8-159. $(15a^3 - 9a^2 + 12a - 6) \div 3$

8-160. $(24a^4 - 16a^2 - 12a) \div 4a$

8-161. $(x^2y - xy^2 - 2xy^3) \div xy$

8-162. $(14a^3b^3 - 21a^2b^2 - 28ab) \div 7ab$

8-163. $(30x^3y^4 + 21x^2y^2 - 18x^2y^4 - 15x^2y^5) \div 3x^2y^2$

8-164. $(a^2 - 7a + 10) \div (a - 2)$

8-165. $(x^2 + 8x + 15) \div (x + 5)$

8-166. $(10x^2 + 7xy - 12y^2) \div (2x + 3y)$

8-167. $(3x^4y^2 + 5x^2yz - 2z^2) \div (x^2y + 2z)$

8-168. $(4x^2 - 20xy + 25y^2) \div (2x - 5y)$

8-169. $(5z^2 - 25zy - 30y^2) \div (5z + 5y)$

8-170. $(15a^2 + 28a - 32) \div (-5a + 4)$

8-171. $(x^3 + 4x^2 + 7x + 6) \div (x + 2)$

8-172. $(2a^3 - 3a^2 - 13a + 12) \div (a - 3)$

8-173. $(8x^3 - 10x^2 - 13x + 15) \div (4x^2 - 5 + x)$

8-174. $(10x^3 - 7x^2y - 16xy^2 + 12y^3) \div (5x - 6y)$

8-175. $(18y^3 - 27y^2z + 16yz^2 - 4z^3) \div (6y^2 - 5yz + 2z^2)$

8-176. $(6a^3 - 13a^2b + 8ab^2 - 3b^3) \div (2a - 3b)$

8-177. $(16a^4 - 9a^2b^2 - 12ab^3 - 4b^4) \div (4a^2 + 3ab + 2b^2)$

8-178. $(15k^3 - 29k^2 + 16) \div (3k - 4)$

8-179. $(a^4 + 2a^2b^2 + b^4) \div (a^2 + 3b^2 + 2ab)$

8-180. $(64a^3 - 729b^6) \div (4a - 9b^2)$

8-181. $(x^2 + 4y^2 + z^2 + 4xy + 2xz + 4yz) \div (x + 2y + z)$

8-182. $(a^2 + 9b^2 + 4c^2 - 6ab + 4ac - 12bc) \div (a - 3b + 2c)$

8-183. $(3k^4 - 31k^3 + 78k^2 - 74k + 30) \div (k^2 - 8k + 6)$

8-184. $(14a^4 + 45a^3 + 78a^2 + 45a + 11) \div (2a^2 + 5a + 7)$

8-185. $(12a^4 - 39a^3b + 4a^2b^2 + 37ab^3 + 10b^4)$
$\div (4a^2 - 5ab - 2b^2)$

8-186. $(6x^4 - x^3y + 5x^2y^2 + 34xy^3 - 14y^4)$
$\div (2x^2 - 3xy + 7y^2)$

8-187. $(42c^4 - 63c^3d - 79c^2d^2 + 45cd^3 + 40d^4)$
$\div (6c^2 - 9cd - 7d^2)$

CHAPTER 9

Linear Equations

9-1 Identical and Conditional Equations. A statement that two quantities are equal is called an equation. The symbol = is used to indicate that two quantities have the same value. That part of an equation which is to the left of the equality sign is called the *left side*, or *left member*, of the equation. That part of an equation which is to the right of the equality sign is called the *right side*, or *right member*, of the equation.

There are two kinds of equations found in the study of elementary algebra. They can be illustrated by the equations (1) $2x + 3x = 5x$ and (2) $4x + 1 = 21$. The first statement is true for any value which may be assigned to the letter x. The second statement is true only if x is replaced by an expression equal to 5. When an equation is true for all values that may be assigned to the letter, the equation is called an *identical equation*, or simply an *identity*. An equation which is true for only some particular value or values for the letters it contains is called a *conditional equation*. The first equation is an identity; the second is a conditional equation.

Sometimes the symbol $\equiv$ is used to indicate an identity. Thus, $a + b \equiv b + a$. However, this is not usually necessary, because the context of the statement will make clear which type is indicated. When the word "equation" is used by itself, we shall mean a conditional equation.

9-2 Solving Equations. Any number which, when substituted for the letter in a conditional equation involving one letter, will make its members equal is called the *root* of the equation. The process of finding the roots of an equation is known as *solving* the equation. The set of roots of an equation is called its *solution*. Thus, the solution of the equation $4x + 1 = 21$ is 5. The root of the equation is 5.

The solution of conditional equations forms a vital part of the mathematics that is found in the study of physics, chemistry, engineering, and engineering technology.

To solve equations, we often make use of several important self-evident truths called *axioms*. These axioms deal with operations which always lead to equivalent equations.

Axiom 1.   Equality is a reflexive relation; that is, $a = a$.

Axiom 2.   Equality is a symmetric relation; i.e., if $a = b$, then $b = a$.

Axiom 3.   Equality is a transitive relation; i.e., if $a = b$, and $b = c$, then $a = c$.

Axiom 4.   The same quantity may be added to both members of an equation; i.e., if $a = b$, then $a + c = b + c$.

Axiom 5.   The same quantity may be subtracted from both members of an equation; i.e., if $a = b$, then $a - c = b - c$.

Axiom 6.   Both members of an equation may be multiplied by the same quantity (except zero); i.e., if $a = b$ and $c \neq 0$, then $ac = bc$.

Axiom 7.   Both members of an equation may be divided by the same quantity (except zero); i.e., if $a = b$ and $c \neq 0$, then $a/c = b/c$.

Axiom 8.   A quantity may be substituted for its equal in an equation.

EXAMPLE 9-1.   Solve the equation $x - 2 = 5$.

Solution

$$x - 2 = 5$$
$$x - 2 + 2 = 5 + 2 \qquad \text{by addition Axiom 4}$$
$$x = 7$$

EXAMPLE 9-2. Solve the equation $x + 4 = 5$.

Solution

$$x + 4 = 5$$
$$x + 4 - 4 = 5 - 4 \qquad \text{by subtraction Axiom 5}$$
$$x = 1$$

EXAMPLE 9-3. Solve the equation $\frac{2}{3}x = 8$.

Solution

$$\frac{2}{3}x = 8$$
$$\frac{3}{2}(\frac{2}{3}x) = \frac{3}{2}(8) \qquad \text{by multiplication Axiom 6}$$
$$x = 12$$

EXAMPLE 9-4. Solve the equation $6x = 18$.

Solution

$$6x = 18$$
$$\frac{6x}{6} = \frac{18}{6} \qquad \text{by division Axiom 7}$$
$$x = 3$$

Usually, before an equation can be solved, several of the axioms on equalities must be used. However, it is often possible to perform some of the operations "in your head."

EXAMPLE 9-5. Solve the equation $7x - 5 = 3x + 19$.

Solution

$$7x - 5 = 3x + 19$$
$$7x = 3x + 24 \qquad \text{by axiom of addition}$$
$$4x = 24 \qquad \text{by axiom of subtraction}$$
$$x = 6 \qquad \text{by axiom of division}$$

EXAMPLE 9.6. Solve the equation $3x + 8 - \frac{1}{2}x - 15 = 2x + 9 + \frac{1}{4}x - 14$.

Solution

$$3x + 8 - \tfrac{1}{2}x - 15 = 2x + 9 + \tfrac{1}{4}x - 14$$

$$\tfrac{5}{2}x - 7 = \tfrac{9}{4}x - 5 \quad \text{by combining similar terms}$$

$$\tfrac{1}{4}x = 2 \quad \text{by axioms of addition and subtraction}$$

$$x = 8 \quad \text{by axiom of multiplication}$$

9-3 Checking Solutions. The practicing scientist, engineer, and technician always should *check* his solution to a problem. An answer to a problem is worthless unless it is "checked out." Therefore, the "check" of a solution is an essential part of the solution.

We have defined the root of an equation as the quantity which, when substituted for the letter in an equation, will reduce it to an identity. Therefore, to check the solution of an equation we must substitute the root in the original equation to see if the process will reduce the original equation to an identity. If it does, the root is said to *satisfy the equation.*

EXAMPLE 9-7.   Check to see if 8 is a root to the equation of Example 9-6.

Check

$$3x + 8 - \tfrac{1}{2}x - 15 = 2x + 9 + \tfrac{1}{4}x - 14$$

substituting 8 for x

$$3(8) + 8 - \tfrac{1}{2}(8) - 15 \stackrel{?}{=} 2(8) + 9 + \tfrac{1}{4}(8) - 14$$

$$24 + 8 - 4 - 15 \stackrel{?}{=} 16 + 9 + 2 - 14$$

$$13 = 13$$

Since the equation is reduced to an identity, 8 is a root of the equation.   8 is said to satisfy the equation.

PROBLEMS

Solve the equations and check the root of each:

9-1. $2x - 5 = 11$ **9-2.** $3x + 4 = 19$
9-3. $18 + 2x = 12$ **9-4.** $17 - 3x = 5$
9-5. $5x - 8 = x + 16$ **9-6.** $6x + 9 = 3 - 6x$
9-7. $9x - 12 = 7x - 11$ **9-8.** $20 - 3x = 6 - 6x$
9-9. $8y - 5 = 3y - 25$ **9-10.** $9z - 11 = 7z - 11$
9-11. $5a + 7 - a = 2a + 15$
9-12. $4k + 3k - 4 = 16 - k + 4$
9-13. $6x - 43 - 28x = 15x - 6 + 37$
9-14. $44a - 129 - 13a = 5a - 65 - 6a$
9-15. $5y - 7 - 4y - 8 + 8y - 15 = 0$
9-16. $21 - 3w = 15 - 2w - 2 - 3w + 2$
9-17. $6 - 4v + 3 = 5v - 3 - 3v$
9-18. $16y - 33 = 3 + 4y - 54 + 10y + 23$
9-19. $6z + 9 - 7z = 9z + 9 + 2z - 6$
9-20. $9t - 48 - 4t + 16 = 6t - 18 - 5t - 19 + 5$

9-4 Transposing. The student should have noted in studying the previous examples and in working problems in the foregoing exercise that, when the proper term is *added to* or *subtracted from* both sides of an equation, one term disappears from one side and reappears on the other side of the equation *with its sign changed*.

This fact leads to a short cut in applying the axioms of addition and subtraction. The process is called *transposition* and can be expressed by the following rule.

▶ *Rule.* If any term in an equation is transposed from one side to the other with its sign changed, an equivalent equation will result.

EXAMPLE 9-8. Solve the equation $7x - 8 = 3x + 12$.

Solution

$$7x - 8 = 3x + 12$$

transposing -8 and $3x$, $\quad 7x - 3x = 12 + 8$

$$4x = 20$$

$$x = 5$$

Check

$$7(5) - 8 \stackrel{?}{=} 3(5) + 12$$

$$35 - 8 \stackrel{?}{=} 15 + 12$$

$$27 = 27$$

9-5 Equations Containing Parentheses. Often, for clarity's sake, symbols of grouping are required in writing equations. In solving such equations, it is necessary to first remove the symbols of grouping. The equation can then be solved in the regular manner.

EXAMPLE 9-9. Solve the equation $7x - 3(2x - 4) = 5(3x - 6)$.

Solution

$$7x - 3(2x - 4) = 5(3x - 6)$$

By distributive law: $7x - 6x + 12 = 15x - 30$

Transpose: $\quad 7x - 6x - 15x = -30 - 12$

Combine similar terms: $\quad -14x = -42$

Divide by -14: $\quad x = 3$

Check

$$7(3) - 3(2 \cdot 3 - 4) \stackrel{?}{=} 5(3 \cdot 3 - 6)$$

$$7(3) - 3(6 - 4) \stackrel{?}{=} 5(9 - 6)$$

$$7(3) - 3(2) \stackrel{?}{=} 5(3)$$

$$21 - 6 \stackrel{?}{=} 15$$

$$15 = 15$$

9-6 Equations with Fractions. An equation with fractional coefficients may be reduced to an equivalent equation with no fractional coefficients by multiplying both members of the equation by the lowest common multiple of the denominators of all the coefficients. It first should be noted that such expressions as $\dfrac{3(x-2)}{4}$ and $\frac{3}{4}(x-2)$ are identical. In like manner $\dfrac{x-5}{6}$ and $\frac{1}{6}(x-5)$ are identical.

EXAMPLE 9-10. Solve the equation $\dfrac{3x-4}{6} + \dfrac{3}{4} = \dfrac{4x+2}{3}$

Solution

$$\frac{3x-4}{6} + \frac{3}{4} = \frac{4x+2}{3}$$

Multiply by 12: $12 \cdot \dfrac{3x-4}{6} + 12 \cdot \dfrac{3}{4} = 12 \cdot \dfrac{4x+2}{3}$

Simplify: $2(3x-4) + 3 \cdot 3 = 4(4x+2)$

Use distributive law: $6x - 8 + 9 = 16x + 8$

Transpose: $6x - 16x = 8 + 8 - 9$

Combine similar terms: $-10x = 7$

Divide by -10: $x = -\frac{7}{10}$

Check

$$\frac{3(-\frac{7}{10})-4}{6} + \frac{3}{4} \overset{?}{=} \frac{4(-\frac{7}{10})+2}{3}$$

$$\frac{-\frac{21}{10} - \frac{40}{10}}{6} + \frac{3}{4} \overset{?}{=} \frac{-\frac{28}{10} + \frac{20}{10}}{3}$$

$$-\frac{61}{60} + \frac{3}{4} \overset{?}{=} -\frac{8}{30}$$

$$-\frac{61}{60} + \frac{45}{60} \overset{?}{=} -\frac{16}{60}$$

$$-\frac{16}{60} = -\frac{16}{60}$$

In solving fractional equations, the student should understand that the fractional line is a symbol of grouping in that the numerator is treated as a whole, i.e., as if the numerator were included in parentheses. Consider the next example.

Example 9-11.   Solve the equation

$$\frac{x}{4} - \frac{2x - 5}{3} = \frac{x}{2} - \frac{5(x - 1)}{12}$$

Solution

$$12 \cdot \frac{x}{4} + 12(-\tfrac{1}{3})(2x - 5) = 12 \cdot \frac{x}{2} + 12(-\tfrac{5}{12})(x - 1)$$
$$3x - 4(2x - 5) = 6x - 5(x - 1)$$
$$3x - 8x + 20 = 6x - 5x + 5$$
$$3x - 8x - 6x + 5x = 5 - 20$$
$$-6x = -15$$
$$x = \tfrac{5}{2} \text{ or } 2\tfrac{1}{2}$$

Check

$$\frac{\tfrac{5}{2}}{4} - \frac{2(\tfrac{5}{2}) - 5}{3} \overset{?}{=} \frac{\tfrac{5}{2}}{2} - \frac{5(\tfrac{5}{2} - 1)}{12}$$
$$\tfrac{5}{8} - 0 \overset{?}{=} \tfrac{5}{4} - \tfrac{5}{8}$$
$$\tfrac{5}{8} = \tfrac{5}{8}$$

PROBLEMS

Solve and check each of the following equations:

9-21. $10x + 2(x - 4) = 3(2x - 1) + 7$
9-22. $7 - (3 - x) + 2x = 11 - (5x - 1)$
9-23. $3(y + 1) = 12 + 4(y - 1)$
9-24. $5a - (a - 6) = 3a - 2(a + 3)$
9-25. $3 - 7(3 + x) = 5x - 6(x - 2)$
9-26. $5d - 19 - 4(3d - 2) = 18 + (6 - 2d)$
9-27. $11 - 6(2x - 3) + 5(3x - 4) = 0$
9-28. $3x(2x - 5) + 7 = 3x(2x - 6) + 13$
9-29. $7y(y - 2) - 3y(2y - 5) = y(y - 4) + 20$
9-30. $(z + 3)(z - 6) = (z - 4)(z + 2)$
9-31. $(2k - 3)(3k + 2) = 3k(2k - 1)$
9-32. $3x^2 - (x + 4)(3x - 2) = 2(1 - 5x) + 6$

9-33. $2a^2 - (2a - 3)(a + 5) = 7(2 - a)$

9-34. $(2y + 3)^2 + 27 = 4y(y - 1) + 7y$

9-35. $9(z - 1)(z - 3) - 7(z - 2)(z - 3) = 2(z - 1)(z - 2)$

9-36. $(2y - 3)(y + 4) - 23 = (y + 7)(2y - 5) - 4y$

9-37. $(t - 1)^2 - (2t - 3)^2 - 46 = 3t(2 - t)$

9-38. $\dfrac{2x - 1}{3} - \dfrac{3x + 1}{4} = x - 6$

9-39. $\dfrac{7y - 1}{9} = 1 + \dfrac{3y + 4}{8}$

9-40. $\dfrac{2x - 3}{7} - \dfrac{6x - 11}{5} = \dfrac{6}{35}$

9-41. $\dfrac{8a + 3}{6} - \dfrac{7a - 1}{4} + \dfrac{1}{2} = 0$

9-42. $\dfrac{x}{6} - \dfrac{3x - 4}{2} = \dfrac{2(2x - 5)}{3}$

9-43. $\dfrac{2x}{3} - \dfrac{x + 5}{2} = \dfrac{3x - 4}{4}$

9-44. $\dfrac{3r}{5} + \dfrac{4(r - 5)}{15} = 2 - \dfrac{5(2 - r)}{6}$

9-7 Literal Equations. A *literal equation* is an equation in which some or all of the known quantities, usually constants, are represented by letters instead of numbers. In literal equations letters appear where numbers usually appear. It is customary in writing literal equations to use letters toward the beginning of the alphabet to represent the known quantities and those toward the end of the alphabet as the unknown quantities.

The solution of a literal equation follows the same steps as those of any other equation. The major difference lies in the nature of the solution. The roots of equations studied to this point have always been numbers. The root of a literal equation is expressed in terms of letters which represent numbers.

EXAMPLE 9-12. Solve the equation $ay - 5b = c$ for y and check the root.

Solution

$$ay - 5b = c$$

Add $-5b$ to both sides: $\quad ay = 5b + c$

Divide both sides by a: $\quad y = \dfrac{5b + c}{a}$

Check

$$a\left(\frac{5b + c}{a}\right) - 5b = c$$

$$5b + c - 5b = c$$

$$c = c$$

EXAMPLE 9-13. Solve for z and check the root if $7(z - 2a) - 4(3z + 11a) = 20$.

Solution

$$7(z - 2a) - 4(3z + 11a) = 20$$

Use the distributive law: $7z - 14a - 12z - 44a = 20$

Collect similar terms: $\qquad\qquad -5z - 58a = 20$

Add $58a$ to both sides: $\qquad\qquad\quad -5z = 58a + 20$

Divide both members by -5: $\qquad\qquad z = \dfrac{58a + 20}{-5}$

or $\qquad\qquad\qquad\qquad\qquad\qquad\quad z = -\dfrac{58a + 20}{5}$

Check

$$7\left[-\frac{58a + 20}{5} - 2a\right] - 4\left[3\left(-\frac{58a + 20}{5}\right) + 11a\right] \overset{?}{=} 20$$

$$7\left[\frac{-58a - 20 - 10a}{5}\right] - 4\left[\frac{-174a - 60 + 55a}{5}\right] \overset{?}{=} 20$$

Multiply both members by 5:

$$7[-58a - 20 - 10a] - 4[-174a - 60 + 55a] \overset{?}{=} 100$$

Apply the distributive law:

$$-406 - 140 - 70a + 696a + 240 - 220 \overset{?}{=} 100$$

Combine similar terms: $100 = 100$

9-8 Formulas. In experimental and theoretical technology many facts are expressed by equations, called formulas. The student should already be familiar with certain mensuration formulas; e.g., $C = 2\pi R$, for the circumference of a circle; $A = \pi R^2$, for the area of a circle; $A = lw$, for the area of a rectangle; $D = rt$, relating distance, rate, and time; etc. The letters in a formula are usually the first letters of the words whose magnitude they represent.

Often a formula will be changed to an equivalent form in order to "solve for a different unknown." Consider the following examples.

EXAMPLE 9-14. The formula relating heat H in calories to current in amperes, resistance R in ohms, and time T in seconds is $H = 0.24I^2RT$. Express T in terms of H, I, and R. (We express this by saying "Solve for T.")

Solution

$$H = 0.24I^2RT$$

By symmetric property of equality: $0.24I^2RT = H$

Divide both members by $0.24I^2R$: $\qquad T = \dfrac{H}{0.24I^2R}$

EXAMPLE 9-15. Solve for r in the formula

$$S = \frac{(a - rL)}{(1 - r)}.$$

Solution

Multiply both members by $(1 - r)$: $S(1 - r) = a - rL$
Apply the distributive law: $\qquad S - Sr = a - rL$
Add $rL - S$ to both members: $\qquad rL - Sr = a - S$
Apply the distributive law: $\qquad r(L - S) = a - S$
Divide both members by $(L - S)$: $\qquad r = \dfrac{a - S}{L - S}$

PROBLEMS

Solve and check each of the following literal equations for x, y, or z:

9-45. $7x + 8a - 3x = 3a + 2x$

9-46. $9y - 12k = 3y + 9k - y$

9-47. $8z + (d - 2z) = 4(d - z)$ **9-48.** $ax - b = c - dx$

9-49. $(y - 3a)(y + 2a) - y(y - 4a) = 9a^2$

9-50. $(2z - b)(2z + b) - b(z - 8) = 4z(z - 5) - 30b$

9-51. $\dfrac{5x}{a} - b = c$ **9-52.** $\dfrac{8y}{3} - \dfrac{3b}{4} = \dfrac{5(y - 2b)}{6}$

Solve each formula for the letter indicated after each formula:

9-53. $V = lwh$; w **9-54.** $R = \dfrac{kl}{d^2}$; l

9-55. $S = 2\pi r^2 + 2\pi rh$; h **9-56.** $y = ax + b$; x

9-57. $V = \frac{1}{3}\pi r^2 h$; h **9-58.** $A = P + Prt$; r

9-59. $v^2 = 2gh$; h **9-60.** $Fd = Wh$; h

9-61. $M = \frac{1}{6}bh^2$; b **9-62.** $Ax + By + C = 0$; y

9-63. $H = \dfrac{PLAN}{33,000}$; P **9-64.** $S = \dfrac{n(a + l)}{2}$; n

9-65. $l = a + (n - 1)d$; d **9-66.** $F = \frac{9}{5}C + 32$; C

9-67. $A = \frac{1}{2}(a + b)$; a **9-68.** $\dfrac{p_1 V_1}{T_1} = \dfrac{p_2 V_2}{T_2}$; V_1

9-69. $F = \dfrac{Wv^2}{gR}$; R **9-70.** $v^2 = v_0^2 + 2gh$; h

9-71. $a = \dfrac{v - v_0}{t}$; v **9-72.** $s = v_0 t + \frac{1}{2}at^2$; a

9-73. $\dfrac{1}{R} = \dfrac{1}{R_1} + \dfrac{1}{R_2}$; R_2 **9-74.** $Ft = mv_2 - mv_1$; m

9-9 Solving Stated Word Problems. The problems to be solved by the engineer, scientist, technician, or whoever uses a mathematical solution is frequently stated in words. The problem usually resolves into finding a number from certain verbal statements about it. Equations are used to solve practical problems, not only in the technical fields, but in all kinds of activity.

The chief difficulty in solving stated problems is that the equations used in solving the problems are not given to us ready made. We must first make up the equations from the information given in the statement of the problem and from any other information we may have that is pertinent to the problem. After the equations are correctly set up, they can usually be solved with little difficulty.

While there is no unique way to solve stated problems, the following general suggestions should prove helpful.

1. Read the statement of the problem to get the general idea.

2. Reread carefully the problem, noting what is given and what is wanted.

3. Let some letter, such as x, represent one of the unknown quantities.

Be certain that the letter represents a number. An explicit statement indicating what the letter stands for should be written; e.g., "Let x = the number of pounds of tin"; "let r = the rate of the plane in feet per second."

4. Express the other unknown quantities using the same letter.

5. From the conditions of the problem, obtain a statement that a certain number can be expressed two ways using the same letter. Indicate the equality of the expression by means of an equation.

6. Solve the equation obtained in step 5 for the unknown letter x. Having x, the other unknowns in step 4 may be determined.

7. Check the results obtained to see whether they fulfill the conditions given in the problem.

It should be clear that the checking must be done against the original worded statement and not against the equation used in solving the problem.

Numerous formulas from mathematics, business, and science can be used to complete step 5 above. Among them are:

The measure of the whole is equal to the sum of the measures of its parts.

Mensuration formulas for geometric figures.

Distance equals the product of rate and time.

Density equals the quotient of weight and volume.

Total cost equals the product of the number of items and the cost of each item.

EXAMPLE 9-16.   What are the dimensions of a rectangular plot of land that can be fenced with 540-ft length of fence if the length of the plot is to be twice its width?

Solution

Let x = width of plot, ft

$2x$ = length of plot, ft

The total distance around the plot can be used to arrive at the equation to be solved.

$$x + 2x + x + 2x = 540$$
$$6x = 540$$
$$x = 90$$
$$2x = 180$$

Answer.   The dimensions of the plot are 90 by 180 ft.

Check.   180 ft is twice 90 ft; the perimeter of the plot is 90 ft + 180 ft + 90 ft + 180 ft = 540 ft.

EXAMPLE 9-17.   Two identical printing presses operating at the same speed printed 25,200 newspapers when the first press operated 120 min and the second press operated 90 min.   How many newspapers did each press print?

Solution

Let x = the number of newspapers per minute each press printed

then $120x$ = the number of newspapers the first press printed

and $90x$ = the number of newspapers the second press printed

The problem states that 25,200 newspapers were printed. Thus,

$$120x + 90x = 25{,}200$$
$$210x = 25{,}200$$
$$x = 120$$
$$120x = 14{,}400$$
$$90x = 10{,}800$$

Answer. The first press printed 14,400 newspapers; the second, 10,800 newspapers.

Check

$$
\begin{array}{r}
14{,}400 \\
10{,}800 \\
\hline
25{,}200
\end{array}
\quad \text{(total production)}
$$

EXAMPLE 9-18. The denominator of a fraction exceeds the numerator by 6. The fraction is equivalent to 3/2. What is the fraction?

Solution

Let $x =$ the numerator

then $\quad x + 6 =$ the denominator

and $\quad \dfrac{x + 6}{x} = 3/2$

Multiplying by $2x$, we get

$$2(x + 6) = 3x$$
$$2x + 12 = 3x$$
$$x = 12$$
$$x + 6 = 18$$

Answer. The fraction is $\frac{18}{12}$.

Check

$$18 - 12 = 6$$
$$\tfrac{18}{12} = \tfrac{3}{2}$$

EXAMPLE 9-19. A collection of 58 coins consisting of dimes and quarters has a value of $9.10. Find the number of coins of each kind in the collection.

Solution

Let x = the number of dimes in the collection

Then $58 - x$ = the number of quarters in the collection

and $10x$ = the value, in cents, of the dimes

$25(58 - x)$ = the value, in cents, of the quarters

Expressing the total value of the coins, in cents, as an equation, we get

$$10x + 25(58 - x) = 910$$
$$1{,}450 - 25x = 910$$
$$-15x = -540$$
$$x = 36$$
$$58 - x = 22$$

Answer. There are 36 dimes and 22 quarters in the collection.

Check

36	$0.10 \times 36 = \$3.60$
22	$0.25 \times 22 = \underline{5.50}$
$\overline{58}$ (total number of coins)	$\overline{\$9.10}$ (total value)

EXAMPLE 9-20. How many pounds each of almonds valued at 40 cents per pound and walnuts valued at 50 cents per pound should be mixed to get a 200-lb mixture which can be sold at 46 cents per pound?

Solution

Let x = no. of lb of almonds

Then $200 - x$ = no. of lb of walnuts

200 = no. of lb of nuts in mixture

and $40x$ = value of almonds, in cents

$50(200 - x)$ = value of walnuts, in cents

$46(200)$ = value of mixture, in cents

Equating expressions for the total value of the ingredients, we get

$$40x + 50(200 - x) = 46(200)$$
$$40x + 10{,}000 - 50x = 9{,}200$$
$$-10x = -800$$
$$x = 80$$
$$200 - x = 120$$

Answer. Eighty pounds of almonds should be mixed with 120 lb of walnuts.

Check

$$80 \times \$0.40 = \$32.00 \qquad 200 \times \$0.46 = \$92.00$$
$$120 \times \$0.50 = \underline{60.00}$$
$$\$92.00 \qquad \text{(total)}$$

EXAMPLE 9-21. Two planes take off from airports which are 1,440 miles apart and fly a collision course. The first plane takes off at 2:00 A.M. and averages 750 mph. The second plane takes off 20 min later and averages 1,800 mph. At what time will the planes meet?

Solution

Let $t =$ time first plane is in flight, hr

Then $\quad t - \frac{1}{3} =$ time second plane is in flight, hr

and $(750 \text{ mph})(t \text{ hr}) = 750t =$ distance first plane covers, miles

$(1{,}800 \text{ mph})(t - \frac{1}{3} \text{ hr}) = 1{,}800(t - \frac{1}{3}) =$ distance second plane covers, miles

$$750t + 1{,}800(t - \tfrac{1}{3}) = 1{,}440$$
$$750t + 1{,}800t - 600 = 1{,}440$$
$$2{,}550t = 1{,}440 + 600$$
$$2{,}550t = 2{,}040$$
$$t = \tfrac{4}{5} \text{ hr or 48 min}$$

Answer. The planes will meet at 2:48 A.M.

Check

$$750(\tfrac{4}{5}) = 600 \text{ miles}$$
$$1{,}800(\tfrac{48}{60} - \tfrac{20}{60}) = \underline{840 \text{ miles}}$$
$$1{,}440 \text{ miles (total distance)}$$

EXAMPLE 9-22. Faucet A can fill a tank in 6 hr; faucet B can fill the tank in 3 hr; outlet C can drain the tank in 4 hr. After the tank is half full, how long will it take to fill the tank if faucets A and B and outlet C are each operating on the tank?

Solution

$\tfrac{1}{6}$ = part of tank filled per hour by faucet A

$\tfrac{1}{3}$ = part of tank filled per hour by faucet B

$\tfrac{1}{4}$ = part of tank drained per hour by outlet C

Let $\quad t$ = hours required to fill tank under above conditions

Then $\quad \dfrac{t}{6}$ = part of full tank delivered by faucet A

$\dfrac{t}{3}$ = part of full tank delivered by faucet B

$\dfrac{t}{4}$ = part of full tank drained by outlet C

and $\quad \dfrac{t}{6} + \dfrac{t}{3} - \dfrac{t}{4} = \dfrac{1}{2}$

$$2t + 4t - 3t = 6$$
$$3t = 6$$
$$t = 2$$

Answer. The tank will be filled in 2 hr.

Check

Faucet A will fill $2(\tfrac{1}{6}) = \tfrac{1}{3}$ of the tank in 2 hr

Faucet B will fill $2(\tfrac{1}{3}) = \tfrac{2}{3}$ of the tank in 2 hr

Outlet C will drain $2(\tfrac{1}{4}) = \tfrac{1}{2}$ of the tank in 2 hr

Together $\tfrac{1}{3} + \tfrac{2}{3} - \tfrac{1}{2} = \tfrac{1}{2}$ of the tank will be filled in 2 hr

PROBLEMS

9-75. A fishing rod and reel together cost $35. The reel costs $5 more than the rod. What is the cost of each?

9-76. The length of a rectangle is 7 in. greater than its width. The distance (called the *perimeter*) around the rectangle is 66 in. Find its length and width.

9-77. A tract of land bordering a river's edge is to be fenced on one side and both ends. The length of the side of the tract is 25 yd less than twice that of its end. What are the length and width of the tract if 87 yd of fence is used?

9-78. Divide 56 into two parts such that the first part is 16 more than the second.

9-79. The numerator of a fraction is 4 less than the denominator. The reduced fraction is equivalent to $\frac{3}{5}$. What is the fraction?

9-80. A board 63 in. long is sawed into two pieces such that one piece is 5 in. shorter than twice the length of the other piece. Find the length of the two pieces.

9-81. A carpenter cuts four pieces with different lengths from a strip of molding 16 ft 9 in. long. Each piece after the first is 3 in. shorter than the preceding piece. How long is each piece?

9-82. The following three men agreed to raise $140,000 to start a business. Mr. Jones agreed to contribute twice as much money as Mr. Smith, and Mr. Smith agreed to contribute twice as much as Mr. Brown. How much did each agree to contribute?

9-83. A man is twice as old as his son. Ten years ago he was three times as old as his son. How old is each now?

9-84. A man is 8 years older than three times his son's age. Four years ago the sum of their ages was 84 years. How old is each now?

9-85. Mr. Tolle went to work for Company A 5 years ago.

Each year he received a $400 raise over his previous year's salary. His total salary for the 5-year period was $28,600. What was his starting salary?

9-86. A pouch contains a collection of nickels, dimes, and quarters worth $2.95. There are in the pouch twice as many nickels as dimes and 8 less quarters than dimes. Find the number of coins of each kind in the pouch.

9-87. How many gallons each of 8 and 20% salt solution must be mixed to get 100 gal of 15% salt solution?

9-88. How many pounds of an alloy containing 40% nickel must be melted with an alloy containing 60% nickel to get 80 lb of an alloy containing 55% nickel?

9-89. How many gallons must be withdrawn from a 100-gal drum full of 75% glycerin solution and replaced by water to get the drum full of a 50% solution of glycerin?

9-90. A jet plane is flying 1,500 mph in pursuit of another plane which started $2\frac{1}{2}$ hr earlier and is traveling 600 mph. (*a*) How long will it take the jet to overtake the slower plane? (*b*) How far will the jet fly before overtaking the second plane?

9-91. A man travels from A to B, a distance of 120 miles, at a constant speed of 40 mph. He returns from B to A at a constant speed of 60 mph. What is his average rate for the round trip?

9-92. Two cars start at 1:00 P.M. going in the same direction. Car A travels at a constant speed of 50 mph. The driver of car B travels 2 hr at a constant speed of 40 mph and then decides to increase his speed to 55 mph until he overtakes car A. At what time does car B overtake car A? How far will car A have traveled before it is overtaken by car B?

9-93. Machine A can complete a job in 18 hr. Machine B can complete the job in 10 hr. How long will it take both machines working simultaneously to complete the job?

9-94. A man invests $50,000, part at 5% interest and the rest at 6% interest.   If his annual income is $2,680 from his investment, how much has he invested at each rate?

9-95. A man in a motorboat traveled across a lake at a speed of 20 mph.   On his return trip he averaged 12 mph.   It took him 4 hr longer on the return trip than on the original crossing.   (*a*) How long did he take for the round trip? (*b*) What was the round-trip distance?

9-96. Company *A* decides to distribute $68,000 in bonuses to its employees according to their lengths of service with the company as follows: 1 to 5 years, a base bonus; 6 to 10 years, twice the bonus of the 1- to 5-year employee; 11 to 15 years, twice the bonus of the 6- to 10-year employee; 16 to 20 years, twice the bonus of the 11- to 15-year employee. There are 8 employees with 16 to 20 years of service, 30 employees with 11 to 15 years of service, 110 employees with 5 to 10 years of service, 542 employees with 1 to 5 years of service.   How much should each employee get?

9-97. A construction foreman signed a contract to supervise the construction of a motel.   He was given a specified time within which to complete the construction.   The contract gave him $35 per each day he worked, plus a bonus of $50 for each day that the job was completed before the specified time.   His crew finished the job in three-fourths of the time allowed.   His total salary (wages plus bonus) amounted to $1,085.   What was the specified time limit of the contract?

9-98. A mechanic was hired to keep the field equipment of a large farm in working condition.   He was paid $30 a day whenever all equipment was in working condition and fined $50 when any piece could not operate on a given day.   At the end of 250 working days he received $7,140 in wages.   How many days was all the equipment in working condition?

CHAPTER 10

Elements of Geometry

10-1   Uses of Geometry.   Geometry had its origin long ago in the measurements by the Babylonians and Egyptians of their lands overswept by the floods of the Nile River.   The word geometry is derived from the words *geo*, meaning "earth," and *metron*, meaning "measure."   As early as 2000 B.C. we find the land surveyors of these people reestablishing vanishing landmarks and boundaries by using the principles of geometry.

Geometry is a science that deals with forms made by lines and surfaces.   The study of geometry is an essential part of the training of the successful engineer, scientist, technician, architect, and draftsman.   The carpenter, machinist, tinsmith, stonecutter, artist, and designer each applies the truths of geometry in his craft.   In the next chapters the student will learn about geometric figures such as lines, rays, angles, triangles, circles, parallelograms, cylinders, spheres, and the like.

10-2   Undefined Terms.   There are many terms in use today that are difficult to define.   They can be defined only in terms of other equally undefinable concepts.   Consider the words success, prosperity, caution, illness, insanity, reasonable, sweet, and delinquent.   The dictionary defines such terms by giving "circular definitions."   For example, happiness may be defined as a state of being glad or contented.   To understand this definition, the reader would have to know the meaning of the words "glad" and "contented."   These words are equally difficult to define.

155

Thus it should be evident that we must start with some undefined terms and define others in terms of these. These are called *undefined elements* or *basic concepts*.

10-3 Points and Lines. The four fundamental undefined geometric basic concepts we shall use in this book are *point*, *line*, *plane*, and *straight*.

What is a point? Everyone has some understanding of the term. Although we can represent a point by marking a small dot on a sheet of paper or on a blackboard, it certainly is not a point. If it were possible to subdivide the marker, then subdivide the smaller dots, and so on indefinitely, we still would not have a point. We would, however, approach a condition which most of us assign to that of a point. Some texts define a point as something which has position but no size or dimensions. However, the words "position" and "size or dimensions" are also basic concepts and can be described only by using circular definitions.

We name a point by a capital letter printed beside it, as "point *A*" in Fig. 10-1. Other geometric figures can be defined in terms of sets of points which satisfy certain restricting conditions.

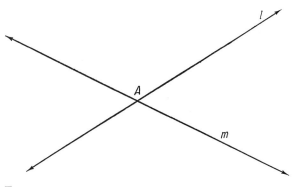

Fig. 10-1

We are all familiar with lines, but no one has seen one. Just as we can represent a point by a marker or dot, we can represent a line by moving the tip of a sharpened pencil across a piece of paper. This will produce an approximation for the meaning given to the word "line." Some authors attempt to define a line as that which has only one dimension. Here, again, use is made of an undefinable concept, dimension.

While we can not define the word "line," we recognize it as a *set of points*.

We could try to define a "straight" line as one no part of which is "crooked" or one which extends infinitely far in opposite "directions." The failure of these attempts should be evident. The line is named by labeling two points on it with capital letters or by one lower-case letter near it. The straight line in Fig. 10-2 is read "line *AB*" or "line 1." Line *AB* is often written

Fig. 10-2

$\overleftrightarrow{AB}$. In this text, unless otherwise stated, when the term *line* is used, the concept *straight* line will be meant.

▶ *Definition.* A set of points are *collinear* if and only if they belong to the same line. *R*, *S*, and *T* of Fig. 10-3 are collinear.

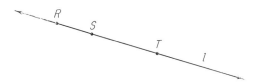

Fig. 10-3

10-4 Solids and Planes. A solid is a three-dimensional figure. Common examples of solids are shown in Fig. 10-4.

The geometric solid shown in Fig. 10-5 has six faces which are smooth and flat. These faces are called *plane surfaces* or sim-

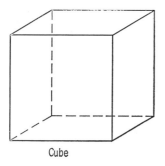

Cube

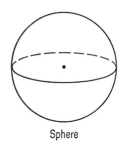

Sphere

Cylinder

Cone

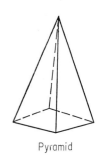

Pyramid

Fig. 10-4

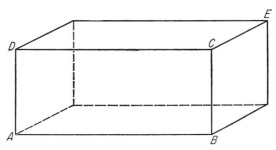

Fig. 10-5

ply *planes*. A plane surface has two dimensions, length and width. The surface of a blackboard or of a table top are examples of plane surfaces. A plane can be thought of as a set of points.

If two lines cross each other, they are called *intersecting lines*. Two straight lines can intersect in only one point (see Fig. 10-1).

10-5 Segments. Rays. Let us next consider that part of a line between two points of the line.

▶ *Definition.* The part of the line between *A* and *B*, together with points *A* and *B* (see Fig. 10-6), is called the *segment AB*.

Fig. 10-6

Symbolically it is written $\overleftrightarrow{AB}$. The points *A* and *B* are called *end points* of $\overleftrightarrow{AB}$. The number which tells how far it is from *A* to *B* is called the *measure* (or *length*) of $\overleftrightarrow{AB}$. We shall use the symbol *AB* to mean the length of $\overleftrightarrow{AB}$.

The student should recognize the difference between the meanings of the symbols $\overleftrightarrow{AB}$ and *AB*. The first refers to the geometric figure; the second to a number.

▶ *Definition.* A point *B* is the midpoint of $\overleftrightarrow{AC}$ if *B* is *between A* and *C* and *AB = BC* (see Fig. 10-7). The midpoint is said to *bisect* the segment.

Fig. 10-7

▶ *Definition.* A *ray* is the part of a straight line extending from a point on the line indefinitely in only one direction (see Fig. 10-8).

Fig. 10-8

The symbol for the ray from A through B is $\overrightarrow{AB}$ and is read "ray AB." The point A is called the *endpoint* of $\overrightarrow{AB}$. $\overrightarrow{AB}$ and $\overrightarrow{AC}$ of Fig. 10-9 are called *opposite rays*.

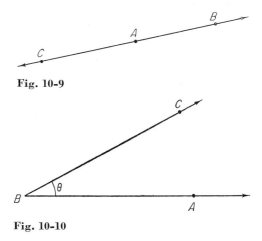

Fig. 10-9

Fig. 10-10

10-6 Angles. The figure drawn in Fig. 10-10 is representative of an angle.

▶ *Definition.* An *angle* is the figure formed by two rays with a common end point. The rays are called the *sides* of the angle, and their common end point is called the *vertex* of the angle.

The symbol for angle is ∠; the plural, ∡. There are three common ways for naming an angle: (1) by three capital letters, the middle letter being the vertex and the other two being points on the sides of the angle, as ∠ *ABC*; (2) by a single capital letter at the vertex if it is clear which angle is meant, as ∠ *B*; and (3) by a small letter in the interior of the angle. In advanced work in mathematics the small letter used to name the angle is often a Greek letter, as ∠ *θ*.

The student should note that the sides of an angle go out infinitely far in two directions. This is because the sides of an angle are rays, not segments. In Fig. 10-11, ∠ *AOD*, ∠ *BOE*, and ∠ *COF* all refer to the same angle.

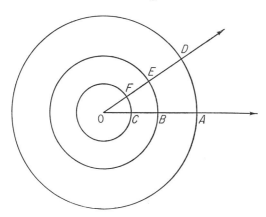

Fig. 10-11

10-7 Measures of Angles. Angles are measured in terms of the degree unit. If a circle is divided into 360 equal arcs and radii are drawn to any two consecutive points of division, the angle formed at the center by these radii has a size of one *degree*. The symbol for degree is °. The degree is quite small. One can gain a rough idea of the size of one degree is he realizes that if in Fig. 10-12 (not drawn to scale), $\overrightarrow{BA}$ and $\overrightarrow{BC}$ are each 57 in. long and $\overleftrightarrow{AC}$ is 1 in. long, ∠ *ABC* has a size of approximately one

Fig. 10-12

degree. If this angle is divided into 60 equal angles, each of the smaller angles has a magnitude of one *minute*. The symbol for the minute is '. If one of these minute angles is divided again into 60 equal angles, each of these very small angles will have a size of one *second*. The symbol for the second is ''. Thus 3,600 seconds are equivalent to one degree. Surveyors, engineers, and astronomers commonly measure angles with accuracy to the second.

The number of degrees in an angle can be measured roughly by the student with the aid of a protractor (Fig. 10-13). The

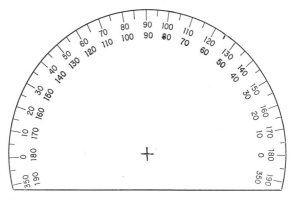

Fig. 10-13

student can also draw an angle to a required measure with the use of this instrument.

The United States Armed Services measures angles in terms of mils. If in Fig. 10-12 $\overset{\leftrightarrow}{BA}$ and $\overset{\leftrightarrow}{BC}$ are 1,000 in. long and $\overset{\leftrightarrow}{AC}$ is 1 in. in length, $\angle ABC$ will have a magnitude of one *mil*. A mil is roughly $\frac{1}{20}$ degree. Students of trigonometry and calculus generally use a larger unit angle than the degree. It is called the radian. It is roughly equivalent to 57°.

We shall write the fact that ∠ *RST* has a measure of k degrees in abbreviated form as $m\angle RST = k°$. Thus, in Fig. 10-14, we

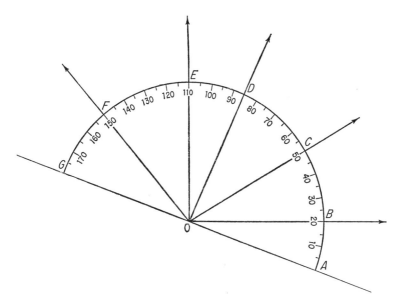

Fig. 10-14

indicate the angle measures as

$$m\angle AOB = 20° \qquad m\angle COD = 36°$$
$$m\angle AOD = 86° \qquad m\angle DOF = 64°$$
$$m\angle AOF = 150° \qquad m\angle BOE = 90°$$

and so on.

PROBLEMS

10-1. Name the three vertices of the figure shown on page 64.
10-2. Which line segments meet at K?

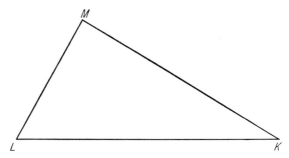

Problems 10-1 to 10-3

10-3. Which angle has the larger measure, $\angle L$ or $\angle K$?   Check your answer by tracing $\angle L$ on a piece of translucent material and superimposing the trace on $\angle K$.

10-4. Which line segment is the longer?   Use tracing paper to check your answer.

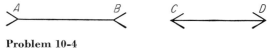

Problem 10-4

10-5. Place a point A on a piece of paper.   Draw a line l through A.   How many other lines can you draw through A?

10-6. Place two distinct points A and B on a piece of paper. Draw a straight line l through these two points.   How many other straight lines can you draw through these two points?

10-7. Using two letters, name line l three ways.

Complete Probs. 10-8 to 10-16.

10-8. $AE = AC + \cdots$

10-9. $OB = \cdots + AB$

10-10. $\cdots = OE + EF$

10-11. $OC = OD - \cdots$

10-12. $AB = \cdots - CD$

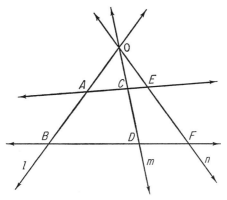

Problems 10-7 to 10-12

10-13. $m\angle DAB = m\angle DAO + m \cdots$

10-14. $m\angle DCO = m\angle DCB - \cdots$

10-15. $m\angle \cdots = m\angle ABO + m\angle OBC$

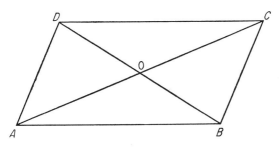

Problems 10-13 to 10-17

10-16. $m\angle AOB = m\angle AOC - \cdots$

10-17. Which angle appears to have the same measure as $\angle AOD$? as $\angle DOC$?

In Probs. 10-18 to 10-32, draw pictures which illustrate the situations described. If the situations cannot occur, tell why.

10-18. l and m are two lines intersecting at P.

10-19. l and m are two lines; P is a point of l; R is a point of l; S is a point of m; $\overleftrightarrow{RS}$ is not the same as $\overleftrightarrow{PR}$.

10-20. C is not a point on $\overleftrightarrow{AB}$, and A and B are two different points.

10-21. r and s are two lines that do not intersect.

10-22. P is not a point of $\overleftrightarrow{KL}$, P is a point of line l, and line l and $\overleftrightarrow{KL}$ do not intersect.

10-23. R, S, and T are three points; T is the point of intersection of $\overleftrightarrow{RT}$ and $\overleftrightarrow{ST}$.

10-24. P, Q, R, and S are four points; Q is a point of $\overleftrightarrow{PR}$; and R is a point of $\overleftrightarrow{PS}$.

10-25. P, Q, R, and S are four distinct points; Q is a point of $\overleftrightarrow{PR}$; and Q is a point of $\overleftrightarrow{PS}$.

10-26. A, B, and C are three collinear points. C, D, and E are three noncollinear points, and E is a point of $\overleftrightarrow{AB}$.

10-27. On line AB, C is between A and B.

10-28. On line AB, B is between A and C.

10-29. On $\overleftrightarrow{AB}$, A is between B and C.

10-30. P, Q, and R are three collinear points; P is a point of $\overrightarrow{QR}$; and R is not a point of $\overrightarrow{PQ}$.

10-31. l, m, and n are three distinct lines. l and m do not intersect, and m and n do not intersect.

10-32. l, m, and n are three distinct lines. l and m do not intersect, m and n do not intersect, but l and n do intersect.

Find the value of each of the following:

10-33. $m\angle\, AJC$

10-34. $m\angle\, CJE$

10-35. $m\angle\, HJC$

10-36. $m\angle\, DJB$

10-37. $m\angle\, BJF$

10-38. $m\angle\, CJD + m\angle\, GJD$

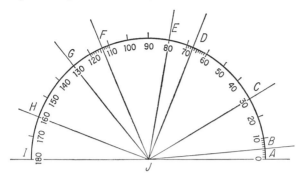

Problems 10-33 to 10-40

10-39. $m\angle HJC + m\angle FJE$

10-40. $m\angle HJB - m\angle FJD$

10-8 Kinds of Angles. Two angles are said to be adjacent angles if they have the same vertex and a common side between them. In Fig. 10-15, $\angle AOB$ and $\angle BOC$ are adjacent angles. $\overrightarrow{OB}$ is said to lie in the interior of $\angle AOC$ (except for point O).

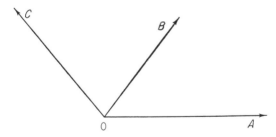

Fig. 10-15

The pairs of nonadjacent angles formed when two lines intersect are termed *vertical angles*. In Fig. 10-16 $\angle \alpha$ and $\angle \alpha'$ are vertical angles. Angles β and $\angle \beta'$ are also vertical angles.

As the measure of an angle increases from 0 to 180°, the following kinds of angles are formed: acute angle, right angle, obtuse angle, and straight angle (see Fig. 10-17).

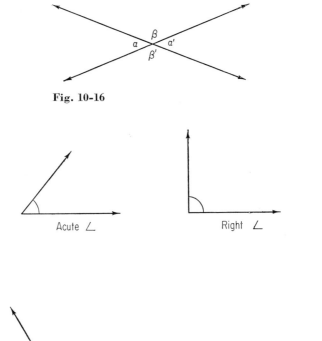

Fig. 10-16

Fig. 10-17

▶ *Definitions.* An angle is an *acute angle* if it has a measure less than 90°. An angle is a *right angle* if it has a measure of 90°. An angle is an *obtuse angle* if its measure is more than 90° and less than 180°. An angle is a *straight angle* if its measure is equal to 180°.

10-9 Congruent Angles. Congruent Segments. A common concept in daily life is that of size and comparative sizes. We frequently speak of two things having the same size. The word *congruent* is used in geometry to define what we intuitively speak of as having the same size.

▶ *Definitions.* Angles are *congruent* if they have the same measure. Segments are *congruent* if they have the same measure. Thus, if we know that $AB = CD$, we can say that $\overleftrightarrow{AB}$ and $\overleftrightarrow{CD}$ are congruent, that $\overleftrightarrow{AB}$ is congruent to $\overleftrightarrow{CD}$, or that $\overleftrightarrow{CD}$ is congruent to $\overleftrightarrow{AB}$. Again, if we know that $m\angle ABC = m\angle RST$, we can say that $\angle ABC$ and $\angle RST$ are congruent angles, $\angle ABC$ is congruent to $\angle RST$, or $\angle RST$ is congruent to $\angle ABC$.

The symbol for "is congruent to" is $\cong$. Thus the following are equivalent statements:

$AB = CD;\ \overleftrightarrow{AB} \cong \overleftrightarrow{CD};\ \overleftrightarrow{CD} \cong \overleftrightarrow{AB}.$

$m\angle ABC = m\angle RST;\ \angle ABC \cong \angle RST;\ \angle RST \cong \angle ABC.$

▶ *Definition.* The *bisector* of an angle is the ray whose end point is the vertex of the angle and which divides the angle into two congruent angles. $\overrightarrow{BD}$ *bisects*, or is the *angle bisector* of, $\angle ABC$ if D is in the interior of $\angle ABC$ and if $\angle ABD \cong \angle DBC$ (see Fig. 10-18).

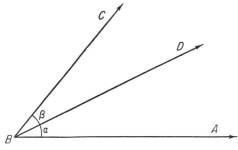

Fig. 10-18

10-10 Perpendicular Lines and Right Angles. Consider the four figures shown in Fig. 10-19. They are examples of representations of right angles and perpendicular lines.

▶ *Definition.* Two lines are *perpendicular* if they intersect to form right angles.

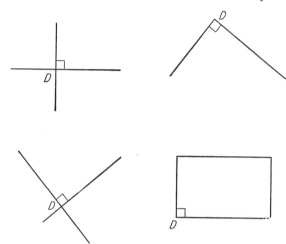

Fig. 10-19

Since rays and segments are parts of lines, we can have rays, segments, and lines perpendicular to each other.

The symbol for perpendicular is ⊥. This symbol may also be read "perpendicular to." The right angle of a figure is often designated by placing a square corner mark where the two sides of the angle meet. The *foot* of the perpendicular to a line is the point where the perpendicular meets the line. Thus, D is the foot of the perpendiculars in Fig. 10-19.

10-11 Distance from a Point to a Line. The *distance* from a point to a line is the measure of the perpendicular line segment from the point to the line. Thus in Fig. 10-20 the measure of $\overrightarrow{PM}$ is the distance from point P to $\overleftrightarrow{AB}$. This *perpendicular distance is the shortest distance from a point to a line.*

10-12 Complementary and Supplementary Angles. Two angles the sum of whose measures is 90° are termed *complementary angles.* In Fig. 10-21 $\angle\,\alpha$ and $\angle\,\beta$ are complementary angles. Each of the angles is the complement of the other. Angle $\angle\,\alpha$ is the complement of $\angle\,\beta$; and $\angle\,\beta$ is the complement of $\angle\,\alpha$.

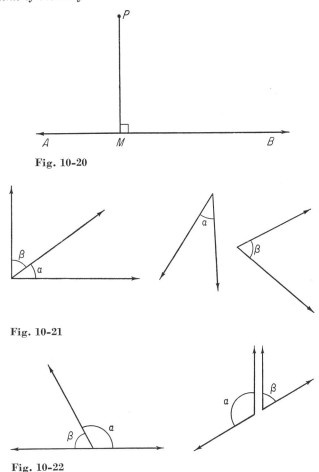

Fig. 10-20

Fig. 10-21

Fig. 10-22

Supplementary angles are two angles the sum of whose measures is 180°. In Fig. 10-22, ∠ α and ∠ β are supplementary angles. Angle ∠ α is the supplement of ∠ β, and ∠ β is the supplement of ∠ α.

10-13 Triangles. Kinds of Triangles. If *A*, *B*, and *C* are three noncollinear points, the figure formed by the joining of the three segments $\overleftrightarrow{AB}$, $\overleftrightarrow{BC}$, and $\overleftrightarrow{AC}$ as shown in Fig. 10-23

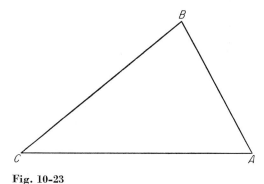

Fig. 10-23

is called a *triangle*. The symbol for a triangle is △ (plural ⚠). Thus, Fig. 10-23 is labeled *ABC*.

Each of the noncollinear points is called a *vertex* of the triangle, and each of the line segments is a *side* of the triangle. Each angle which contains two sides of the triangle is an *angle* of the

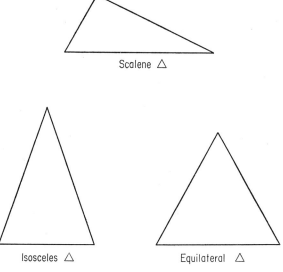

Fig. 10-24

triangle. In Fig. 10-23, A, B, and C are vertices of $\triangle ABC$; $\overset{\bullet\longrightarrow\bullet}{AB}$, $\overset{\bullet\longrightarrow\bullet}{BC}$, and $\overset{\bullet\longrightarrow\bullet}{CA}$ are the sides of $\triangle ABC$; and $\angle A$, $\angle B$, and $\angle C$ are the angles of ABC. Angle C is *opposite* side AB; $\overset{\bullet\longrightarrow\bullet}{AB}$ is *opposite* $\angle C$. The sides AC and BC are said to *include* $\angle C$. $\angle C$ and $\angle A$ *include* side CA.

Triangles may be classified by their sides (Fig. 10-24). A *scalene* triangle is a triangle with no two sides that are congruent. An *isosceles* triangle is a triangle with two congruent sides. An *equilateral* triangle has three congruent sides. The parts of an isosceles triangle are labeled as in Fig. 10-25. In

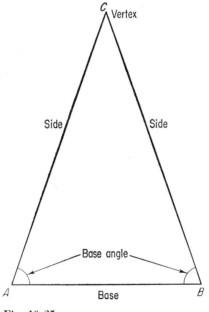

Fig. 10-25

the figure, $AC = BC$. Angle A, opposite $\overset{\bullet\longrightarrow\bullet}{BC}$, and $\angle B$, opposite $\overset{\bullet\longrightarrow\bullet}{AC}$, are called the *base angles* of the isosceles triangle. Side AB

is the *base* of the triangle.   Angle *C*, opposite the base, is the *vertex angle.*

Triangles may also be classified according to the kind of angles they contain (see Fig. 10-26).   An *acute* triangle is one that has

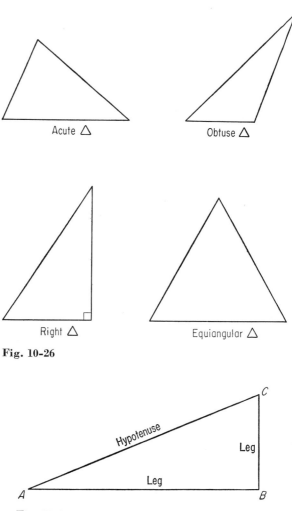

Fig. 10-26

Fig. 10-27

three acute angles.   An *obtuse* triangle has one obtuse angle.   A *right* triangle has one right angle.   The sides which form the right angle of the triangle are termed *legs* of the triangle, and the side opposite the right angle is called the *hypotenuse*.   In Fig. 10-27, $\overrightarrow{AB}$ and $\overrightarrow{BC}$ are the legs and $\overrightarrow{AC}$ is the hypotenuse of the right triangle.   An *equiangular* triangle has three congruent angles.

PROBLEMS

10-41. Using a protractor and a ruler, construct a triangle with $AB = 4$ in., $m\angle A = 110°$, and $m\angle B = 25°$.   Give two names for this kind of triangle.

10-42. In the figure, what side is common to $\triangle ADC$ and $\triangle DBC$?   What vertices are common to the two triangles?

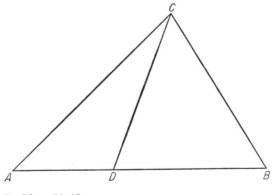

Problem 10-42

In Probs. 10-43 to 10-52, state the kind of triangle each figure seems to be (*a*) according to the sides of the triangles and (*b*) according to the angles of the triangles.

10-43. △ *KLM*   **10-44.** △ *ABC*   **10-45.** △ *DEF*

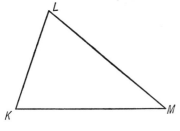

Problem 10-43

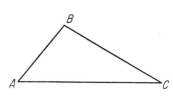

Problem 10-44

10-46. △ *GHI*   **10-47.** △ *JKL*   **10-48.** △ *ABC*

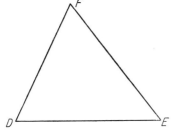

Problem 10-45

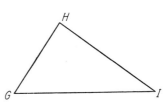

Problem 10-46

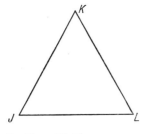

Problem 10-47

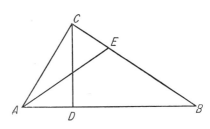

Problems 10-48 to 10-52

10-49. △ *ADC*   **10-50.** △ *BDC*   **10-51.** △ *AEC*

10-52. △ *ABE*

10-53. In the figure for Probs. 10-48 to 10-52, indicate two pairs of perpendicular lines.

10-54 to 10-56. Name a pair of complementary ∡ in each of the diagrams.

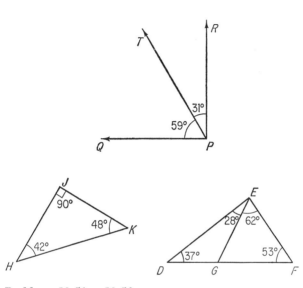

Problems 10-54 to 10-56

10-57. Tell why ∠ α and ∠ β are complementary angles.

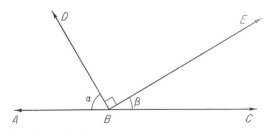

Problem 10-57

10-58 to **10-60.** Name a pair of supplementary angles in each of the following diagrams.

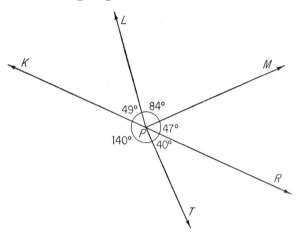

Problem 10-58

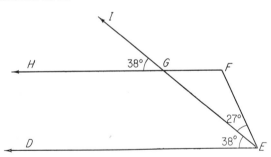

Problem 10-59

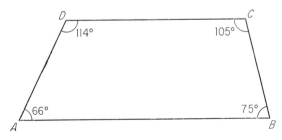

Problem 10-60

10-61 to **10-63.** Name two pairs of adjacent angles in each of the following figures.

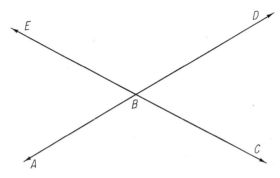

Problem 10-61

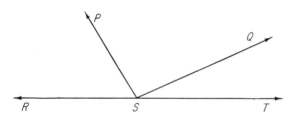

Problem 10-62

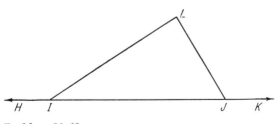

Problem 10-63

10-64. Find the complement of (*a*) 30°, (*b*) 55°, (*c*) 80°, (*d*) $k°$.

10-65. Find the supplement of (*a*) 30°, (*b*) 65°, (*c*) 90°, (*d*) 135°, (*e*) $h°$.

10-14   The Method of Geometry.   In the study of geometry the student begins with certain basic assumptions which can be agreed upon, even though they cannot be proved.   In Chap. 9 we listed a few basic general assumptions called axioms. Let us next list a few fundamental geometric assumptions, called *postulates*, which also are accepted as true without proof.

Postulate 1.   Through two given points, one, and only one, straight line can be drawn.

Postulate 2.   Two lines can intersect in at most one point.

Postulate 3.   If B is between A and C on segment AC, then $AC = AB + BC$.

Postulate 4.   If D is a point in the interior of $\angle ABC$, then $m\angle ABC = m\angle ABD + m\angle DBC$.

Postulate 5.   A line segment has one, and only one, midpoint.

Postulate 6.   An angle has one, and only one, bisector.

With these axioms and postulates and a set of definitions, plus a few more postulates, it is possible to *prove* deductively many new statements called *theorems*.   These theorems can then be used to prove new theorems.

Some of the more important theorems proved in geometry follow:

Theorem 10-1.   All right angles are congruent.

Theorem 10-2.   All straight angles are congruent.

Theorem 10-3.   Vertical angles are congruent.

Theorem 10-4.   A straight-line segment is the shortest line segment that can be drawn between two points.

Theorem 10-5.   At any point on a straight line one, and only one, perpendicular can be drawn to the line.

Theorem 10-6.   From any point outside a straight line one, and only one, perpendicular to the line can be drawn.

Theorem 10-7.   The perpendicular from a point to a straight line is the shortest path to the straight line.

EXAMPLE 10-1. If, in the figure, we know that $RS = QT$, $RN = MT$, show that $NS = QM$.

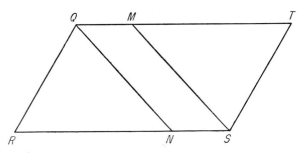

Example 10-1

Discussion. If RN is subtracted from RS, NS remains. If MT is subtracted from QT, QM remains. Axiom 5 states that, if equals are subtracted from equals, the remainders are equal. Thus,

$$RS = QT \qquad \text{given}$$
$$RN = MT \qquad \text{given}$$
Then $\qquad \overline{NS = GM} \qquad \text{by Axiom 5}$

EXAMPLE 10-2

Given. $m\angle ABC = m\angle RST$; $\overrightarrow{BD}$ bisects $\angle ABC$; $\overrightarrow{SP}$ bisects $\angle RST$.

Prove. $m\angle \alpha = m\angle \beta$.

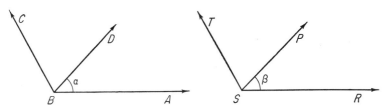

Example 10-2

Discussion. We know that "to bisect" means to divide by 2. Since ∠ *ABC* and ∠ *RST* have the same measures and each are bisected, then each of the angles is divided by 2 to form angles whose measures are half as large as the measures of the original ones. Axiom 7 states that both members of an equation may be divided by the same quantity. Hence,

$$m\angle\, ABC = m\angle\, RST \qquad \text{given}$$
$$\tfrac{1}{2}m\angle\, ABC = \tfrac{1}{2}m\angle\, RST \qquad \text{by Axiom 7}$$

Then $\qquad m\angle\, \alpha = m\angle\, \beta \qquad$ by definition of bisector

PROBLEMS

In the following exercises discuss how the conclusions can be reached, based upon your list of axioms, postulates, and definitions.

10-66. If $a = c$ and $b = c$, then $a + b = 2c$.
10-67. If $a = c$, then $a - b = c - b$.
10-68. If $4x = 20$, then $x = 5$.
10-69. If $AC = DE$ and $BC = EF$, then $AB = DF$.

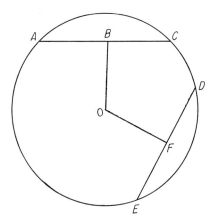

Problem 10-69

10-70. If $HI = JK$, then $HJ = IK$.

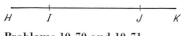

Problems 10-70 and 10-71

10-71. If $HJ = IK$, then $HI = JK$.

10-72. $m\angle RSK = m\angle TSL$, then $m\angle RSL = m\angle TSK$.

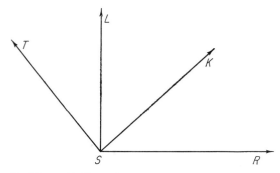

Problems 10-72 and 10-73

10-73. If $m\angle RSL = m\angle TSK$, then $m\angle RSK = m\angle TSL$.

10-74. If $m\angle A = m\angle B$, $m\angle \alpha = \frac{1}{2}m\angle A$ and $m\angle \beta = \frac{1}{2}m\angle B$, then $m\angle \alpha = m\angle \beta$.

10-75. If $\overleftrightarrow{LT} \perp \overleftrightarrow{KM}$, then $\angle \alpha$ and $\angle \beta$ are both right angles (why?) and $\angle \alpha \cong \angle \beta$.

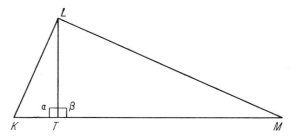

Problem 10-75

10-76. If $\overleftrightarrow{AB}$ and $\overleftrightarrow{CD}$ intersect at O, then $\angle AOC \cong \angle BOD$.

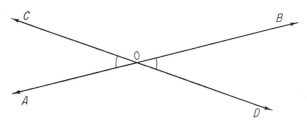

Problem 10-76

10-77. If $PS = PR$ and $TS = QR$, then $PT = PQ$.

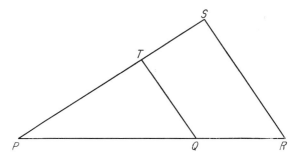

Problem 10-77

10-78. *Given.* $m\angle ABC = m\angle RST$ and $m\angle ABD = m\angle RSP$.
Prove. $m\angle DBC = m\angle PST$.

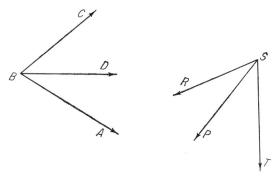

Problem 10-78

10-79. *Given.* l is a straight line and $m\angle \alpha = m\angle \beta$.
Prove. $m\angle x = m\angle y$.

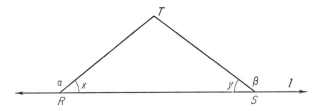

Problem 10-79

10-80. *Given.*   *l*, *m*, and *n* are straight lines, and $m\angle\,\alpha = m\angle\,\beta$.
        Prove. $m\angle\,\gamma = m\angle\,\beta$.

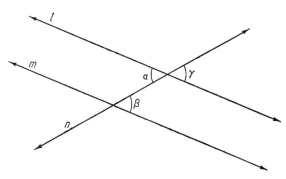

Problem 10-80

10-81. *Given.* $m\angle\,DFE = m\angle\,FDE$, $m\angle\,EFG = m\angle\,EDH$.
        Prove. $m\angle\,GFD = m\angle\,HDF$.

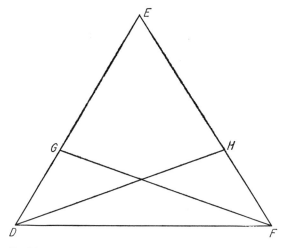

Problem 10-31

10-82. *Given.* $AC = BC$; $AL = BM$.
   Prove. $LC = MC$.

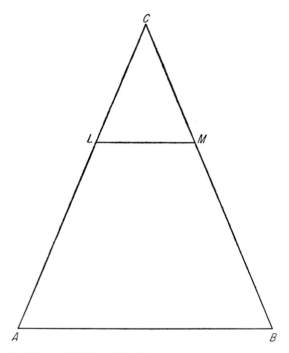

Problems 10-82 and 10-83

10-83. *Given.* $AL = BM$; $LC = MC$.
   Prove. $AC = BC$.

10-84. *Given.* ∠ K and ∠ I are right angles; m∠ x = m∠ y.
    Prove. m∠ α = m∠ β.

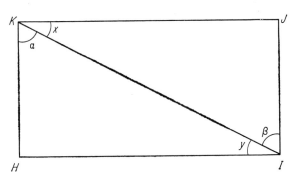

Problem 10-84

10-85. *Given.* l is a straight line; ∠ ABC is a right angle.
    Prove. ∠ x is the complement of ∠ y.

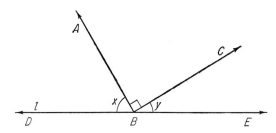

Problem 10-85

CHAPTER 11

Congruence

11-1 Congruent Figures. Two figures are *congruent* if they can be made to coincide in all their parts. Congruent figures therefore have the same shape and size. Conversely, two figures whose corresponding parts can be made to coincide are congruent. The coincident parts are called *corresponding parts*.

Congruent figures are common in modern technology. For example, industry today relies a great deal on mass production and assembly-line manufacture. Often each part of a machine or household article is made by precision manufacture to have exactly the same shape and size. These parts are then sent to an assembly plant where the parts can be fitted together to form a complete unit.

The mass production and repair of automobiles, airplanes, television sets, automatic washers, refrigerators, and many other products of modern industry depend on the manufacture of thousands of parts having exactly the same shape and size. It is especially important in repairing a complex machine that the necessary replacement parts match exactly the original parts.

The symbol for congruence is $\cong$. Thus, $\triangle ABC \cong \triangle DEF$ is read "triangle ABC is congruent to triangle DEF." If the triangles are congruent (see Fig. 11-1), we know that $AB = DE$, $BC = EF$, $AC = DF$, $m\angle A = m\angle D$, $m\angle B = m\angle E$, and $m\angle C = m\angle F$. In like manner, if we know that the three corresponding pairs of sides and the three pairs of angles have the same measures, we can state that the triangles are congruent.

189

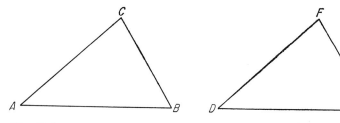

Fig. 11-1

11-2 Congruence of Triangles. The triangle is the most widely used of all the geometric figures formed by straight lines. The engineer uses triangles in his work because the triangle is rigid in structural design. Triangular braces and structures are common place in bridges, towers, and gates.

The engineer, by applying principles of congruent triangles, is able to duplicate structures. He is able to measure the sides and angles of a triangle and compute its area.

It is not the purpose of this text to develop theorems relating conditions for congruence of triangles. We shall simply list the various methods for establishing congruence and then determine if certain figures are congruent.

While we *define* two triangles as congruent if three pairs of sides and three pairs of angles have equal measures, triangles can be *proved* congruent if fewer corresponding parts are known to have the same measures. Another postulate must first be accepted.

> *Postulate* 7 (the SAS postulate). Two triangles are congruent if two sides and the included angle of one are, respectively, congruent to the two sides and included angle of the other.

Thus, Postulate 7 states that, in Fig. 11-2, if $AB = DE$, $AC = DF$, and $\angle A \cong \angle D$, then $\triangle ABC \cong \triangle DEF$.

The student will often find he is aided in checking for congruence of triangles if he designates congruent sides and angles

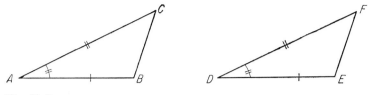
Fig. 11-2

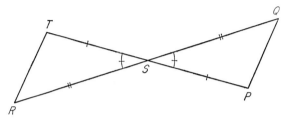
Fig. 11-3

by similar check marks. Thus, in Fig. 11-3, if it is given $RS = QS$, $m\angle RST = m\angle QSP$, and $TS = PS$, the student can readily see that the conditions of Postulate 7 are satisfied and that $\triangle RST \cong \triangle QSP$.

It is important that the student recognize, in using Postulate 7 to prove triangles congruent, that the congruent angles must be *between* (formed by) the corresponding sides. If the congruent angles are not between the two known congruent sides, it does not necessarily follow that the correspondence will give a congruence. In $\triangle RST$ and $\triangle KLM$ (Fig. 11-4) note that, though

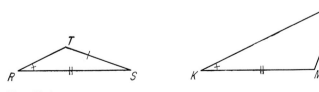
Fig. 11-4

$RS = KM$, $ST = ML$, and $\angle R \cong \angle K$, the triangles certainly are not congruent.

Thus, whenever we know or can prove that two sides and the included angle of one triangle are congruent to two sides and the included angle of the other, we can give Postulate 7 as the reason for stating that the two triangles are congruent. We shall abbreviate the words of the postulate with the letters SAS.

EXAMPLE 11-1

Given. $\overleftrightarrow{CD} \perp \overleftrightarrow{AB}$; $\overleftrightarrow{CD}$ bisects $\overleftrightarrow{AB}$ at D.

Prove. $\triangle ADC \cong \triangle BDC$.

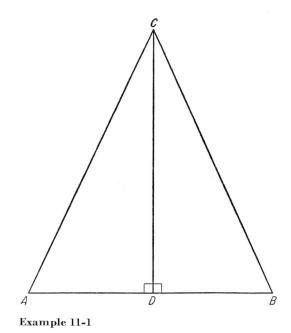

Example 11-1

Proof

1. $\overleftrightarrow{CD} \perp \overleftrightarrow{AB}$, given.
2. $\angle ADC$ is a right $\angle$ because $\perp$ lines form right angles.

3. ∠ *BDC* is a right ∠ because ⊥ lines form right angles.

4. ∠ *ADC* ≅ ∠ *BDC* because right angles are congruent.

5. $\overleftrightarrow{CD}$ bisects $\overleftrightarrow{AB}$, given.

6. *AD* = *BD* because a bisector divides a segment into two congruent parts.

7. *CD* = *CD*, by reflexive property (Axiom 1).

8. Then △ *ADC* ≅ △ *BDC*, by SAS.

EXERCISES

The triangles in Probs. 11-1 to 11-15 are marked to indicate congruent sides and angles. Indicate which pairs of triangles can be proved congruent by using the SAS postulate, definitions, axioms, and the other postulates listed so far in this text. If the triangles cannot be proved by the SAS postulate, tell why.

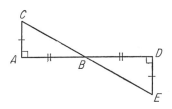

Problem 11-1

Problem 11-2

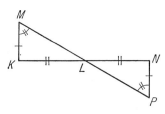

Problem 11-3

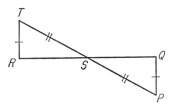

Problem 11-4

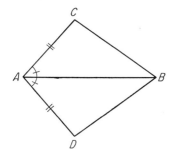

Problem 11-5

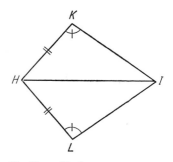

Problem 11-6

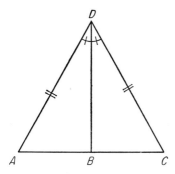

Problem 11-7

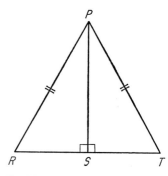

Problem 11-8

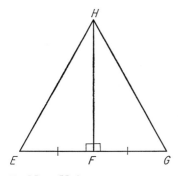

Problem 11-9

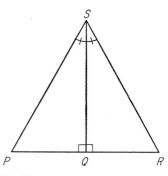

Problem 11-10

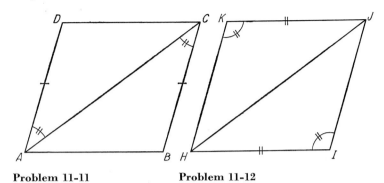

Problem 11-11   **Problem 11-12**

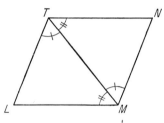

Problem 11-13

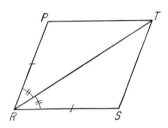

Problem 11-14

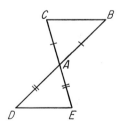

Problem 11-15

In Probs. 11-16 to 11-20, prove the triangles congruent by proving that the conditions for SAS are met.

11-16. *Given.* $\overleftrightarrow{AB}$ and $\overleftrightarrow{CD}$ bisect each other at E.

    Prove. $\triangle ACE \cong \triangle BDE$.

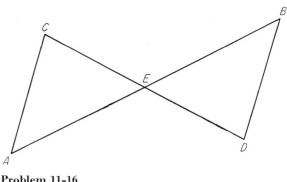

Problem 11-16

11-17. *Given.* $\overleftrightarrow{PR} \perp \overleftrightarrow{RT}$; $\overleftrightarrow{QT} \perp \overleftrightarrow{RT}$; $PR = QT$; S bisects $\overleftrightarrow{RT}$.

    Prove. $\triangle RSP \cong \triangle TSQ$.

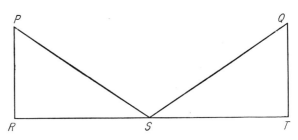

Problem 11-17

11-18. *Given.* $AD = CD$; $\overleftrightarrow{DB}$ bisects $\angle ADC$.

Prove. $\triangle ABD \cong \triangle CBD$.

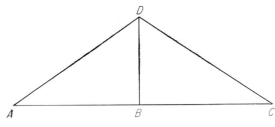

Problem 11-18

11-19. *Given.* $RS = TS$; $RP = TP$; $m\angle\,\alpha = m\angle\,\alpha'$; $m\angle\,\beta = m\angle\,\beta'$.

Prove. $\triangle RSP \cong \triangle TSP$.

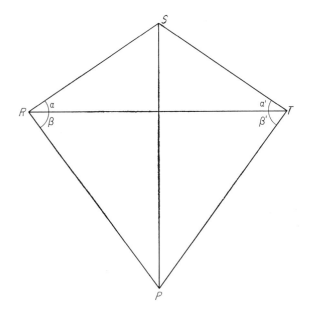

Problem 11-19

11-20. *Given.* $AC = BC$; M is the midpoint of $\overleftrightarrow{AC}$; N is the midpoint of $\overleftrightarrow{BC}$.

Prove. $\triangle ACN \cong \triangle BCM$.

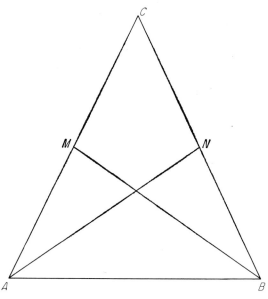

Problem 11-20

11-3 Theorems on Congruence. Once it is agreed to accept the SAS postulate, it is possible to *prove* additional theorems for triangles. The proofs are beyond the scope of this book. We shall just list some of the more important ones.

> *Theorem* 11-1 (ASA theorem). If two triangles have two angles and the included side of one congruent to the corresponding two angles and the included side of the other, the triangles are congruent.
>
> *Theorem* 11-2 (SSS theorem). If three sides of one triangle are congruent, respectively, to the three sides of another, the triangles are congruent.

Theorem 11-3 (hypotenuse–acute-angle theorem). If two right triangles have the hypotenuse and acute angle of one congruent, respectively, to the hypotenuse and acute angle of the other, the triangles are congruent.

Theorem 11-4 (hypotenuse-leg theorem). If two right triangles have the hypotenuse and a leg of one congruent to the hypotenuse and a leg of the other, the triangles are congruent.

Theorem 11-5. The base angles of an isosceles triangle are congruent.

EXAMPLE 11-2

Given. $AC = BC$; $\angle APM \cong \angle BPN$; P is the midpoint of $\overleftrightarrow{AB}$.

Prove. $\triangle APM \cong \triangle BPN$.

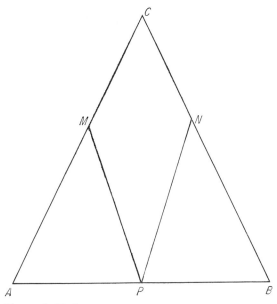

Example 11-2

Proof

1. $AC = BC$ given.

2. $\angle MAP \cong \angle NBP$ because the base angles of an isosceles $\triangle$ are $\cong$.

3. P is the midpoint of $\overleftrightarrow{AB}$, given.

4. $AP = BP$ because the midpoint of a segment divides it into two congruent segments.

5. $\angle APM \cong \angle BPN$ given.

6. $\triangle APM \cong \triangle BPN$ by ASA.

EXERCISES

The triangles in Probs. 11-21 to 11-35 are marked to indicate congruent sides and angles. Indicate which pair of sides and angles is given or can be proved congruent, and if possible, indicate the theorem or postulate that can be used to prove pairs of triangles congruent. Indicate which triangles cannot be proved congruent by any of the methods discussed thus far.

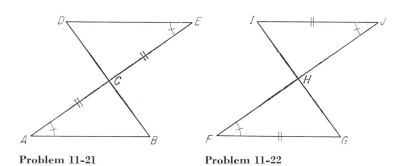

Problem 11-21   **Problem 11-22**

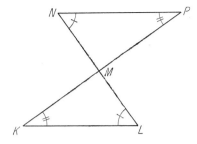

Problem 11-23

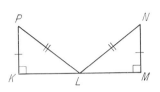

Problem 11-24

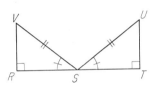

Problem 11-25

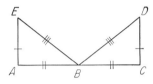

Problem 11-26

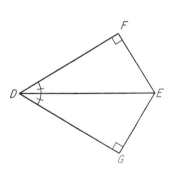

Problem 11-27

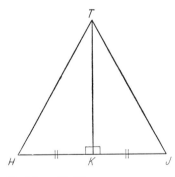

Problem 11-28

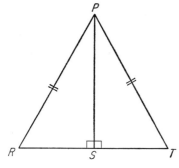

Problem 11-29

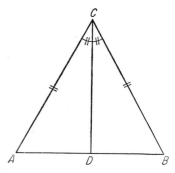

Problem 11-30

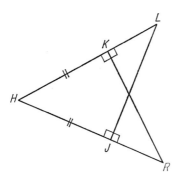

Problem 11-31

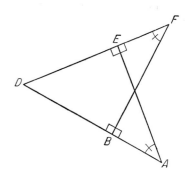

Problem 11-32

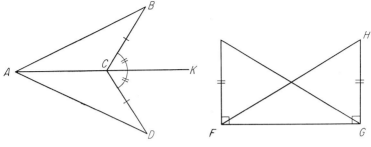

Problem 11-33

Problem 11-34

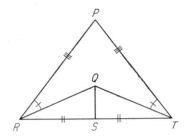

Problem 11-35

11-36. *Given.* $AC = BC$; $\overrightarrow{CM}$ bisects $\angle ACB$.
  Prove. $\triangle AMC \cong \triangle BMC$.

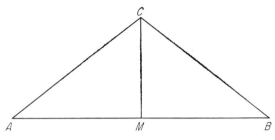

Problem 11-36

11-37. *Given.* $AC = BC$; $AD = BE$.
  Prove. $\triangle ABD \cong \triangle BAE$.

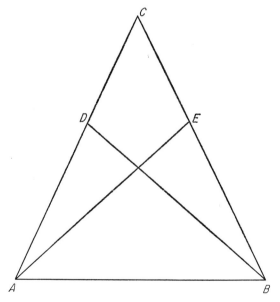

Problem 11-37

11-38. *Given.* $RP = QP$; $RS = QT$.
      Prove. $\triangle RTP \cong \triangle QSP$.

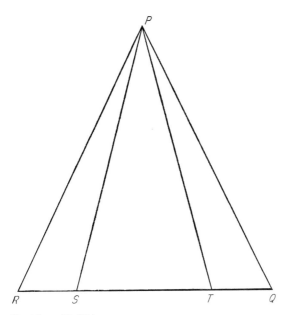

Problem 11-38

11-39. *Given.* $AE = DE$; $m\angle AEB = m\angle DEC$; $BE = CE$.
      Prove. $\triangle AEC \cong \triangle DEB$.

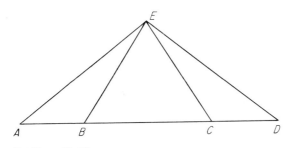

Problem 11-39

11-40. *Given.* $\angle DAB \cong \angle CBA$; $\angle DAC \cong \angle CBD$.

  Prove. $\triangle ADB \cong \triangle BCA$.

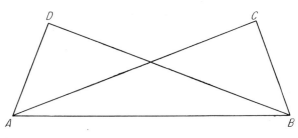

Problem 11-40

11-4 Corresponding Parts of Congruent Triangles.

Since congruent triangles have the same shape and size, we know that corresponding sides and corresponding angles of congruent triangles are congruent.   In two congruent triangles, corresponding sides are found opposite corresponding angles.   Conversely, corresponding angles are found opposite corresponding sides.   Thus, in Fig. 11-5, $\triangle ABC$ and DEC can be proved congruent by having given or by proving the following corresponding

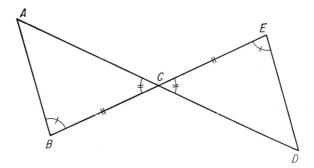

Fig. 11-5

pairs congruent: $\angle E \cong \angle B$; $EC = BC$; $\angle ECD \cong \angle BCA$.
Now, since we have proved the triangles congruent, we can state

that other pairs of corresponding parts are congruent; namely, $\angle D \cong \angle A$, $ED = BA$, and $DC = AC$.

We now have an additional method of proving segments and angles congruent. If we can show that the segments and angles are corresponding parts of congruent figures, we know that they are congruent.

EXAMPLE 11-3

Given. $\overrightarrow{AD}$ bisects $\angle CAB$; $\overleftrightarrow{DB} \perp \overleftrightarrow{AB}$, $\overleftrightarrow{DC} \perp \overleftrightarrow{AC}$.

Prove. $DB = DC$.

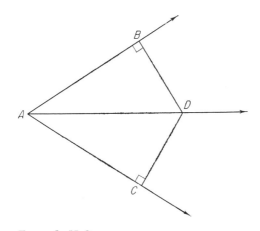

Example 11-3

Proof

1. $\overrightarrow{AD}$ bisects $\angle CAB$, given.

2. $m\angle DAB = m\angle DAC$ because a bisector divides an angle into two angles with equal measures.

3. $\overleftrightarrow{DB} \perp \overleftrightarrow{AB}$ and $\overleftrightarrow{DC} \perp \overleftrightarrow{AC}$ because it is given.

4. $\angle ABD$ and $\angle ACD$ are right angles because $\perp$ lines form right $\angle$.

5. $\triangle ABD$ and $\triangle ACD$ are right $\triangle$ by definition of "right triangle."

6. $AD = AD$ by the reflexive property (Axiom 1).

7. $\triangle ABD \cong \triangle ACD$ by hypotenuse–acute-angle theorem.

8. $DB = DC$ because corresponding parts of congruent triangles are congruent.

11-5 Special Lines and Angles of a Triangle. Several special lines, line segments, and angles have particular significance when associated with triangles.

The *base* of a triangle is the side upon which it appears to rest. Any one of the three sides may be designated as the base of a given triangle. The angle opposite the base of a triangle is called the *vertex angle*. A triangle has three bases and three vertex angles. The angles adjacent to the base are termed *base angles*.

An *altitude* of a triangle is the perpendicular segment drawn from a vertex to the line containing the opposite side. Every triangle has three altitudes. The dotted-line segments of Fig. 11-6 illustrate the three altitudes of an acute triangle and an

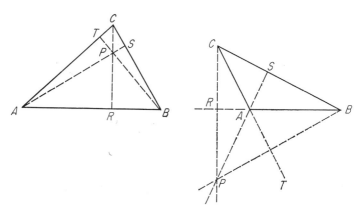

Fig. 11-6

obtuse triangle. The term altitude is also often used to refer to the measure of the line segment. It can be shown that the three altitudes (or extension of the altitudes) will pass through a common point.

The *median* of a triangle is a line segment whose end points are any vertex and the midpoint of the opposite side. Every triangle has three medians. The dotted-line segments of Fig. 11-7 illustrate medians of a triangle. It can be shown that the

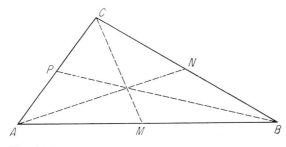

Fig. 11-7

three medians of a triangle pass through a common point, called the *centroid*. This point is also called the *center of gravity* in the study of mechanics. If a sheet of material is cut into a triangular shape, it will balance on a suspension point through the centroid.

The *angle bisector* of a triangle is a segment which divides an angle of the triangle into two congruent angles. The angle

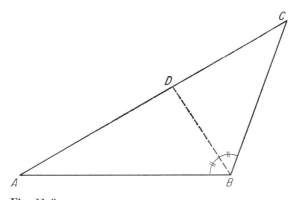

Fig. 11-8

bisector has its end points on a vertex and a side opposite the angle. $\overleftrightarrow{BD}$ is the bisector of $\angle B$ of $\triangle ABC$ in Fig. 11-8. Every triangle has three angle bisectors. It can be shown that the three angle bisectors meet in a common point which is equidistant from the three sides of the triangle.

In Fig. 11-9, if S is between R and Q, then $\angle QST$ is an *exterior angle* of $\triangle RST$. Every triangle has six exterior angles. These

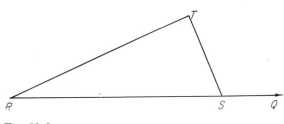

Fig. 11-9

exterior angles form three pairs of vertical angles. $\angle R$ and $\angle T$ are called *nonadjacent interior angles* of $\angle QST$.

PROBLEMS

11-41. *Given.* $LM = MN$; $m\angle\,\alpha = m\angle\,\beta$; $PM = TM$.

Prove. $m\angle P = m\angle T$.

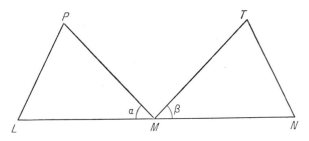

Problem 11-41

11-42. *Given.* $\overleftrightarrow{TM}$ bisects $\angle RTS$; $RT = ST$.

   Prove. $RM = SM$.

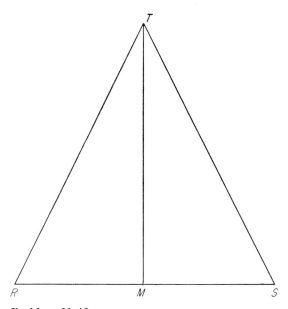

Problem 11-42

11-43. *Given.* $\overrightarrow{AP}$ bisects $\angle BAC$; $\overleftrightarrow{PB} \perp \overleftrightarrow{AB}$; $\overleftrightarrow{PC} \perp \overleftrightarrow{AC}$.

   Prove. $PB = PC$.

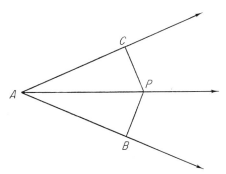

Problem 11-43

11-44. *Given.* $\overleftrightarrow{PQ} \perp \overleftrightarrow{PS}$; $\overleftrightarrow{RS} \perp \overleftrightarrow{PS}$; T bisects $\overleftrightarrow{PS}$.

  Prove. T bisects $\overleftrightarrow{RQ}$.

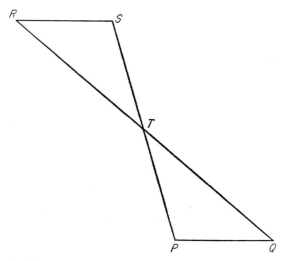

Problem 11-44

11-45. *Given.* $CD = CE$; $m\angle CDB = m\angle CEA$.
        Prove. $m\angle A = m\angle B$.

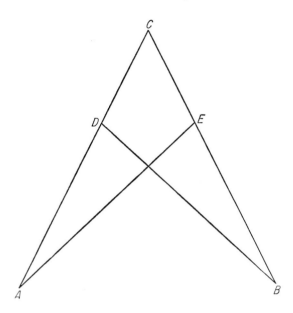

Problem 11-45

11-46. *Given.* $ST = SR;\ \overrightarrow{PT} \perp \overrightarrow{ST};\ \overrightarrow{PR} \perp \overrightarrow{SR}.$

Prove. $\overleftrightarrow{SP}$ bisects $\angle RST.$

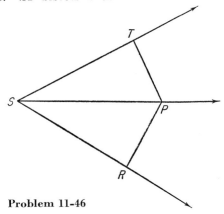

Problem 11-46

11-47. *Given.* $KM = LM;\ \overleftrightarrow{MN}$ bisects $\angle KML.$

Prove. $\overleftrightarrow{MN}$ is an altitude.

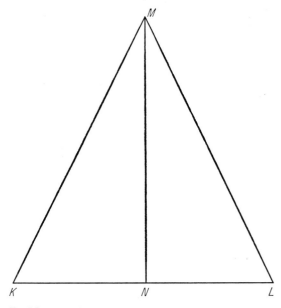

Problem 11-47

11-48. *Given.* M is the midpoint of $\overset{\longleftrightarrow}{AB}$; $AC = BC$.

       Prove. $\overset{\longleftrightarrow}{CM} \perp \overset{\longleftrightarrow}{AB}$.

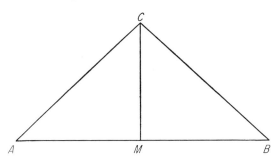

Problem 11-48

11-49. *Given.* $AC = BC$; $\overset{\longleftrightarrow}{CM}$ is a median of $\triangle\ ABC$.

       Prove. $\overset{\longleftrightarrow}{CM}$ is also an altitude.

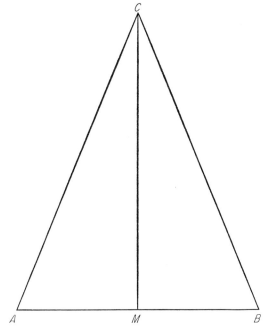

Problem 11-49

215

CHAPTER **12**

Parallel Lines and Parallelograms

12-1 Parallel Lines Are Commonplace. Two straight lines can intersect in at most one point. If they do not intersect, they are parallel or do not lie in the same plane.

▶ *Definition.* Two lines which lie in the same plane and do not intersect if extended indefinitely are parallel lines.

Examples of parallel lines can be found in many places. The opposite edges of this page are parallel. Two railroad tracks, the yardage markers on the football field, and the pickets of a fence are approximations of parallels.

The symbol for "parallel" or "is parallel to" is ∥. Rays and segments are considered parallel if the lines which contain them

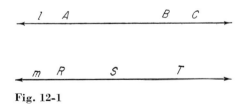

Fig. 12-1

are parallel. Thus, in Fig. 12-1, the statements $\overleftrightarrow{AC} \parallel \overleftrightarrow{RT}$, $\overrightarrow{AB} \parallel \overrightarrow{RS}$, $\overrightarrow{AC} \parallel \overrightarrow{RT}$ are each equivalent to the statement $l \parallel m$.

One of the most important postulates in the study of geometry is the parallel postulate.

▶ *Postulate* 8. *Parallel postulate.* Through a given point not on a given line there is at most one line which can be drawn parallel to the given line.

This postulate tells us that, if, in Fig. 12-2, it is given that $\overleftrightarrow{CD} \parallel \overleftrightarrow{AB}$ and passes through P, we know that, if $\overleftrightarrow{RS} \parallel \overleftrightarrow{AB}$, it

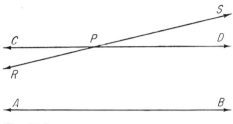

Fig. 12-2

cannot pass through P or, if $\overleftrightarrow{RS}$ passes through P, it cannot be parallel to $\overleftrightarrow{AB}$.

12-2 Transversals and Angles. A line which cuts two or more lines is called a *transversal*. In Fig. 12-3, $\overleftrightarrow{GK}$ is a transversal

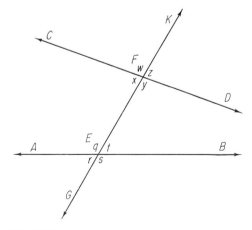

Fig. 12-3

of $\overleftrightarrow{AB}$ and $\overleftrightarrow{CD}$. When two straight lines are cut by a transversal, eight angles are formed. These angles have the following names. The pairs $\angle x$, $\angle t$ and $\angle q$, $\angle y$ are called *alternate interior angles*. The pairs $\angle w$, $\angle s$ and $\angle z$, $\angle r$ are *alternate exterior angles*. The pairs $\angle z$ and $\angle t$, $\angle y$ and $\angle s$, $\angle w$ and $\angle q$, and $\angle x$ and $\angle r$ are called *corresponding angles*. A study of the figure will reveal why the terms are used.

12-3   Theorems on Parallel and Perpendicular Lines. If Postulate 8 is accepted, it becomes possible to prove many theorems relating parallel and perpendicular lines. We shall now state some of the more important ones. These theorems are often used by the designer, the engineer, the technician, and the craftsman.

> *Theorem* 12-1. Two lines each parallel to a third line are parallel to each other. Thus if, in Fig. 12-4, $l \parallel n$ and $m \parallel n$, then $l \parallel m$.

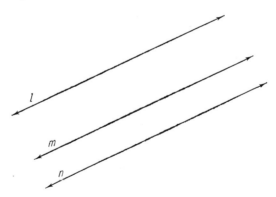

Fig. 12-4

> *Theorem* 12-2. If two straight lines form congruent alternate interior angles when they are cut by a transversal, they are parallel.

> *Theorem* 12-3. If two parallel lines are cut by a transversal, they form congruent alternate interior angles.

The last two theorems are known as *converse statements.* If, in Fig. 12-5, it is given that transversal t cuts $\overleftrightarrow{AB}$ and

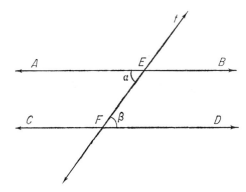

Fig. 12-5

$\overleftrightarrow{CD}$ so as to make $m\angle\,\alpha = m\angle\,\beta$, we can conclude that $\overleftrightarrow{AB} \parallel \overleftrightarrow{CD}$. Conversely, if we know that $m\angle\,\alpha = m\angle\,\beta$, we know that $\overleftrightarrow{AB} \parallel \overleftrightarrow{CD}$.

Theorem 12-4. If two straight lines form congruent corresponding angles when cut by a transversal, the lines are parallel.

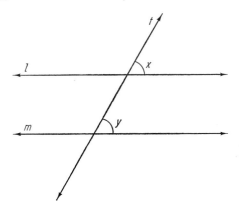

Fig. 12-6

Theorem 12-5.   If two parallel lines are cut by a transversal, they form congruent corresponding angles.

If, in Fig. 12-6 it is known that transversal t cuts lines l and m so that $m\angle x = m\angle y$, we can be certain that $l \parallel m$. Conversely, if it is given that $l \parallel m$, we know that $m\angle x = m\angle y$.

PROBLEMS

In Probs. 12-1 to 12-10, congruent angles are marked with similar hash marks and right angles are indicated with the ⌐ symbol.   Indicate whether or not l and m are parallel.

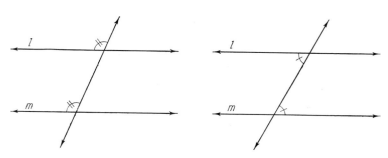

Problem 12-1   **Problem 12-2**

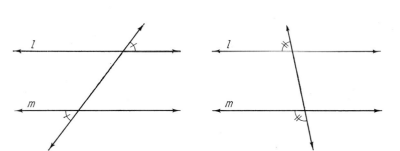

Problem 12-3   **Problem 12-4**

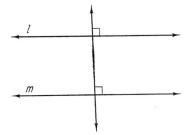

Problem 12-5

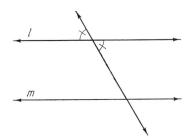

Problem 12-6

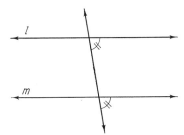

Problem 12-7

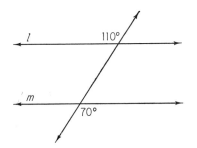

Problem 12-8

Problem 12-9

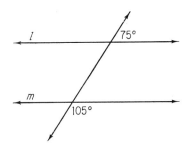

Problem 12-10

12-11. *Given.* $\overleftrightarrow{AH} \parallel \overleftrightarrow{EI}$; $\overleftrightarrow{AH} \parallel \overleftrightarrow{CG}$; $m\angle ABD = 55°$; $m\angle BDE$
= 100°.

What is the measure of $\angle DFE$?

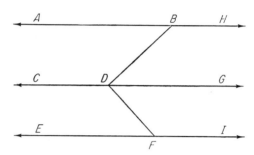

Problem 12-11

12-12. *Given.* $\overleftrightarrow{AB} \parallel \overleftrightarrow{CE}$; $\overleftrightarrow{BG} \parallel \overleftrightarrow{EF}$; $m\angle B = 75°$.

What is the measure of $\angle CEF$?

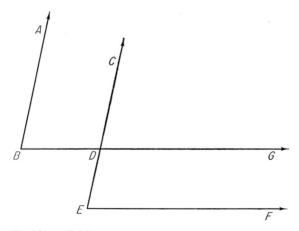

Problem 12-12

12-13. *Given.* $AC = BC$; $\overleftrightarrow{CE} \parallel \overleftrightarrow{AB}$; $m\angle A = 70°$.
What is the measure of $\angle BCD$?

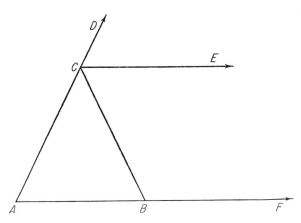

Problem 12-13

12-14. *Given.* $\overleftrightarrow{AB} \parallel \overleftrightarrow{GH}$; $\overleftrightarrow{EB} \parallel \overleftrightarrow{FH}$; $m\angle EBC = 80°$.
What is the measure of $\angle GHF$?

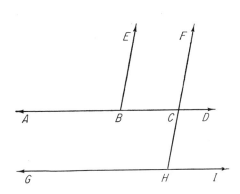

Problem 12-14

12-15. Indicate which pairs of lines are parallel.

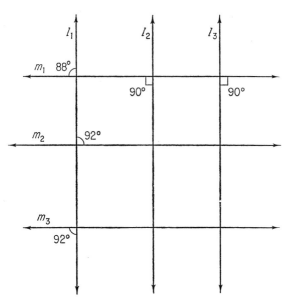

Problem 12-15

12-16. *Given.* $\overleftrightarrow{AB}$ and $\overleftrightarrow{CD}$ bisect each other at M.

Prove. $\overleftrightarrow{AC} \parallel \overleftrightarrow{BD}$.

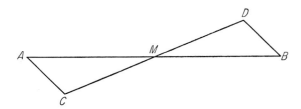

Problem 12-16

12-17. *Given.* $\overrightarrow{RP} \parallel \overrightarrow{TQ}$; $RP = TQ$.
     Prove. $RS = TS$; $PS = QS$.

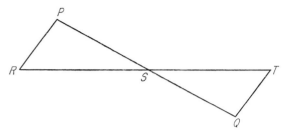

Problem 12-17

12-18. *Given.* $AB = CD$; $AD = CB$.
     Prove. $\overrightarrow{AB} \parallel \overrightarrow{CD}$.

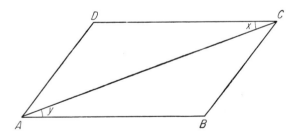

Problem 12-18

12-19. *Given.* $\overrightarrow{PT} \parallel \overrightarrow{RS}; PT = RS.$
Prove. $PR = ST.$

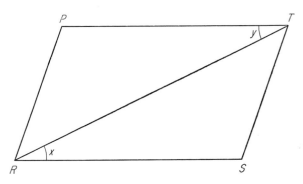

Problem 12-19

12-4 Sum of the Angles of a Triangle.   We shall now prove
a theorem with which many students are already familiar, having learned inductively about it in other classes.

Theorem 12-6.   The sum of the measures of the angles of a
triangle is equal to 180°.

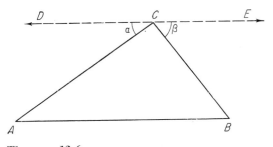

Theorem 12-6

Given.   Any triangle ABC.
Prove. $m\angle A + m\angle B + m\angle C = 180°.$

Proof

1. Through C draw $\overleftrightarrow{DE} \parallel \overrightarrow{AB}$. Postulate 8 tells us this is possible.

2. $m\angle \alpha = m\angle A$ by Theorem 12-3.

3. $m\angle \beta = m\angle B$ by Theorem 12-3.

4. $m\angle ACB = m\angle ACB$ by Axiom 1 (reflexive property).

5. $m\angle \alpha + m\angle \beta + m\angle ACB = m\angle A + m\angle B + m\angle ACB$ because, if equals are added to equals, the sums are equal.

6. But $m\angle \alpha + m\angle \beta + m\angle ACB = 180°$ because the measure of a straight angle is $180°$.

7. The $m\angle A + m\angle B + m\angle ACB = 180°$, by Axiom 8 (substitution property).

12-5   Exterior Angle of a Triangle.   Theorem 12-6 can now be used to prove the following important theorem.

Theorem 12-7.   The measure of an exterior angle of a triangle is equal to the sum of the measures of the two nonadjacent interior angles.

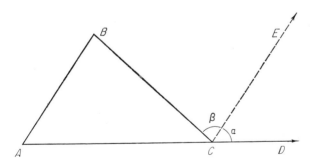

Theorem 12-7

Given. $\angle BCD$ is an exterior angle of $\triangle ABC$.

Prove. $m\angle BCD = m\angle A + m\angle B$.

Proof

1. Draw $\overrightarrow{CE} \parallel \overleftrightarrow{AB}$.   Postulate 8 allows this.
2. $m\angle \alpha = m\angle A$ by Theorem 12-5.
3. $m\angle \beta = m\angle B$ by Theorem 12-3.
4. $m\angle BCD = m\angle \alpha + m\angle \beta$ by Postulate 4.
5. $m\angle BCD = m\angle A + m\angle B$ by   Axiom   8   (substitution property).

PROBLEMS

12-20.   *Given.* $AC = BC$; $m\angle A = 60°$.
           Find. $m\angle DCB$.

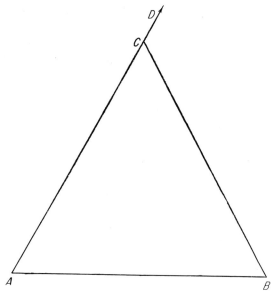

Problem 12-20

12-21. *Given.* $RT = ST = RS.$
       Find. $m\angle T.$

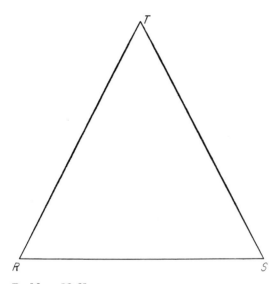

Problem 12-21

12-22. *Given.* $GI = HI$; $m\angle I = 40°$.

Find. $m\angle H$.

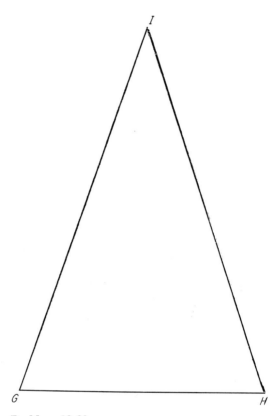

Problem 12-22

12-23. *Given.* $FE \perp DE$; $FE = DE$.
       Find. $m\angle D$.

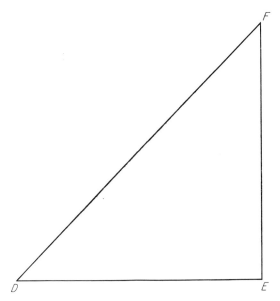

Problem 12-23

12-24. *Given.* $m\angle D = 80°$; $m\angle C = 60°$.
       Find. $m\angle ABD$.

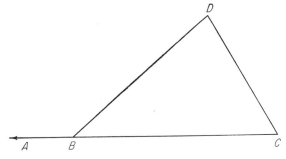

Problem 12-24

12-25. *Given.* $m\angle P = 65°$; $m\angle SQR = 135°$.
  Find. $m\angle S$.

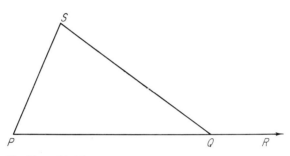

Problem 12-25

12-26. *Given.* $\overrightarrow{FJ}$ bisects $\angle EFH$; $m\angle H = 82°$; $m\angle G = 44°$.
  Find. $m\angle JFH$.

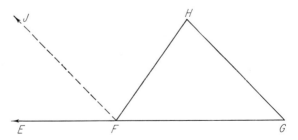

Problem 12-26

12-27. *Given.* $KN = KL$; $\overleftrightarrow{KN} \perp \overleftrightarrow{KL}$.
   Find. $m\angle MLN$.

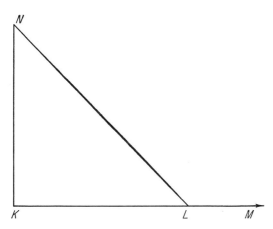

Problem 12-27

12-28. *Given.* $\angle CDE \cong \angle B$; $m\angle CED = 82°$.
   Find. $m\angle A$.

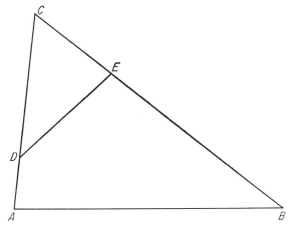

Problem 12-28

12-29. *Given.* $\overleftrightarrow{QS} \perp \overrightarrow{RT}$; $RL = TL$; $m\angle Q = 48°$.
Find. $m\angle LPQ$.

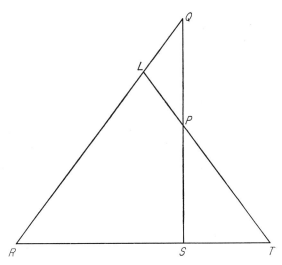

Problem 12-29

12-30. *Given.* $\overleftrightarrow{CD} \perp \overrightarrow{PT}$; $\overleftrightarrow{CA} \perp \overrightarrow{PR}$; $m\angle P = 28°$.
Find. $m\angle C$.

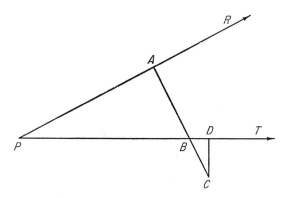

Problem 12-30

12-31. *Given.* $\overleftrightarrow{AE} \perp \overleftrightarrow{BC}$; $\overleftrightarrow{BD} \perp \overleftrightarrow{AC}$; $m\angle CAE = 20°$.

Find. $m\angle DBC$.

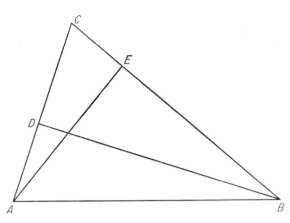

Problem 12-31

12-32. *Given.* $\overleftrightarrow{CD} \perp \overleftrightarrow{AB}$; $\overleftrightarrow{BC} \perp \overleftrightarrow{AC}$; $m\angle A = 40°$.

Find. $m\angle BCD$

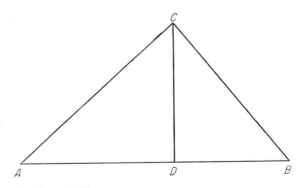

Problem 12-32

12-33. *Given.* $\overrightarrow{AB} \parallel \overrightarrow{CD}$; $\overrightarrow{AP}$ bisects $\angle CAB$; $\overrightarrow{CP}$ bisects $\angle ACD$.
Find. $m\angle P$.

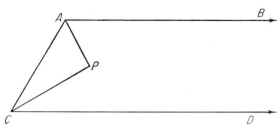

Problem 12-33

12-34. *Given* $m\angle P = 130°$; $\overrightarrow{RP}$ bisects $\angle TRS$; $\overrightarrow{SP}$ bisects $\angle RST$.
Find. $m\angle T$.

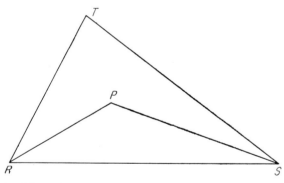

Problem 12-34

12-6 Polygons. A closed figure bounded by straight lines lying in the same plane is called a *polygon*. The segments forming the boundary are the *sides* of the polygon. The sum of the measures of the sides is the *perimeter*. Each point where two sides meet is called a *vertex*.

The simplest polygon is the triangle. A polygon has as many angles as it has sides. A *regular polygon* is one which is both equilateral and equiangular. The meanings of the terms *diagonal, interior angle,* and *exterior angle* can be recognized by studying Fig. 12-7.

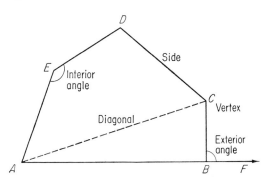

Fig. 12-7

Polygons are named according to the number of sides they have (see Fig. 12-8). A polygon of four sides is called a *quadrilateral;* a polygon of five sides is called a *pentagon;* a polygon of six sides is called a *hexagon;* a polygon of seven sides is a *heptagon;* a polygon of eight sides is an *octagon.*

12-7 Quadrilaterals. Quadrilaterals have various shapes and sizes. Those with at least one pair of parallel sides are the most important. These we shall now consider.

A quadrilateral the opposite sides of which are parallel is a *parallelogram* (symbol $\square$). Any side of the parallelogram may be called the base, as $\overleftrightarrow{AB}$ of $\square$ $ABCD$ (Fig. 12-9). The *altitude* of a parallelogram is the perpendicular distance between a pair of bases, as DE. Each parallelogram has two altitudes.

An equilateral parallelogram is called a *rhombus* (see Fig. 12-10).

A parallelogram whose angles are right angles is called a *rectangle* (see Fig. 12-10).

A rectangle whose sides are congruent is called a *square* (see Fig. 12-10).

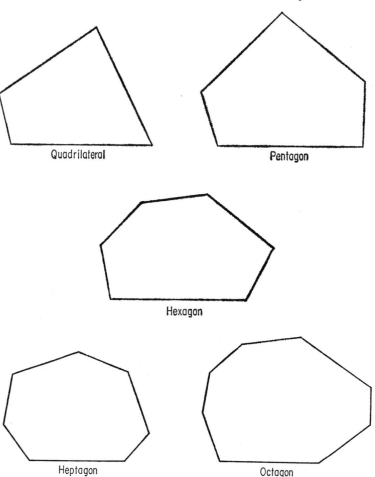

Fig. 12-8. Polygons.

12-8 Theorems on Parallelograms. It should be noted that rhombuses, rectangles, and squares are special parallelograms. The following properties common to all parallelograms can be proved, based upon the axioms, postulates, and theorems we have thus far discussed. The student is advised to make a sketch which will check out the properties.

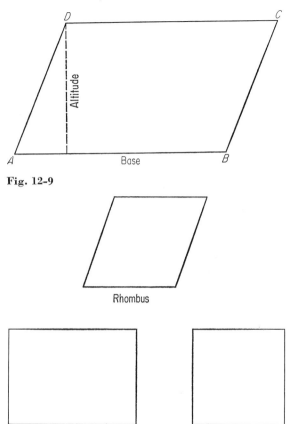

Fig. 12-9

Rhombus

Rectangle   Square

Fig. 12-10. Quadrilaterals

Theorem 12-8. The opposite sides of a parallelogram are congruent.

Theorem 12-9. The opposite angles of a parallelogram are congruent.

Theorem 12-10. Either diagonal divides a parallelogram into two congruent triangles.

Theorem 12-11. Any two adjacent angles of a parallelogram are supplementary.

Theorem 12-12.   The diagonals of a parallelogram bisect each other.

Theorem 12-13.   The diagonals of a rectangle have the same measure.

Theorem 12-14.   The diagonals of a rhombus are perpendicular to each other.

Theorem 12-15.   If the opposite sides of a quadrilateral are congruent, the quadrilateral is a parallelogram.

Theorem 12-16.   If two sides of a quadrilateral are congruent and parallel, the quadrilateral is a parallelogram.

Theorem 12-17.   The sum of the measures of the interior angles of a quadrilateral is 360°.

12-9   Trapezoid.   A *trapezoid* is a quadrilateral having one, and only one, pair of sides parallel (see Fig. 12-11).   The parallel sides are the *bases* (upper and lower) of the trapezoid.   The nonparallel sides are called *legs*.   The pair of angles adjacent to a

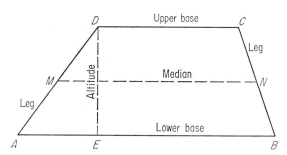

Fig. 12-11.   Trapezoid.

base are called *base angles*.   The *altitude* is the perpendicular distance, as *DE*, between the bases.   An *isosceles trapezoid* is one the legs of which are congruent (see Fig. 12-12).

The *median* of a trapezoid is the line segment connecting the midpoints of the legs.   It can be shown that the measure of the median of a trapezoid is equal to one-half the sum of the measures of the bases.

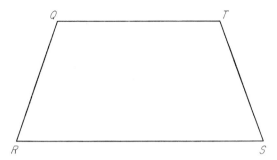

Fig. 12-12. Isosceles trapezoid.

PROBLEMS

In Probs. 12-35 to 12-59, indicate whether the statement is *always true* (mark *T*) or *not always true* (mark *F*).

12-35. A square is a rectangle.

12-36. A square is a rhombus.

12-37. A square is a parallelogram.

12-38. A rectangle is a square.

12-39. A rectangle is a rhombus.

12-40. A rectangle is a parallelogram.

12-41. A quadrilateral is a polygon.

12-42. A quadrilateral is a trapezoid.

12-43. A quadrilateral is a rectangle.

12-44. A polygon is a quadrilateral.

12-45. A quadrilateral is a parallelogram.

12-46. A polygon is a trapezoid.

12-47. The diagonals of a parallelogram bisect each other.

12-48. The diagonals of a parallelogram are congruent.

12-49. The diagonals of a rhombus are perpendicular to each other.

12-50. The lines through the vertices of a parallelogram parallel to the diagonals form another parallelogram.

12-51. If the diagonals of a parallelogram are perpendicular, the parallelogram is a square.

12-52. If the diagonals of a quadrilateral are perpendicular to each other, the quadrilateral is a parallelogram.

12-53. The nonparallel sides of an isosceles trapezoid make congruent angles with either base.

12-54. If two sides of a quadrilateral are congruent, it is a parallelogram.

12-55. A pentagon has six sides.

12-56. The sum of the measures of the interior angles of a parallelogram is 180°.

12-57. The opposite angles of a parallelogram are supplementary.

12-58. A pentagon has three diagonals.

12-59. Two consecutive angles of a parallelogram are complementary.

In Probs. 12-60 to 12-70 indicate the word(s) or number that will make the statement true.

12-60. A trapezoid the nonparallel sides of which are congruent is called a(n) . . . trapezoid.

12-61. A quadrilateral that has two and only two sides parallel is called a(n) . . . .

12-62. The bases of a trapezoid are the . . . sides of the figure.

12-63. An equilateral parallelogram is a(n) . . . .

12-64. An equilateral rectangle is a(n) . . . .

12-65. Either diagonal of a parallelogram divides it into two . . . triangles.

12-66. The opposite sides of a parallelogram are . . . and . . . .

12-67. The diagonals of a rhombus are . . . to each other.

12-68. The measure of each interior angle of a regular hexagon is . . . degrees.

12-69. The measure of the median of a trapezoid whose bases measure 12 in. and 18 in. is . . . in.

12-70. The number of diagonals that can be drawn in a polygon of 100 sides is . . . .

CHAPTER **13**

The Circle

13-1 Uses of the Circle. The circle is one of the most common and useful of all curved lines. Man's perfection of the wheel as an application of the circle has been classified by many as one of the most important inventions in the history of civilization. Without the wheel most of the world's work would cease. Industry would be completely crippled without wheels, gears, and axles with circular cross sections. Transportation would revert back to conditions of prehistoric times without the wheel.

Every year many millions of feet of circular pipe and wire are manufactured. Most canned goods come in circular cylinders. Circular shapes are found in many ornamental and landscape designs. Traffic circles are used to direct and divert the flow of vehicles of transportation.

13-2 Definitions. A *circle* is defined as the set of points lying in one plane each of which is the same distance from a fixed point, called the *center*. The symbol for circle is ⊙ (plural ⊚). Sometimes the term *circle* is used to refer to the region enclosed by the curve. A line segment one of whose end points is the center of the circle and the other one a point on the circle is called a *radius* (plural radii) of the circle. In Fig. 13-1, O is the center of O. $\overrightarrow{OA}$, $\overrightarrow{OB}$, and $\overrightarrow{OC}$ are radii. A *diameter* is a line segment through the center of a circle with end points on the circle. The measure of the diameter of a circle is twice the measure of its radius. A *chord* is a line segment with its end

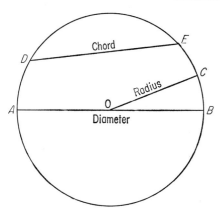

Fig. 13-1

points on the circle. Thus, the diameter is a special chord—
the longest one for a given circle.

It will be noted that we defined "radius" and "diameter" as
a segment, that is, a set of points. Common usage, however,
often lets the words denote their measures. Thus, we speak of a
circle with a radius of, say, 10 in. In general, no confusion should
arise in this dual meaning of the word.

A *secant*, as $\overleftrightarrow{MN}$ in Fig. 13-2, is a line which intersects a circle
at two points.

A *tangent* is a line which touches a circle at one, and only one,
point. This point is called the *point of tangency*. In Fig. 13-2,
$\overleftrightarrow{RT}$ is tangent to $\odot O$ at P.

13-3   Arcs and Angles.   The length (measure of) of a circle
is called its *circumference*. Any part of a circle is called an *arc*
of the circle, such as arc AE (written $\overparen{AE}$) of Fig. 13-3. Since
any two points on a circle divide it into two arcs, we shall call the
shorter arc a *minor arc* and the longer arc a *major arc*. We shall
agree in this text to let $\overparen{AE}$ stand for the minor arc. We shall
write $\overparen{ABE}$ for the major arc.

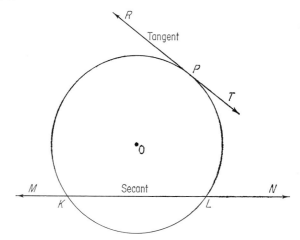

Fig. 13-2

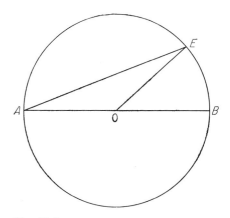

Fig. 13-3

The diameter of a circle divides it into two congruent *semi-circles.*

A *central angle*, as ∠ *AOE* of Fig. 13-3, is an angle whose vertex is the center of the circle. Angle *AOE* is said to *intercept* arc *AE* and chord *AE*. Arc *AE* and chord *AE* are said to *subtend* the central angle *AOE*.

An arc of a circle is measured by its central angle. Thus, if $m\angle BOE = 46°$, then $m\overset{\frown}{BE} = 46°$ and $m\overset{\frown}{BAE} = 314°$. Conversely, the measure of a central angle of a circle is equal to the measure of its intercepted arc. If $m\overset{\frown}{AE} = 134°$, then $m\angle AOE = 134°$.

13-4 Congruent Circles and Arcs. Circles are *congruent* if they have congruent radii. Two arcs of the same, or congruent, circles are *congruent* if they have the same measure. The relationship between arc length and arc degrees can be illustrated by referring to Fig. 13-4. In the figure are two cir-

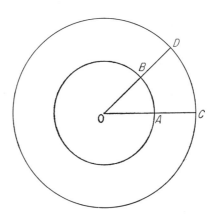

Fig. 13-4

cles, called *concentric circles*, with the same center. Since both $\overset{\frown}{AB}$ and $\overset{\frown}{CD}$ subtend the same central angle, they must have the same measure. Thus, $m\overset{\frown}{AB} = m\overset{\frown}{CD}$. However, it will be noted that the lengths of the arcs are not equal; that is, $\overset{\frown}{AB} \neq \overset{\frown}{CD}$. Here we have two arcs of different circles with the same number of arc degrees but with unequal lengths. The student should recognize that $m\overset{\frown}{AB} = m\overset{\frown}{CD}$ states that the measures *in degrees* of the two arcs are equal while $\overset{\frown}{AB} = \overset{\frown}{CD}$ states the measures in *length units* are equal.

13-5 Inscribed Angles. An angle is *inscribed* in an arc of a circle if the end points of the arc are points on the two sides of the angle and if the vertex of the angle is a point but not an end point of the arc. In Fig. 13-5a $\angle RST$ is inscribed in minor arc RST. In Fig. 13-3b $\angle ABC$ is inscribed in major arc ABC.

Angle RST is said to intercept $\overset{\frown}{RT}$; $\angle ABC$ intercepts $\overset{\frown}{AC}$.

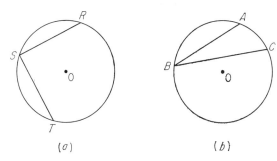

(*a*)   (*b*)

Fig. 13-5

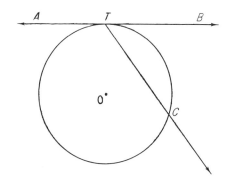

Fig. 13-6

In Fig. 13-6 $\angle BTC$ is formed by a tangent and a secant with a common point on the circle. $\angle BTC$ is said to intercept $\overset{\frown}{TC}$.

The following statements can be proved.

Theorem 13-1. The measure of an inscribed angle is equal to half the measure of its intercepted arc. Thus if, in Fig. 13-5b, $m\overset{\frown}{AC} = 40°$, then $m\angle ABC = 20°$.

Theorem 13-2. The measure of the angle formed by a tangent and a secant drawn from the point of tangency is half the measure of its intercepted arc. Thus if, in Fig. 13-6, $m\overset{\frown}{TC} = 80°$, then $\angle BTC = 40°$.

Theorem 13-3. If a line is tangent to a circle, it is perpendicular to the radius drawn to the point of tangency. If, in Fig. 13-7, $\overset{\leftrightarrow}{AB}$ is tangent to $\odot O$ at T, then $\overset{\leftrightarrow}{AB}$ is perpendicular to radius OT.

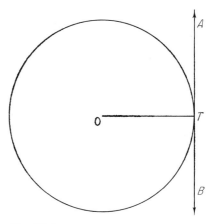

Fig. 13-7

Theorem 13-4. If a line is perpendicular to a radius at its point on the circle, it is tangent to the circle. Theorem 13-4 is the converse of Theorem 13-3. It states that, if in Fig. 13-7, $\overset{\leftrightarrow}{AB} \perp \overset{\bullet\!\!\!\!\!\!\rightarrow}{OT}$, then $\overset{\leftrightarrow}{AB}$ is tangent to $\odot O$ at T.

PROBLEMS

Find the number of degrees in the measures of ∠ α, ∠ β, and arc *m*. *O* is the center of the circle. *T* is the point of tangency.

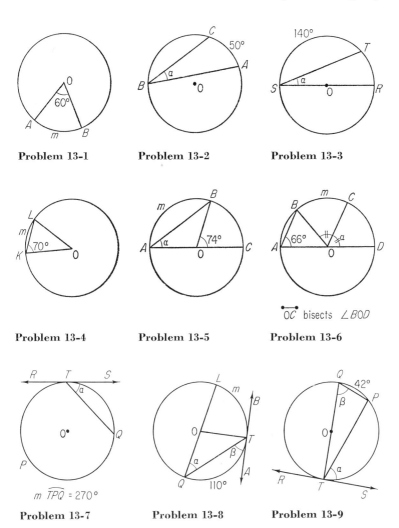

Problem 13-1

Problem 13-2

Problem 13-3

Problem 13-4

Problem 13-5

$\overset{\bullet\quad\bullet}{OC}$ bisects ∠*BOD*

Problem 13-6

m $\widehat{TPQ}$ = 270°

Problem 13-7

Problem 13-8

Problem 13-9

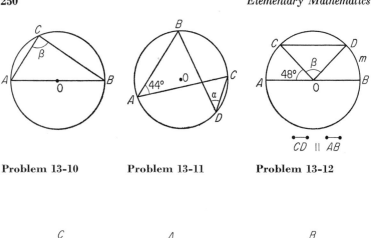

Problem 13-10   **Problem 13-11**   **Problem 13-12**

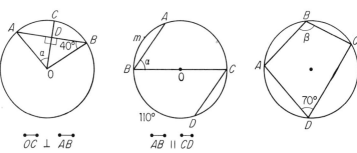

Problem 13-13   **Problem 13-14**   **Problem 13-15**

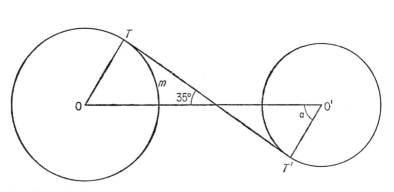

Problem 13-16

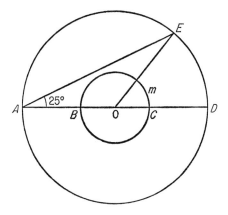

Problem 13-17

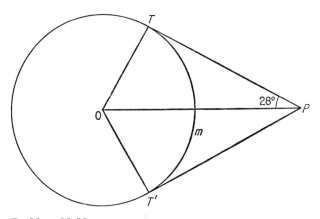

Problem 13-18

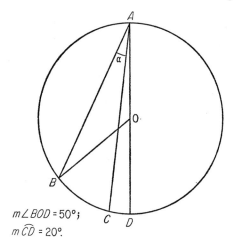

$m\angle BOD = 50°;$
$m\,\widehat{CD} = 20°.$

Problem 13-19

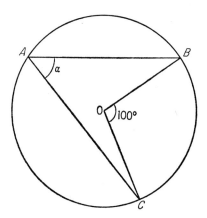

Problem 13-20

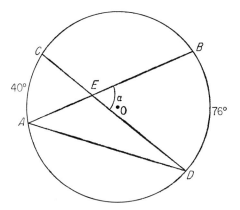

Problem 13-21

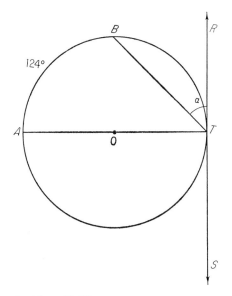

Problem 13-22

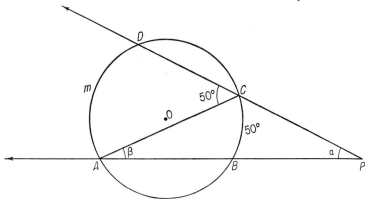

Problem 13-23

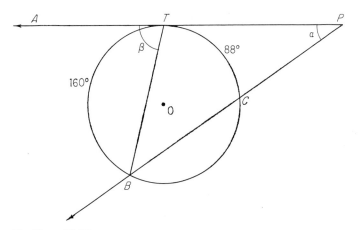

Problem 13-24

13-6 Chords and Angles. When two chords of the same circle intersect within the circle, they form two pairs of vertical angles. Consider the angle α (Fig. 13-8) formed by two intersecting chords. If we draw chord AB, two inscribed angles are formed. From Theorem 12-7 we know that $m\angle \alpha = m\angle A + m\angle B$. From Theorem 13-1 we know that $m\angle A = \frac{1}{2}m\widehat{BC}$ and

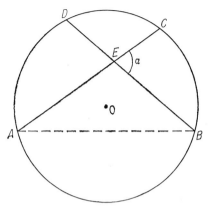

Fig. 13-8

$m\angle B = \frac{1}{2}m\widehat{AD}$.   Then, using Axiom 8 (the substitution axiom), we can show that $m\angle\alpha = \frac{1}{2}(m\widehat{BC} + m\widehat{AD})$.

Theorem 13-5.   The measure of an angle formed by two chords intersecting within a circle is half the sum of the measures of the arcs intercepted by it and its vertical angle.

13-7   Tangents and Secants.   In Fig. 13-9, $\angle APD$ intercepts $\widehat{AD}$ and $\widehat{AB}$.   Angle DPE intercepts $\widehat{DE}$ and $\widehat{BC}$.   The following theorems are proved in the study of geometry.

Theorem 13-6.   The measure of the angle formed by two secants or two tangents intersecting outside a circle is half the difference between the measures of the intercepted arcs.   In Fig.   13-9, $m\angle DPE = \frac{1}{2}(m\widehat{DE} - m\widehat{BC})$ and $m\angle APF = \frac{1}{2}(m\widehat{ADF} - m\widehat{ABF})$.

Theorem 13-7.   The measure of the angle formed by a secant and a tangent intersecting outside a circle is half the difference between the measures of the intercepted arcs.   In Fig. 13-9, $m\angle APD = \frac{1}{2}(m\widehat{AD} - m\widehat{AB})$.

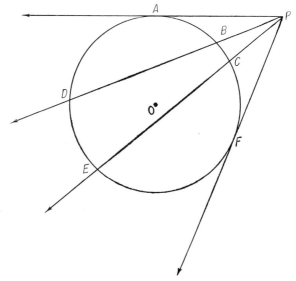

Fig. 13-9

EXERCISES

Find the number of degrees in the measures of ∠α, ∠β, and arc *m*. *O* is the center of the circle. *T* is a point of tangency.

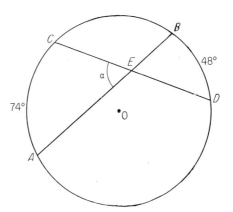

Problem 13-25

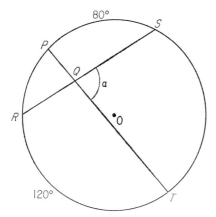

Problem 13-26

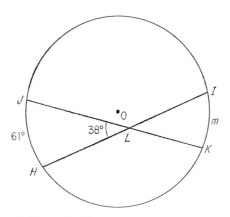

Problem 13-27

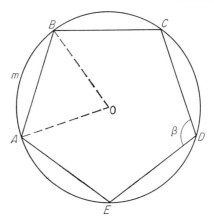

ABCDE is a regular pentagon

Problem 13-28

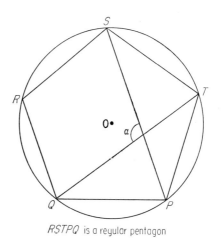

RSTPQ is a regular pentagon

Problem 13-29

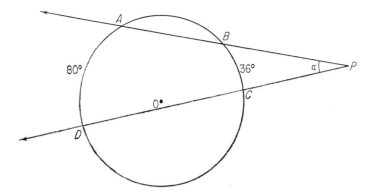

Problem 13-30

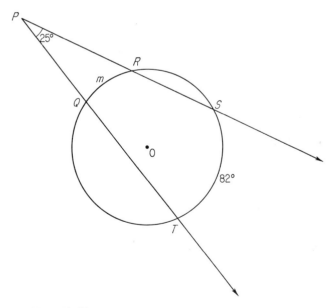

Problem 13-31

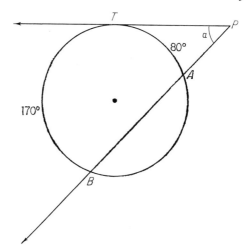

Problem 13-32

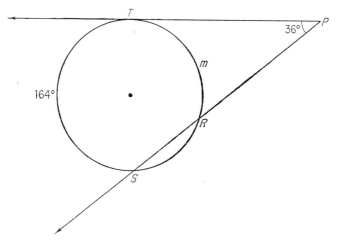

Problem 13-33

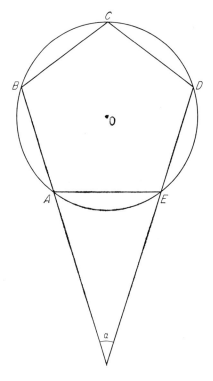

ABCDE is a regular pentagon

Problem 13-34

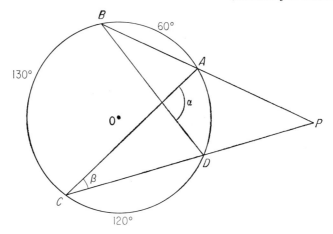

Problem 13-35

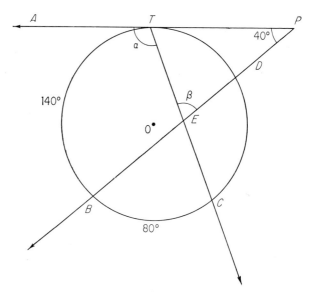

Problem 13-36

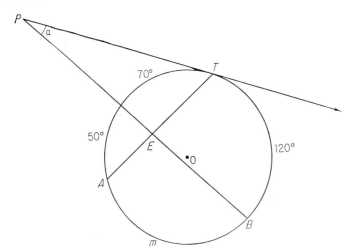

Problem 13-37

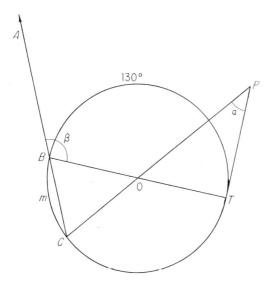

Problem 13-38

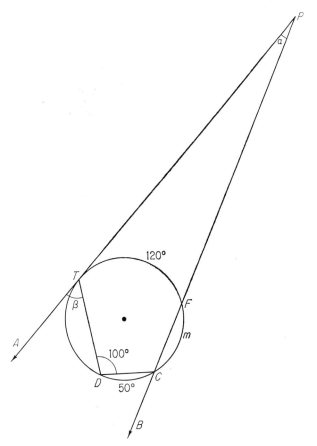

Problem 13-39

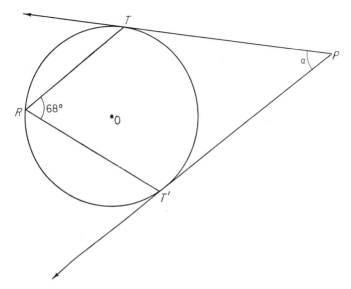

Problem 13-40

CHAPTER 14

Ratio, Proportion, and Similar Polygons

14-1 Ratio. Much communication today is concerned with comparing quantities. When one person weighs 150 lb and another 200 lb, we say that the first weighs $\frac{150}{200}$ or $\frac{3}{4}$ as much as the second or the second weighs $\frac{4}{3}$ as much as the first. If one person pays $1,000 in Federal taxes and $100 in state taxes, we compare his taxes by saying his Federal and state taxes are in the ratio of 10 to 1.

▶ *Definition.* The *ratio* of one quantity to another like quantity is the quotient of the first divided by the second.

A ratio is a fraction, and all the rules govering a fraction apply to ratios. A ratio can be written with a fraction bar, a solidus, a division sign, or the symbol : (which is read "is to"). Thus the ratio of 3 to 4 is $\frac{3}{4}$, 3/4, 3 ÷ 4, or 3:4. The 3 and 4 are called *terms* of the ratio.

It is important to note that only measures of *like* quantities can be compared. We cannot compare, for instance, 200 lb and 1,000 dollars. Pounds and dollars do not measure the same kind of quantity. However, we can compare 2 yd and 5 ft by first converting 2 yd to 6 ft. The ratio, then, becomes 6/5. The ratio of the measures of two straight angles and three right angles is 4/3.

It will be noted that a ratio is always an *abstract* number;

i.e., it has no units. Unless there is an important reason to the contrary, a ratio should be expressed in its simplest form. Therefore, we should express, for example, a ratio as $\frac{3}{4}$ rather than $\frac{150}{200}$.

14-2 Proportion. A *proportion* is a statement of equality of two or more ratios. For example, since 6/8 and 3/4 have the same value, the ratios can be equated to form a proportion: $\frac{6}{8} = \frac{3}{4}$ or $6:8 = 3:4$. If the ratios $a:b$ and $c:d$ are equal, the expression $a:b = c:d$ is a proportion. This is read "*a* is to *b* as *c* is to *d*." In the proportion, *a* is referred to as the *first term*, *b* as the *second term*, *c* as the *third term*, and *d* as the *fourth term*.

The first and fourth terms are called the *extremes*, and the second and third terms are called the *means*. It should be noted that four terms are necessary to form a proportion. Care should be taken not to use such a meaningless expression as "*a* is proportional to *b*."

The *fourth proportional* to three quantities is the fourth term of the proportion, the first three terms of which are taken in order. Thus, 3 is the fourth proportional of 8, 6, and 4.

When the two means of a proportion are equal, either is said to be the *mean proportional* between the first and fourth terms of the proportion. If $a:b = b:c$, then *b* is the mean proportional between *a* and *c*. Since $3:6 = 6:12$, 6 is the mean proportional between 3 and 12.

14-3 Theorems about Proportions. Since a proportion is a fractional equation, all the axioms which deal with equalities can be applied to a proportion. Applying these axioms to propositions leads to the following important theorems. The student may wish to develop his own proofs for each of the theorems.

Theorem 14-1. In a proportion, the product of the extremes is equal to the product of the means.

Example 1	Example 2
If $2/3 = 4/6$	If $a:b = c:d$
then $2(6) = 3(4)$	then $ad = bc$

Theorem 14-2.   In a proportion, the means may be interchanged.

Example 1   Example 2

If $12/8 = 3/2$ If $a:b = c:d$

then $12/3 = 8/2$ then $a:c = b:d$

Theorem 14-3.   In a proportion the ratios may be inverted.

Example 1   Example 2

If $\frac{5}{6} = \frac{10}{12}$ If $\dfrac{a}{b} = \dfrac{c}{d}$

then $\frac{6}{5} = \frac{12}{10}$ then $\dfrac{b}{a} = \dfrac{d}{c}$

Theorem 14-4.   If the product of two quantities is equal to the product of two other quantities, either pair of quantities can be used as the means and the other pair as the extremes of a proportion.

Example 1   Example 2

If $4(5) = 2(10)$ If $xy = rs$

then $\frac{4}{2} = \frac{10}{5}$ then $x:r = s:y$

Theorem 14-5.   If four quantities are in proportion, the terms are in proportion by addition or subtraction; that is, the sum (or difference) of the first and second terms is to the second term as the sum (or difference) of the third and fourth terms is to the fourth term.

Example 1   Example 2

If $\frac{3}{4} = \frac{9}{12}$ If $\dfrac{a}{b} = \dfrac{c}{d}$

then $\dfrac{3 + 4}{4} = \dfrac{9 + 12}{12}$ then $\dfrac{a + b}{b} = \dfrac{c + d}{d}$

PROBLEMS

14-1.   Express the following ratios in lowest terms.

    (*a*) 10 to 15   (*b*) 64:36

    (*c*) 2/3 to 3/4

    (*d*) 4 right $\measuredangle$ to 3 straight $\measuredangle$

    (*e*) 2 in. to 1 ft   (*f*) 5 hr to 15 min

    (*g*) 2 yd to 1 ft 3 in.   (*h*) 3 in.:5 cm

14-2. Prove Example 2 of Theorem 14-1 by using Axiom 6.

14-3. Prove Example 2 of Theorem 14-3 by using Axiom 7.

14-4. Prove Example 2 of Theorem 14-5 by adding 1 to both sides of the original proportion.

14-5. Find the values of x which make each proportion a truth statement.

    (*a*) $3:x = 4:24$

    (*b*) $5:20 = x:100$

    (*c*) $9:6 = 15:x$

    (*d*) $x:5 = 3:8$

    (*e*) $1\frac{1}{4}$ ft:3 in. = 2 yd:x in.

    (*f*) 28 in.:x ft = 4 yd:2 ft

14-6. Change each of the following proportions to another whose first term is a and whose second is b.

    (*a*) $\dfrac{b}{a} = \dfrac{5}{6}$ (*b*) $\dfrac{a}{4} = \dfrac{b}{3}$

    (*c*) $\dfrac{6}{a} = \dfrac{7}{b}$ (*d*) $\dfrac{4}{b} = \dfrac{12}{a}$

    (*e*) $b:4 = a:7$ (*f*) $a:2 = b:5$

14-7. Find the ratio of r to s in each of the following:

    (*a*) $3r = 4s$ (*b*) $8r = 6s$

    (*c*) $\frac{2}{3}r = 1\frac{2}{3}s$ (*d*) $r = \frac{1}{4}s$

    (*e*) $ar = bs$ (*f*) $xs = yr$

14-8. Find the fourth proportional to 4, 5, and 8.

14-9. Find the mean proportional between

    (*a*) 2 and 18   (*b*) 4 and 16

    (*c*) 20 and 5   (*d*) 2 and 32

    (*e*) $\frac{3}{4}$ and $\frac{4}{27}$ (*f*) 5 and 4

14-10. In a draftsman's scale drawing, $\frac{1}{8}$ in. represents 1 ft. What length will be represented by a segment $2\frac{5}{8}$ in. long in the drawing?

14-11. If a machine can produce 60 bolts in 2 min, how many bolts can it produce in 8 hr?

14-4   Similar Polygons.   In Chap. 11 we studied a relationship between figures called congruence.   Congruent figures are alike in every respect.   They have the same shape and size.   We shall now define polygons which have the same shape but not necessarily the same size.

▶ *Definition.*   Two polygons are said to be similar to each other if their corresponding angles are congruent and their corresponding sides are proportional.   These polygons have the same shape.

Design engineers and architects are continually dealing with similar figures.   A newly designed structure is first drawn to scale on paper.   The design is much smaller than the structure itself, but all parts have the shape of the finished product.   Blueprints of these drawings are made.   The blueprint can be read by the manufacturer.   By using a ruler and a scale, he can determine the true dimensions of any part of the structure represented in the blueprint.

The surveyor continually uses the properties of similarity of triangles in his work.

The symbol for "similar to" or "is similar to" is $\sim$.   In Fig. 14-1, $ABCDE \sim A'B'C'D'E'$ if:

1. $\angle A \cong \angle A'$, $\angle B \cong \angle B'$, $\angle C \cong \angle C'$, $\angle D \cong \angle D'$, $\angle E \cong \angle E'$.

2. $\dfrac{AB}{A'B'} = \dfrac{BC}{B'C'} = \dfrac{CD}{C'D'} = \dfrac{DE}{D'E'} = \dfrac{EA}{E'A'}.$

Conversely, if two polygons are similar, their corresponding angles are congruent and their corresponding sides are proportional.

It is important to note that the definition of similar polygons has two parts.   In order for polygons to be similar, (1) corresponding angles must be congruent and (2) corresponding sides must be proportional.

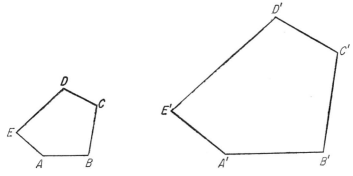

Fig. 14-1

14-5 Theorems on Similar Triangles. The following theorems can be proved and have wide application in mathematics, science, and engineering.

Theorem 14-6. If two triangles have two angles of one congruent to two angles of the other, they are similar.

Theorem 14-7. A line parallel to one side of a triangle and intersecting the other two sides divides these sides proportionally. This theorem states that if, in Fig. 14-2, it is given that $\overleftrightarrow{DE} \parallel \overleftrightarrow{AB}$, then we can conclude that $CD/DA = CE/EB$.

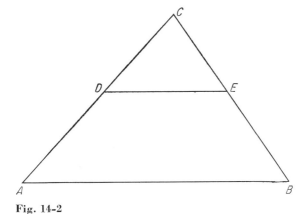

Fig. 14-2

It is then a simple matter to apply Theorem 14-5 to show that

$$\frac{CD + DA}{DA} = \frac{CE + EB}{EB}$$

or

$$\frac{CA}{DA} = \frac{CB}{EB}.$$

Theorem 14-8.   Parallel lines cut off proportional segments on two transversals.   This theorem states that if, in Fig. 14-3, it is given that $m \parallel n \parallel p$, then $AB/BC = DE/EF$.

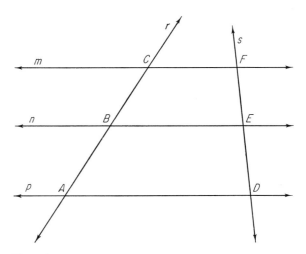

Fig. 14-3

If we apply Theorem 14-5, we can show that

$$\frac{AB + BC}{BC} = \frac{DE + EF}{EF}$$

or

$$\frac{AC}{BC} = \frac{DF}{EF}$$

PROBLEMS

In Probs. 14-12 to 14-21 it is given that $\overleftrightarrow{DE} \parallel \overleftrightarrow{AB}$. In each exercise the lengths of three segments are given. Find the value of x in each exercise.

	14–12	14–13	14–14	14–15	14–16	14–17	14–18	14–19	14–20	14–21
AD	4	5	x	6	8	8	3		8	
DC	6	15	9	x			4	10		
AC					x	32		x	12	
BE	8	x	12	9	10	10	6	9		6
EC	x	21	18	15	14			15		15
BC						x	x			
AB									x	21
DE									16	x

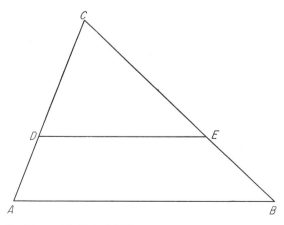

Problems 14-12 to 14-21

In Probs. 14-22 to 14-27 it is given that $m \parallel n \parallel p$.   Find the value of x in each exercise.

	14–22	14–23	14–24	14–25	14–26	14–27
AB	12	x	3		12	
BC	x	25		15	18	8
AC			x	24		12
DE	16	24	9	x		
EF	12	15	15	10	x	10
DF					40	x

Problems 14-22 to 14-27

In Probs. 14-28 to 14-33 determine the pairs of corresponding sides of similar triangles; then find the length of x. Right angles are marked ∟ and congruent angles are marked with the same mark.

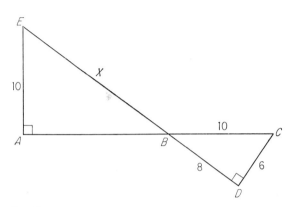

Problem 14-28

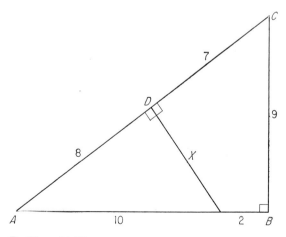

Problem 14-29

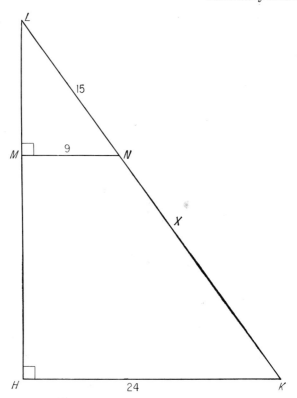

Problem 14-30

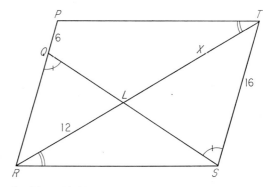

Problem 14-31

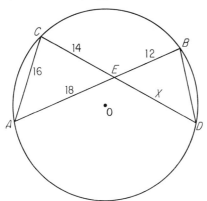

Problem 14-32

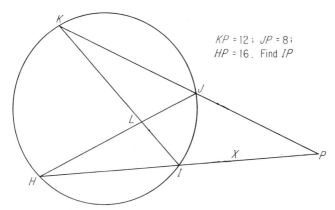

$KP = 12$; $JP = 8$;
$HP = 16$. Find IP

Problem 14-33

14-6 Pythagorean Theorem. The altitude on the hypotenuse of a right triangle divides it into two triangles which are each similar to the given triangle and to each other. Let us assume in Fig. 14-4 that, in $\triangle ABC$, $\angle ACB$ is a right angle and CD (an altitude) is perpendicular to hypotenuse AB. Consider the angles of $\triangle ADC$ and ABC. $\angle ADC \cong \angle ACB$, since they are both right angles. $\angle A \cong \angle A$, by the reflexive property of equality. Hence, the triangles are similar by Theorem 14-6. We also can then show that $\angle ACD$, the third angle of $\triangle ACD$, is congruent to the third angle ($\angle B$) of $\triangle ABC$. In like man-

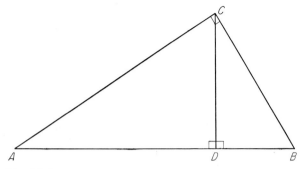

Fig. 14-4

ner, we can prove that $\triangle BDC \sim \triangle ABC$ by showing that $\angle BDC \cong \angle ACB$ and $\angle B \cong \angle B$. Lastly, we can show that $\triangle ADC \sim \triangle BDC$ by showing that $\angle ADC \cong \angle BDC$ and $\angle ACD \cong \angle B$.

We are now ready to prove one of the most useful theorems in geometry.

Theorem 14-9 (*Pythagorean theorem*). The square of the measure of the hypotenuse of a right triangle is equal to the sum of the squares of the measures of the legs.

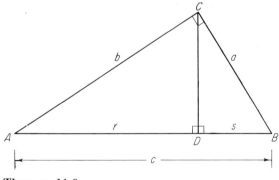

Theorem 14-9

1. Assume that ABC is a right $\triangle$ with $\angle ACB$ a right $\angle$.

2. Draw $\overleftrightarrow{CD} \perp \overleftrightarrow{AB}$.

3. $\triangle ABC \sim \triangle BDC$, since $\angle B \cong \angle B$ and $rt\angle ACB \cong rt\angle BDC$.

4. $\triangle ABC \sim \triangle ADC$, since $\angle A \cong \angle A$ and $rt \angle ACB \cong rt\angle ADC$.

5. Then $c:a = a:s$ and $c:b = b:r$, since corresponding sides of similar polygons are proportional.

6. $a^2 = cs$ and $b^2 = cr$ by Theorem 14-1.

7. $a^2 + b^2 = cs + cr = c(s + r)$ by adding equals and using the distributive law.

8. But $s + r = c$ by Postulate 3.

9. Then $a^2 + b^2 = c^2$ by Axiom 8.

EXAMPLE 14-1

Given. $\overset{\bullet\quad\bullet}{CB} \perp \overset{\bullet\quad\bullet}{AB}$; $AB = 8$ in.; $BC = 15$ in.

Find. AC.

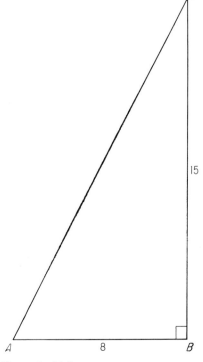

Example 14-1

Solution

By the Pythagorean theorem $(AC)^2 = (AB)^2 + (BC)^2$

Substituting known values, $(AC)^2 = (8)^2 + (15)^2$

$$= 64 + 225$$
$$= 289$$

Then $AC = \sqrt{289} = 17$ in.

EXAMPLE 14-2

Given. $\overleftrightarrow{TR} \perp \overleftrightarrow{RS}$; $TS = 45$ ft; $RT = 27$ ft.

Find. RS.

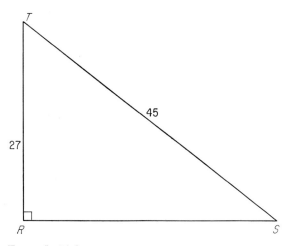

Example 14-2

Solution

$$(TS)^2 = (RT)^2 + (RS)^2$$
or
$$(RS)^2 = (TS)^2 - (RT)^2$$
$$= (45)^2 - (27)^2$$
$$= 2{,}025 - 729$$
$$= 1{,}296$$
$$RS = \sqrt{1{,}296} = 36 \text{ ft}$$

14-7   Similar Triangles Associated with Circles.   Consider Fig. 14-5 in which two chords intersect within a circle.   If

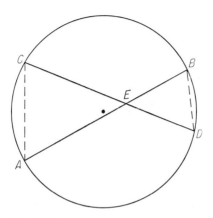

Fig. 14-5

we draw chords AC and BD, two triangles are formed. $\angle A \cong \angle D$, since they intercept the same arc.   In like manner, $\angle C \cong \angle B$. $\angle AEC \cong \angle BED$, since they are vertical angles.   Therefore $\triangle AEC \sim \triangle BED$ and $AE:DE = CE:BE$ or $AE \times BE = DE \times CE$.   This can be stated as a theorem.

> *Theorem* 14-10.   If two chords intersect within a circle, the product of the measures of the segments of one chord is equal to the product of the measures of the segments of the other.

In Fig. 14-6 let PA and PD be secants of $\odot O$ drawn from the point P.   If we draw chords AC and BD, two similar triangles are formed.   It can be shown that $\angle A \cong \angle D$, $\angle ACP \cong \angle DBP$, and $\angle P \cong \angle P$.   Therefore, we can form the proportion $PA:PD = PB:PC$.   Using Theorem 14-1, we can then prove that $PA \times PB = PD \times PC$.

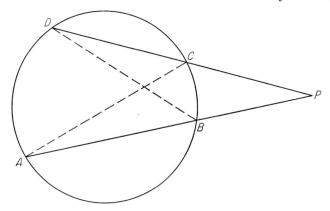

Fig. 14-6

Theorem 14-11.   If two secants are drawn from the same point outside a circle, the product of the measures of one secant and its external segment is equal to the product of the measures of the other secant and its external segment.

PROBLEMS

In Probs. 14-34 to 14-43 $\angle ACB$ is a right $\angle$, $\overset{\longleftrightarrow}{CD} \perp \overset{\longleftrightarrow}{AB}$.

14-34. Find AB if $AC = 16$ and $BC = 12$.
14-35. Find BC if $BD = 9$ and $CD = 12$.
14-36. Find CD if $AC = 17$ and $AD = 15$.

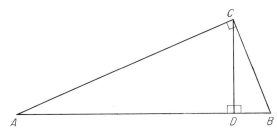

Problems 14-34 to 14-43

14-37. Find AC if $AB = 40$ and $BC = 25$.
14-38. Find CD if $AD = 18$ and $BD = 8$.
14-39. Find BC if $AB = 8$ and $BD = 2$.
14-40. Find AC if $AD = 24$, $CD = 18$, and $BC = 22.5$.
14-41. Find AC if $BD = 18$, $BC = 30$, and $CD = 24$.
14-42. Find BD if $AD = 5$ and $CD = 10$.
14-43. Find DC if $AD = 16$ and $BD = 4$.

In Probs. 14-44 to 14-47 find the lengths of x. Draw a perpendicular if necessary. Right angles and congruent sides are marked.

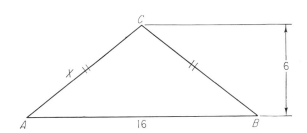

Problem 14-44

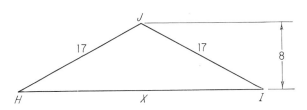

Problem 14-45

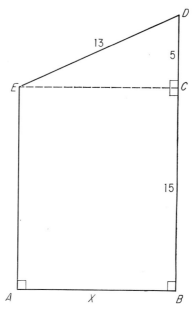

Problem 14-46

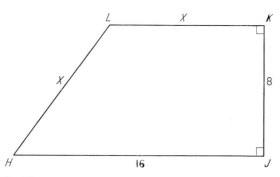

Problem 14-47

14-48. Find CE if $AE = 4$, $EB = 45$, $ED = 15$.
14-49. Find ED if $CE = 20$, $EB = 12$, $AE = 15$.
14-50. Find AE if $EB = 4$, $CE = 8$, $ED = 5$.

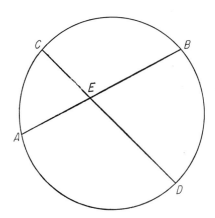

Problems 14-48 to 14-51

14-51. Find AC if $BD = 16$, $AE = 15$, $BE = 20$, $DE = 25$.
14-52. Find RP if $PT = 24$, $PS = 10$, $PQ = 8$.
14-53. Find PS if $RP = 36$, $PT = 48$, $PQ = 12$.

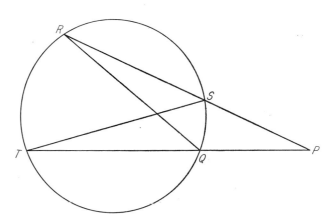

Problems 14-52 to 14-55

14-54. Find *PT* if *PQ* = 3, *PS* = 4, *RS* = 5.

14-55. Find *PQ* if *PS* = 4, *RQ* = 5, *TS* = 8.

14-56. Find *QS* if *OR* = 16, *QT* = 6, *RQ* = 10.

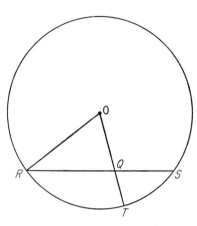

Problems 14-56 and 14-57

14-57. Find *OR* if *RQ* = 16, *QS* = 10, *QT* = 8.

14-58. A 25-ft ladder is placed against a vertical wall of a building. The foot of the ladder is 7 ft from the wall. If the top of the ladder slips 4 ft, how far will the foot of the ladder slide?

CHAPTER 15

Perimeters and Areas

15-1 The Circumference of a Circle. Finding the length and area of a circle have been two of the greatest historic problems in mathematics.

▶ *Definition.* The *circumference* of a circle is the length of the circle (sometimes called the *perimeter*).

The following theorem can be proved:

Theorem 15-1. The ratio of the circumference to the diameter is the same for all circles. This ratio is represented by the Greek letter π (pi). Thus, in Fig. 15-1, if we let

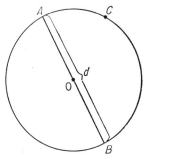 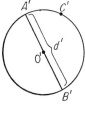

Fig. 15-1

C and C' be circumferences and d and d' diameters of Ⓢ O and O', respectively, $C/D = C'/d' = \pi$.

If we multiply each side of the equation $C/d = \pi$ by d, we obtain the formula for the circumference of the circle. Since the measure of a diameter is two times the measure of the radius, we can express the following rule.

▶ *Formula.* The circumference of a circle is expressed by the formula $C = \pi d$ or $C = 2\pi r$.

The number π is what is called an irrational number; i.e., regardless of the degrees of accuracy to which the number is determined, it will never be exact. In advanced studies it can be shown that $\pi = 4(1 - \frac{1}{3} + \frac{1}{5} - \frac{1}{7} + \frac{1}{9} - \frac{1}{11} + \cdot \cdot \cdot)$. The right-hand expression is called an *infinite series*.

By the use of modern computers, the value of π has been found accurate to more than 100,000 digits. This is a degree of accuracy which has no practical value. The value of π accurate to 10 decimals is 3.1415926536.

In using the formula for circumference it is best to use π rounded off to one more digit than the given data. Then the computed values should be rounded off to the degree of accuracy of the given data.

EXAMPLE 15-1.   Find the circumference of a circle the length of whose diameter is 6.8 in.

Solution

$$
\begin{aligned}
C &= \pi d \\
  &= (3.14)(6.8) \\
  &= 21.352 \\
  &\approx 21.4 \text{ in.}
\end{aligned}
$$

EXAMPLE 15-2.   Find the radius of a circle whose circumference is 7.65 ft.

Solution

$$C = 2\pi r$$
$$r = \frac{C}{2\pi}$$
$$= \frac{7.65}{2(3.142)}$$
$$= 1.201$$
$$\approx 1.20 \text{ ft}$$

15-2 Meaning of Area. A *unit of area* is the measure of the surface within a square whose sides have unit lengths. Thus, if *ABCD* in Fig. 15-2 is a square each side of which has a length of 1 in., the measure of the region enclosed is called a *square inch*.

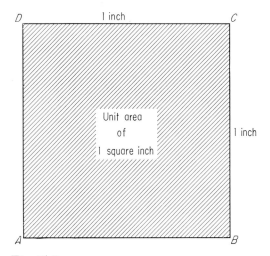

Fig. 15-2

Other common units of area are the *square foot, square yard, square mile,* and *square centimeter.*

The area of a polygon is the number which tells how many times a given unit area is contained in the region bounded by the polygon.

Formulas have been developed by which areas can be computed when certain linear measurements are known. It should be noted that the length of a line segment can be *measured* directly by using a ruler or tape measure but the area of a region is *computed by formula*. Formulas have been developed for areas of the rectangle, triangle, parallelogram, trapezoid, and circle. The areas of other figures can often be found by partitioning them into triangles, rectangles, and trapezoids and then summing up the areas of these figures.

15-3 Area of a Rectangle. If in rectangle *ABCD* of Fig. 15-3 *AB* = 5 in. and *BC* = $3\frac{1}{2}$ in., we can draw the lines shown

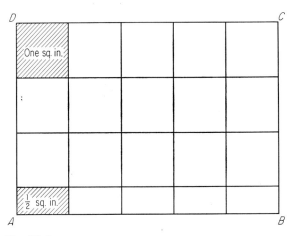

Fig. 15-3

and then count 15 square-inch units and 5 one-half square-inch units. These 5 one-half square-inch units are equivalent to $2\frac{1}{2}$ square-inch units. The total area is then $17\frac{1}{2}$ in². This number could also be obtained by multiplying $5 \times 3\frac{1}{2}$. This example suggests the following postulate.

▶ *Postulate* 9. The area of a rectangle is equal to the product of its base and its altitude ($A = bh$).

Since a square is an equilateral rectangle, we can state: The area of a square is equal to the square of the sides ($A = s^2$).

PROBLEMS

15-1. Find the circumference of a circle with a diameter of (*a*) 3.7 yd, (*b*) 5.07 in., (*c*) 1.912 miles.

15-2. Find the circumference of a circle with a radius of (*a*) 2.5 in., (*b*) 6.37 ft, (*c*) 41.08 cm.

15-3. Find the diameter of a circle whose circumference is (*a*) 4.5 ft, (*b*) 2.51 in., (*c*) 6.283 yd.

15-4. Find the radius of a circle whose circumference is (*a*) 28 in., (*b*) 503 ft, (*c*) 90.14 yd.

15-5. Find the area of a rectangle with base 7.3 ft and altitude 2.4 ft.

15-6. Find the altitude of the rectangle with area of 12.4 in.^{2} and base 2.6 in.

15-7. Find the area of a floor, in square feet, that is 15 ft 8 in. long and 12 ft 9 in. wide.

15-8. How many square inches are in the six sides of a box $7\frac{1}{2}$ by 5 by $3\frac{1}{2}$ in.?

15-9. What is the cost of carpeting the floor of a room with dimensions 15 ft 4 in. by 24 ft 6 in. if carpeting costs $7.75 a square yard?

15-10. How long must the floor of a factory be if it is 45 ft 6 in. wide and has an area of 5584.25 ft^2?

In Probs. 15-11 to 15-20 divide the figures into rectangles and then find the areas of each figure.

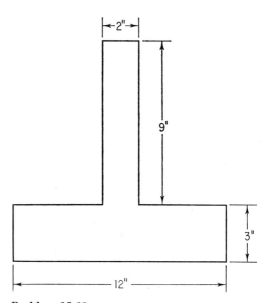

Problem 15-11

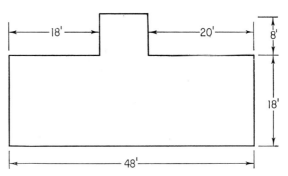

Problem 15-12

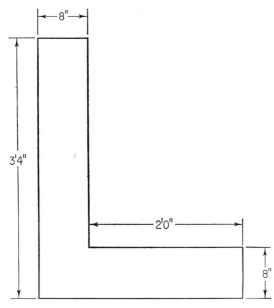

Problem 15-13

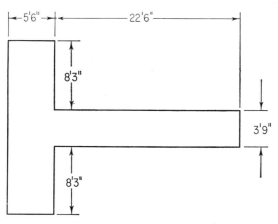

Problem 15-14

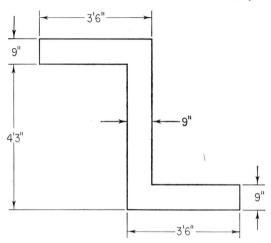

Problem 15-15

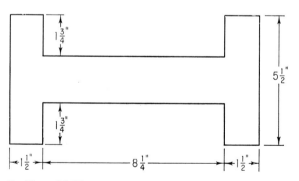

Problem 15-16

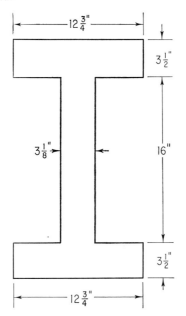

Problem 15-17

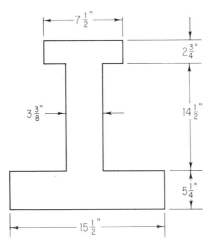

Problem 15-18

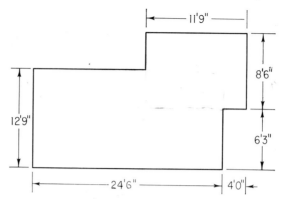

Problem 15-19

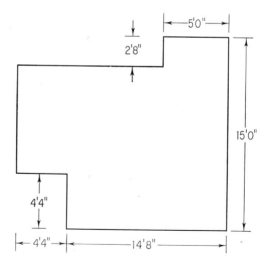

Problem 15-20

15-21. A barn with a flat roof is rectangular in shape, 10 yd wide, 12 yd long, and 5 yd high. It is to be painted inside and outside and on the ceiling but not on the roof or floor. Find the total number of square yards to be painted.

15-4 Area of a Parallelogram. Consider the parallelogram shown in Fig. 15-4. Let h be the length of the altitude and b

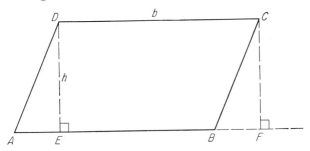

Fig. 15-4

the length of the base. Since $\triangle ADE \sim \triangle BCF$, it can be shown that the area of $\square ABCD$ equals the area of $\square EFCD$. We can then state the following theorem.

Theorem 15-2. The area of a parallelogram is equal to the product of its base and its altitude ($A = bh$).

15-5 Area of a Triangle. Consider $\triangle ABC$ of Fig. 15-5. If we draw $\overleftrightarrow{CD} \parallel \overleftrightarrow{AB}$ and $\overleftrightarrow{BD} \parallel \overleftrightarrow{AC}$, $\square ABDC$ will be formed. Theorem 15-2 states that the area of $\square ABDC = bh$. Diagonal

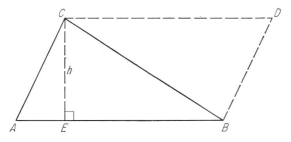

Fig. 15-5

BC separates the parallelogram into two triangles which can be proved congruent. Hence it can be shown that the area of $\triangle ABC = \frac{1}{2}bh$.

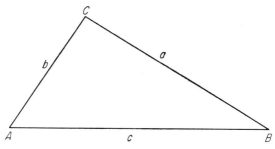

Fig. 15-6

Theorem 15-3. The area of a triangle is equal to half the product of its base and its altitude ($A = \frac{1}{2}bh$).

Occasionally the three sides of a triangle are known but not the altitude or base. It is possible to find the area of such a triangle by using a formula attributed to Heron (first century A.D.) of Alexandria. The proof of the formula can be found in many geometry texts.

Theorem 15-4 (Heron's formula). The area of a triangle with sides a, b, c is given by the formula $A = \sqrt{s(s - a)(s - b)(s - c)}$ where $s = \frac{1}{2}(a + b + c)$.

EXAMPLE 15-3. Find the area of $\triangle ABC$ if $a = 12$ ft, $b = 15$ ft, $c = 19$ ft.

Solution

$$s = \frac{1}{2}(a + b + c)$$
$$= \frac{1}{2}(12 \text{ ft} + 15 \text{ ft} + 19 \text{ ft})$$
$$= 23 \text{ ft}$$
$$A = \sqrt{23(23 - 12)(23 - 15)(23 - 19)}$$
$$= \sqrt{8{,}096}$$
$$= 89.98$$
$$\approx 90 \text{ ft}^2$$

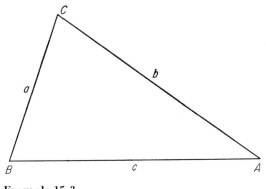

Example 15-3

15-6   Area of a Trapezoid.   Let trapezoid $ABCD$ (Fig. 15-7) have bases b_1 and b_2 and altitude h.   If we draw diagonal AC, the trapezoid will be partitioned into $\triangle ABC$ and ACD.   By

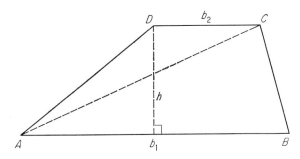

Fig. 15-7

Theorem 15-3, the area of $\triangle ABC = \frac{1}{2}b_1h$ and the area of $\triangle ACD = \frac{1}{2}b_2h$.   Adding, we get the area of $ABCD = \frac{1}{2}b_1h + \frac{1}{2}b_2h$.   Then, by applying the distributive law of multiplication (see Sec. 1-6), we get area $ABCD = \frac{1}{2}h(b_1 + b_2)$.

Theorem 15-5.   The area of a trapezoid is equal to half the product of its altitude and the sum of its bases.

PROBLEMS

15-22. Find the area of a parallelogram with base 18 in. and altitude 24 in.

15-23. Find the area of a parallelogram with base 15.4 in. and altitude 10.3 in.

15-24. Find the altitude of the parallelogram with an area of 408 in.² and a base of 26 in.

15-25. Find the area of the square whose diagonal has a length of 32 in.

15-26. Find the area of the rhombus the diagonals of which are 36 and 24 in.

15-27. Find the area of $\triangle ABC$, in square feet, if $\overleftrightarrow{CD} \perp \overleftrightarrow{AB}$, $AB = 15$ ft 6 in., $CD = 8$ ft 3 in.

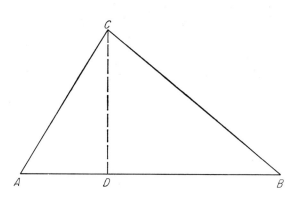

Problem 15-27

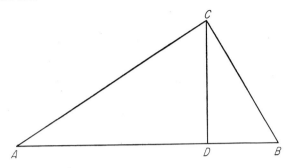

Problem 15-28

15-28. Find the area of $\triangle ABC$ if $\angle ACB$ is a right angle, $\overleftrightarrow{CD} \perp$ $\overleftrightarrow{AB}$, $AD = 16$ ft, $BD = 4$ ft.

15-29. Find the length of ST if $RS = ST$. $\angle S$ is a right $\angle$, and the area of $\triangle RST$ is 128 in.^{2}

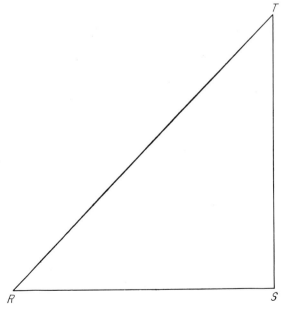

Problem 15-29

15-30. Find the altitude of $\triangle ABC$.

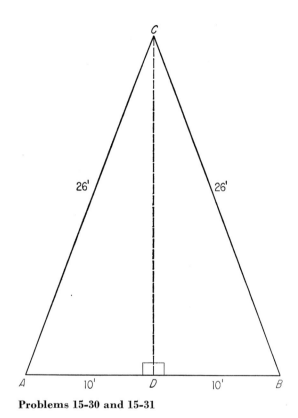

Problems 15-30 and 15-31

15-31. Find the area of $\triangle ABC$.

15-32. Find the area of $\triangle RST$ if $m \angle S = 90°$, $RT = 34$ ft, $ST = 30$ ft.

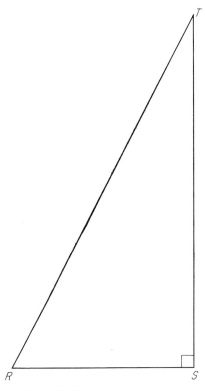

Problem 15-32

15-33. Find the area of a triangle the length of whose sides is 9, 12, and 15 ft.

15-34. Find the area of $\triangle RST$ (accurate to one decimal place) if $RS = 8$ in., $ST = 12$ in., $RT = 16$ in.

15-35. Find the altitude of equilateral $\triangle ABC$ if $AC = 9$ ft.

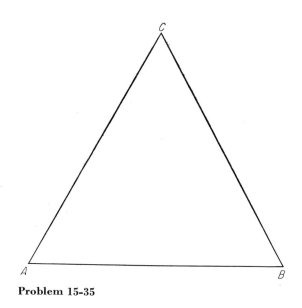

Problem 15-35

In Probs. 15-36 to 15-41 find the areas of the trapezoids.

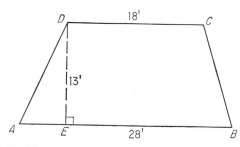

Problem 15-36

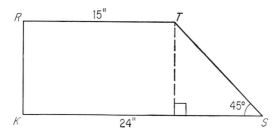

Problem 15-37

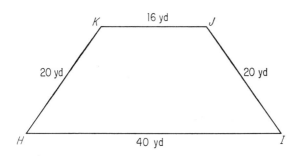

Problem 15-38

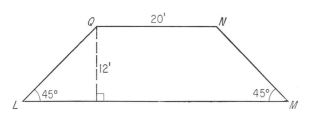

Problem 15-39

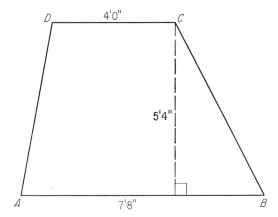

Problem 15-40

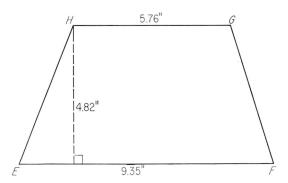

Problem 15-41

In Probs. 15-42 and 15-43 find the area of each figure.

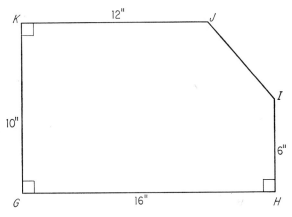

Problem 15-42

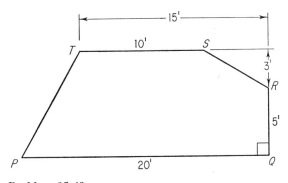

Problem 15-43

15-7   Area of a Circle.   In Sec. 15-1 we learned that the ratio of the circumference and diameter of any circle is equal to the constant π.   It can be proved that this constant is also equal to the ratio of the area to the square of its radius for any circle.

Theorem 15-6.   The ratio of the area to the square of the radius is the same for all circles.

In Fig. 15-8

$$\frac{A}{r^2} = \frac{A}{r'^2} = \pi$$

Multiplying each term of the equation $A/r^2 = \pi$ by r^2, we obtain the formula for the area of a circle.

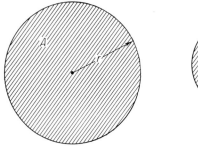

Fig. 15-8

▶ *Formula.* The formula for the area of a circle is $A = \pi r^2$. Since $r = d/2$, we can substitute in the formula and get $A = \pi d^2/4$.

15-8 Length of an Arc. Since the measure of an arc is equal to the measure of its central angle, we know that the lengths of two arcs of a circle are proportional to the measures of their central angles. Thus, in Fig. 15-9, $l/s = \theta/\phi$. If we let C be the circumference of the circle, $l/C = \theta/360$. Multiplying each term by C and then replacing C by $2\pi r$, we get $l = (\theta/360)C = \theta/360(2\pi r)$.

▶ *Formula.* The formula for the length of an arc of a circle is $l = r\theta/180$.

15-9 Area of a Sector. A *sector of a circle* is a region bounded by two radii and an arc (see Fig. 15-10). The areas of two sectors of a circle are proportional to the measures of their central angles. Thus, if K is the area of the sector and A is the

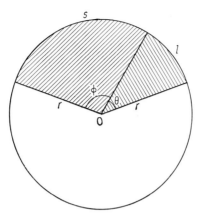

Fig. 15-9

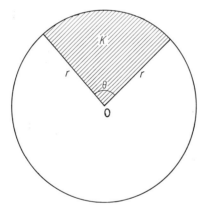

Fig. 15-10

area of the circle, $K/A = \theta/360$. Multiplying each term by A and then replacing A by πr^2, we get the following.

▶ *Formula.* The formula for the area of a sector of a circle is $K = \pi r^2 \theta/360$.

15-10 Area of a Segment. A *segment of a circle* is the region bounded by a chord and an arc of the circle. The shaded

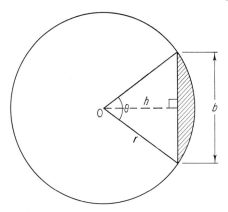

Fig. 15-11

region of Fig. 15-11 represents a segment of the circle.   The area
of the segment can be found by subtracting the area of the triangle formed by the chord and the two radii to its end points
from the area of the sector.   Thus the area is found by $K = \pi r^2 \theta / 360 - \frac{1}{2}bh$.

PROBLEMS

15-44. The radius of a circle is 18 in.   What is the length of an
arc of (*a*) 30°, (*b*) 90°, (*c*) 36°, (*d*) 72°?

15-45. The radius of a circle is 15 in.   What is the area of a sector
with a central angle whose measure is (*a*) 60°, (*b*) 90°, (*c*)
36°, (*d*) 45°?

15-46. The radius of a circle is 12 in.   What is the area of the
segment whose arc subtends a central angle with a measure of (*a*) 60°, (*b*) 90°, (*c*) 120°?

15-47. Find the area of the shaded portion of the square.

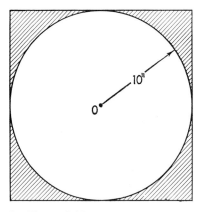

Problem 15-47

15-48. *ABCD* is a square.   Find the area of the shaded portion of the circle.

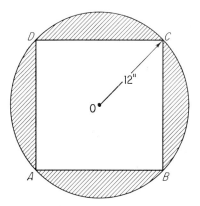

Problem 15-48

15-49. Find the area of the shaded portion of the figure.

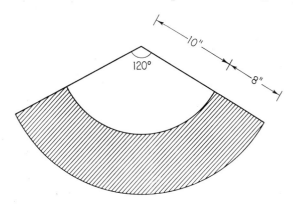

Problem 15-49

15-50. Find the area of the shaded portion (called a fillet) of the square $ABCD$.

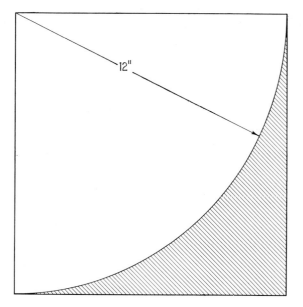

Problem 15-50

15-51. In the figure, L, M, N, T are midpoints of the square $ABCD$ the length of whose side is 4 in. $\overset{\frown}{PC}$ and $\overset{\frown}{AP}$ are circular arcs with centers at T and M, respectively. Find the area of the shaded portion.

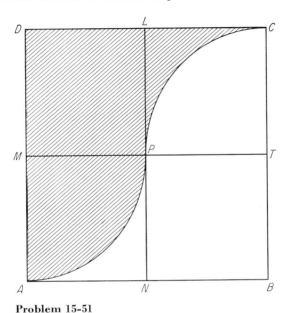

Problem 15-51

15-52. Find the area of the shaded portion of the semicircle.

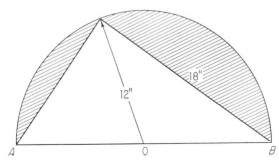

Problem 15-52

15-53. A continuous belt runs around two wheels as shown in
the figure.   Compute the length of the belt.

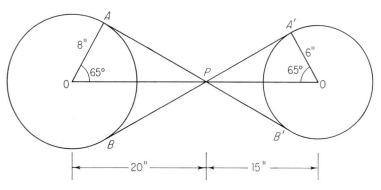

Problem 15-53

15-54. Find the area of the shaded portion of the larger circle.

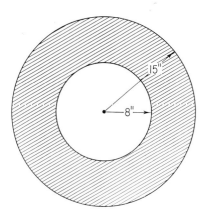

Problem 15-54

15-55. Find the area of the shaded portion of the trapezoid.

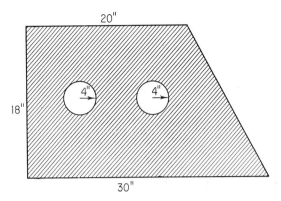

Problem 15-55

15-56. Find the area of the shaded region.

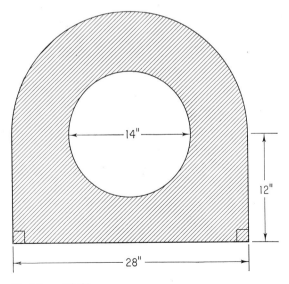

Problem 15-56

15-57. Find the area of the shaded region if the diameter of each of the smaller circles is 3 in. and the larger circle has a diameter of 8 in.

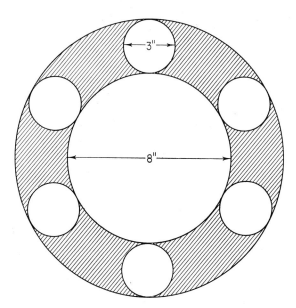

Problem 15-57

15-58. Find the area of the gasket with dimensions shown in the figure.

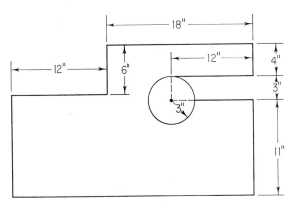

Problem 15-58

15-59. Find the number of circular pipes with an inside diameter of 1 in. which will carry the same amount of water as a pipe with an inside diameter of 4 in.

CHAPTER 16

Surface Areas and Volumes

16-1 Geometric Solids. The figures we have studied thus far are called plane figures, since all the points and lines of each figure lie in the same plane.

Solid geometry (often called *geometry of space*) is the study of figures whose parts do not lie in the same plane. Such figures are called *geometric solids*. Examples of solid figures are the cube, sphere, cone, and pyramid.

The word *solid* in the study of geometry has a meaning different from that in everyday conversation. We often speak of a block of solid wood or solid metal. A geometric solid does not

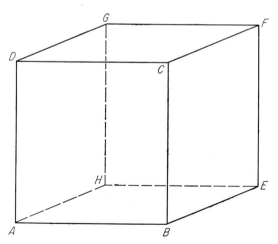

Fig. 16-1. Geometric solid.

refer to the material of which it is made but refers to the configuration formed by points in space. Figure 16-1 represents a solid figure. It is a combination of points, lines, and surfaces. The 8 corners of the figure are points; the 12 edges, such as AB and EF, are line segments; the 6 faces, such as $ABCD$, are portions of flat surfaces or planes.

16-2 Polyhedron. A *polyhedron* is a solid bounded by portions of plane surfaces. The *faces* are the portions of the bounding planes; the *edges* are the lines of intersection of the faces;

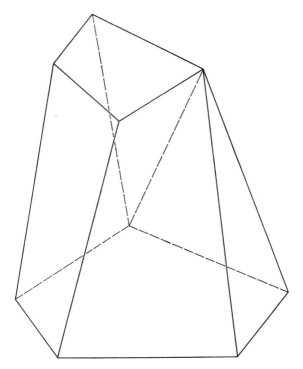

Fig. 16-2. Polyhedron.

the *vertices* are intersections of the edges. Figure 16-2 represents a polyhedron of 8 faces, 15 edges, and 9 vertices.

16-3 Prism. A prism is a polyhedron having two parallel and congruent faces, called *bases*, and the remaining faces are

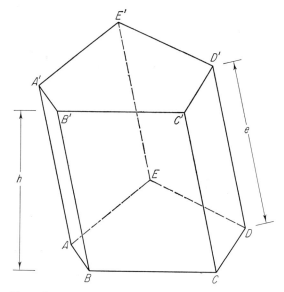

Fig. 16-3. Prism.

parallelograms (see Fig. 16-3). The bases may be triangles, quadrilaterals, or any other kind of polygon. In the prism, base $ABCDE$ is congruent to base $A'B'C'D'E'$. The faces which are parallelograms are called *lateral faces*, and their intersections (such as DD') are called *lateral edges*. It should be evident that the lateral edges are congruent and parallel. The *lateral area* is the sum of the areas of the lateral faces. The *total area* is the sum of the lateral areas and the areas of the two bases. The *altitude h* of a prism is the perpendicular distance between the planes of the bases.

A *right prism* is a prism having its lateral edges perpendicular to the bases (Fig. 16-4). It can be shown that, in a right prism, the lateral faces are rectangles and the lateral edges equal the altitude. A *regular prism* is a right prism whose bases are regular polygons.

If the edges of a prism are not perpendicular to the bases, the prism is called an *oblique prism* (see Fig. 16-3).

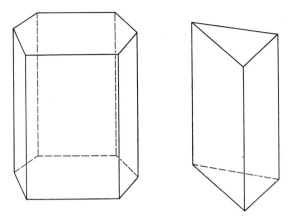

Fig. 16-4. Right prisms.

16-4 Parallelepiped. A parallelepiped is a prism with parallelograms as faces (Fig. 16-5). A *rectangular parallelepiped*

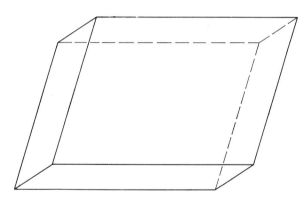

Fig. 16-5. Parallelepiped.

(Fig. 16-6) is a parallelepiped the faces of which are rectangles. All the lateral edges of a rectangular parallelepiped are perpendicular to the planes of the parallel faces.

The most common prism is the rectangular parallelepiped. A cube is a rectangular parallelepiped the faces of which are squares.

Elementary Mathematics

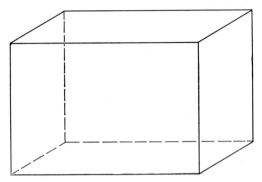

Fig. 16-6.   Rectangular parallelepiped.

16-5   Area of a Right Prism.   The lateral area of a right
prism is found by computing the areas of each face and then
summing the areas.   It can also be found by multiplying the
perimeter of the base by the altitude (see Fig. 16-7).

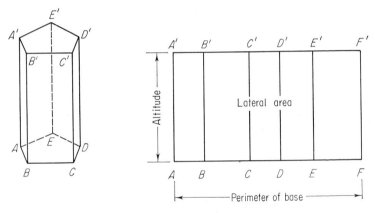

Fig. 16-7

If we denote the total area of a right prism by T, the lateral
area by L, and the area of a base by B, we get the formula

$$T = L + 2B$$

The total area of a rectangular parallelepiped (Fig. 16-8) with

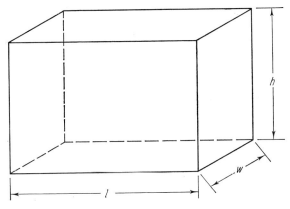

Fig. 16-8

length, width, and height, l, w, and h, respectively, is equal to $2lw + 2wh + 2lh$ or

$$T = 2(lw + wh + lh)$$

For a cube with lateral edge

$$T = 6e^2$$

16-6 Volume of a Prism. The volume of a solid is defined as the number of units of space measured in the solid. This unit of space, called a cubic unit, is that of a cube the edges of which are equal to some unit of measurement for length. Consider the rectangular parallelepiped, shown in Fig. 16-9, which is 4 units long, 3 units wide, and 2 units high. If planes are passed parallel to the faces of the solid as shown, the solid will consist of two layers, each layer containing 4 × 3, or 12, cubic units.

The two layers contain 2 × 12, or 24, cubic units. Thus the volume of the solid equals 24 cubic units. Common units for volume are cubic inches, cubic feet, cubic yards, and cubic centimeters. It will be noted that the numerical value for the volume above was obtained by multiplying together the linear dimensions or by multiplying the area of the base by the altitude.

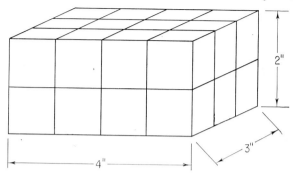

Fig. 16-9

Thus, in Fig. 16-8, if we denote the volume by V and the area of the base by A, we get the formulas

$$V = lwh \qquad \text{or} \qquad V = Ah$$

▶ *Formula.* The volume of any prism is the product of the area of its base and its altitude.

EXAMPLE 16-1.   A classroom is 40 ft long, 30 ft wide, and 12 ft high.   What is the volume of the room in cubic yards?   What is the lateral area in square yards?

Solution

$$
\begin{aligned}
V &= lwh \\
  &= (40 \text{ ft})(30 \text{ ft})(12 \text{ ft}) \\
  &= 14{,}400 \text{ ft}^3 \\
  &= 14{,}400 \text{ ft}^3 \times \frac{1 \text{ yd}^3}{27 \text{ ft}^3} \\
  &= 533\tfrac{1}{3} \text{ yd}^3 \\
L &= 2(lw + wh + lh) \\
  &= 2(40 \text{ ft} \times 30 \text{ ft} + 30 \text{ ft} \times 12 \text{ ft} + 40 \text{ ft} \times 12 \text{ ft}) \\
  &= 4{,}080 \text{ ft}^2 \\
  &= 4{,}080 \text{ ft}^2 \times \frac{1 \text{ yd}^2}{9 \text{ ft}^2} \\
  &= 453\tfrac{1}{3} \text{ yd}^2
\end{aligned}
$$

PROBLEMS

16-1. How many cubic yards of earth are removed in digging a pit 24 ft long, 18 ft wide, and 10 ft deep?

16-2. How many cubic yards of concrete are needed to pour a driveway 45 yd long, 15 ft wide, and 4 in. deep?

16-3. Find the volume of a cube with edge 15 in. long.

16-4. Find the total area of a cube with edge 15 in. long.

16-5. The inside dimensions of a fruit box are $22\frac{1}{2}$ by 17 by 6 in. How many cubic inches will it hold?

16-6. Find the volume in cubic feet of a beam 6 by 8 by 15 in.

16-7. What must be the dimensions of a cube that will give the same volume as a rectangular parallelepiped with dimensions 8 by 18 by 24 in.?

16-8. Find the volume of the right prism shown in the figure. The base is a right triangle with legs at 8 and 15 in.

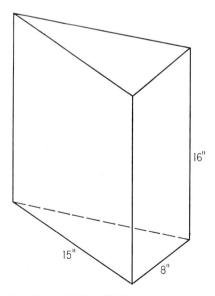

Problems 16-8 to 16-10

16-9. Find the lateral area of the right prism.

16-10. Find the total area of the right prism.

16-11. Find the volume of a triangular right prism 20 in. high if the sides of the bases are 6, 8, and 12 in. (HINT: Use Heron's formula for the area of the base.)

16-12. Find the total area of the prism of Prob. 16-11.

16-13. Find the weight of a block of ice 2 ft by 4 ft by 16 in. if ice weighs 57.2 lb per cubic foot.

16-14. Find the volume of a right prism if its altitude is 30 in. long and the bases are rhombuses having diagonals 10 and 16 in. long.

16-15. Find the lateral area of the prism of Prob. 16-14.

16-16. Find the total area of the prism of Prob. 16-14.

16-17. How many gallons in a reservoir 50 ft long, 30 ft wide, and 10 ft deep? (NOTE: 1 gal is equivalent to 231 in.^{3})

16-18. How many gallons of paint will be needed to paint the walls and ceiling of a room 45 ft long, 30 ft wide, and 12 ft high if 1 gal will cover 400 ft^2?

16-19. Each edge of a cube is increased by 50. What is the resultant percent increase in the surface area of the cube?

16-7 Cylindrical Surface. A surface generated by a straight line that moves parallel to itself is called a *cylindrical surface*. The moving line is called the *generatrix*. A *cylinder* is a geometric solid formed by that part of a cylindrical surface bounded by two parallel planes (see Fig. 16-10).

The intersections of the cylindrical surface and the parallel planes are the *bases* of the cylinder formed. The bases of a cylinder are congruent and have equal areas. The bounding cylindrical surface is the *lateral surface* of the cylinder. The *altitude* of a cylinder is the perpendicular distance between the bases. The *radius r* of a cylinder is the radius of the bases.

A *circular cylinder* is one the bases of which are circles. It is the most common form of cylinder. A *right circular cylinder* Fig. 16-10a) is a circular cylinder in which the generatrix is perpendicular to the bases. If the generatrix is not perpendicular

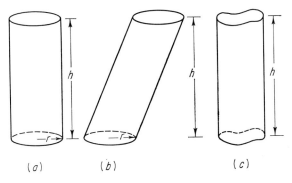

Fig. 16-10. Cylinders.

to the bases, the cylinder is called an *oblique cylinder* (see Fig. 16-10*b*).

16-8   Area of a Right Cylinder.   If the wrapper is removed from a can and spread along a plane (see Fig. 16-11), a rectangle

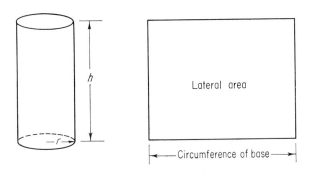

Fig. 16-11

will be formed with height equal to that of the can and length equal to the circumference of the base of the can. This will point up the following formula.

▶ *Formula.*   The lateral area L of a right cylinder is equal to the circumference of the base $\times$ altitude. (For a circle, $L = 2\pi r h$.)

The total area of a cylinder is equal to the sum of the lateral area and the area of the two bases.

▶ *Formula.*   The total area T of a right circular cylinder is
$T = 2\pi rh + 2\pi r^2 = 2\pi r(h + r)$.

16-9   Volume of a Cylinder.   The volume of a cylinder is equal to the product of the area of its base and the length of its altitude.   This will be true whether the cylinder is a right or an oblique cylinder.

▶ *Formula.*   The volume of a circular cylinder is $V = Ah = \pi r^2 h$.

A common type of problem involves finding the volume of cylindrical shells or hollow cylinders (see Fig. 16-12).   If we

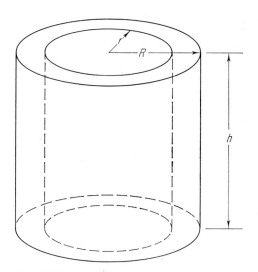

Fig. 16-12

let R be the outer radius, r the inner radius, and h the height of the shell, the volume can be found by subtracting the volume of the smaller cylinder from that of the larger one.

▶ *Formula.* The volume V of a circular cylindrical shell with outside radius R, inside radius r, and altitude h is

$$V = V_1 - V_2$$
$$= \pi R^2 h - \pi r^2 h$$
$$= \pi h (R^2 - r^2)$$

PROBLEMS

16-20. A silo is 10 ft in diameter and 30 ft tall. What is the volume of the silo?

16-21. A cylindrical water tank is 16 ft in diameter and 10 ft tall. How many gallons will it hold? (1 gal = 231 in.^{3})

16-22. Find the lateral surface of a right circular cylinder whose base has a diameter of 16 in. and whose height is 12 in.

16-23. Find the total area of the right circular cylinder with a radius of 10 ft and height of 8 ft.

16-24. A 100-gal cylindrical water tank is 5 ft high. What is its diameter?

16-25. A 50-gal tank has a radius of 16 in. What is its height?

16-26. How many gallons of gasoline will a right circular cylindrical tank hold that is 6 ft in diameter and 25 ft long? (NOTE: 1 ft^3 = 7.5 gal.)

16-27. How much does a mile-long copper wire weigh if the wire has a diameter of $\frac{3}{16}$ in.? Assume that copper has a density of 555 lb/ft^3.

16-28. An iron pipe has an inside diameter of 1 in. and is $\frac{1}{8}$ in. thick. How much will 1,000 ft of the pipe weigh? Assume that the density of the pipe is 450 lb/ft^3.

16-29. How many steel rods $\frac{5}{8}$ in. in diameter and 15 ft long can be made from a steel ingot with dimensions 14 in. by 16 in. by 4 ft?

16-30. How many square feet of asbestos are needed to wrap 500 ft of 6-in. pipe?

16-31. How much water, in gallons, will flow in a 1-in. pipe in a day if the flow speed is 2 ft/sec? (1 gal = 231 in.^{3})

16-10 Pyramid. A pyramid is a polyhedron with one face, called the *base*, a polygon of any number of sides, and the other faces triangles that meet in a common point called the *vertex*. The triangular faces are called the *lateral faces*, and the meeting of the lateral faces are *lateral edges*. The *altitude* of the pyramid

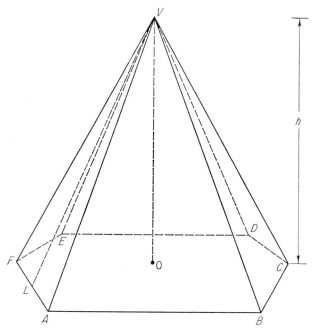

Fig. 16-13.   Pyramid.

is the distance from the vertex to the base.   The *lateral area* of a pyramid is equal to the sum of the areas of the lateral faces of the pyramid.   The *total area* of a pyramid is equal to the sum of the lateral area and the area of the base.

A *regular pyramid* is one whose base is a regular polygon and whose altitude from the vertex passes through the center of the base.   The lateral edges of a regular pyramid are congruent. The lateral faces of a regular pyramid are congruent isosceles triangles. The *slant height* of a regular pyramid is the altitude of any of its lateral faces.

16-11 Volume of a Pyramid. The volume of any pyramid is equal to one-third the product of the area of its base and altitude.

$$\text{Volume} = \tfrac{1}{3} \text{ area of base} \times \text{altitude}$$
$$= \tfrac{1}{3}Ah$$

16-12 Area of a Regular Pyramid. The *lateral area* of a regular pyramid is equal to half the product of its slant height s and the perimeter p of its base.

$$\text{Lateral area} = \tfrac{1}{2} \text{ slant height} \times \text{perimeter of base}$$
$$S = \tfrac{1}{2}sp$$

EXAMPLE 16-2. A regular pyramid has a regular hexagon (six sides) with sides equal to 6 in. and an altitude of 10 in. Find (*a*) the volume and (*b*) the lateral area of the pyramid.

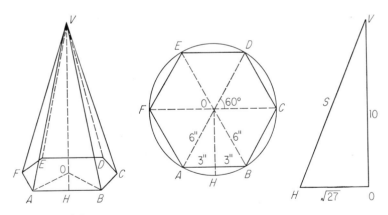

Example 16-2

Solution. (*a*) To solve for the volume, we must first find the area of the base. Let us imagine a circle with a 6-in. radius. If we divide the central angle into six congruent angles of 60°, measure each, and then join the six chords as shown in the figure, regular polygon $ABCDEF$ will be formed. It can be proved that this polygon is divided into six congruent equilateral triangles with sides of 6 in.

$$OA = 6 \text{ in.} \qquad HB = 3 \text{ in.}$$
$$(OH)^2 = (OB)^2 - (HB)^2$$
$$= (6)^2 - (3)^2$$
$$OH = \sqrt{27}$$
$$= 5.196 \text{ in.}$$
$$\text{Area of } AOB = 3(5.196)$$
$$= 15.588 \text{ in.}^2$$
$$\text{Area of } ABCDEF = 6(15.588) \text{ in.}^2$$
$$= 93.528 \text{ in.}^2$$
$$\text{Volume} = \tfrac{1}{3}Ah$$
$$= \tfrac{1}{3}(93.528)(10)$$
$$= 311.76 \text{ in.}^3$$

(b) To find the lateral area, we must next find the slant height VH.

$$(VH)^2 = (OH)^2 + (OV)^2$$
$$= (\sqrt{27})^2 + (10)^2$$
$$= 127$$
$$VH = 11.27 \text{ in.}$$
$$L = \tfrac{1}{2}sp$$
$$= \tfrac{1}{2}(11.27)(6 \times 6)$$
$$= 202.86 \text{ in.}^2$$

PROBLEMS

16-32. Find the volume of a pyramid whose base has an area of 54 in.^{2} and whose altitude is 8 in.

16-33. Find the lateral area of a pyramid whose base has a perimeter of 108 in. and whose slant height equals 15 in.

16-34. What is the volume of a pyramid whose base is a square 18 ft on a side and whose altitude is 10 ft?

16-35. What is the lateral area of a pyramid whose base is a square 12 in. on a side and whose altitude is 8 in.?

16-36. Find the volume of a pyramid whose base is a triangle with sides equal in length to 18, 24, and 30 ft and whose altitude is 20 ft.

16-37. A marble pyramid has a square base 20 in. on a side and is 6 ft high. How heavy is the pyramid if the density of marble is 170 lb/ft³?

16-38. A pyramid has an equilateral triangle for its base and is 8 ft tall. What is the volume of the pyramid if the side of the triangular base is 3 ft?

16-39. A regular pyramid has an equilateral triangle with sides equal to 10 in. as a base and slant height of 20 in. What is its lateral area?

16-40. What is the volume of a regular pyramid whose base is a regular hexagon 10 in. on a side and whose altitude is 20 in.?

16-41. What is the lateral area of a regular pyramid with a regular hexagon with sides of 8 in. for a base and an altitude of 12 in.?

16-13 Conical Surface. A *conical surface* is a surface that is generated by moving a straight line so that it turns around one of its points (see Fig. 16-14). The moving line, such as $\overleftrightarrow{PQ}$, is called the *generatrix*. V is the *vertex* of the surface.

16-14 Cone. A *cone* is that part of a conical surface which is bounded by the vertex and a plane cutting the surface (Fig. 16-15). There are many uses for cones in industry and everyday affairs. We have conical tents, ice-cream cones, conical horns, etc.

The *base RST* of the cone is the curve cut from the conical surface of the plane. The *altitude* of a cone is the perpendicular distance from the vertex to the plane of the base. The *lateral area* of a cone is the area of the lateral surface.

A cone whose base is a circle is called a *circular cone*. If the

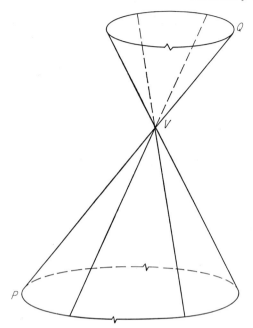

Fig. 16-14.   Conical surface.

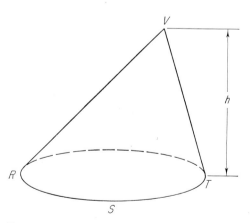

Fig. 16-15.   Cone.

line passing through the vertex of the cone and the center of its base is perpendicular to the base, the figure is called a *right circular cone* (see Fig. 16-16). The length of $\overrightarrow{VR}$ (or $\overrightarrow{VS}$, $\overrightarrow{VP}$, etc.) is called the *slant height* of the right circular cone.

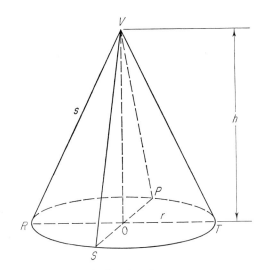

Fig. 16-16. Right circular cone.

16-15 Volume of a Cone. It can be shown that the volume of a cone is equal to one-third the product of the area of its base and its altitude. For the circular cone with radius of the base r and altitude h we get

▶ *Formula*

$$\text{Volume} = \tfrac{1}{3}\ \text{area of base} \times \text{altitude}$$
$$= \tfrac{1}{3}\pi r^2 h$$

The student should notice that, if a cone and a cylinder have the same base and the same altitude (Fig. 16-17), the volume of the cone is exactly $\frac{1}{3}$ the volume of the corresponding cylinder. This same relationship exists between a pyramid and a prism with equal bases and altitudes.

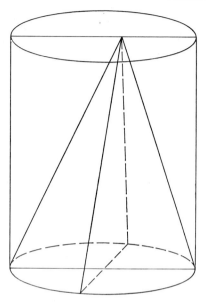

Fig. 16-17

16-16 Lateral Area of a Right Circular Cone. The lateral area of a right circular cone is equal to half the product of its slant height and the circumference of its base. Thus, in Fig. 16-16, we get

▶ *Formula*

Surface area = $\frac{1}{2}$ circumference of base × slant height

$$L = \frac{1}{2}(2\pi r)s$$
$$L = \pi r s$$

The total area T of a cone is equal to the sum of the lateral area and the area of the base.

▶ *Formula*

Total area = lateral area + area of base
$$T = \pi r s + \pi r^2$$

PROBLEMS

16-41. Find the volume of a circular cone 36 in. high and having a base diameter of 18 in.

16-43. What is the lateral area of the right circular cone having an altitude of 36 in. and a base radius of 27 in.?

16-44. Find the total area of a right circular cone having a slant height of 30 ft and a base radius of 18 ft.

16-45. Find the volume of a right circular cone with slant height of 17 ft and an altitude of 15 feet.

V-ABCD is a right circular cone.

16-46. Find the volume of cone *V-ABCD*.

16-47. Find the volume of cone *V-EFGH*.

16-48. Find the lateral area of cone *V-ABCD*.

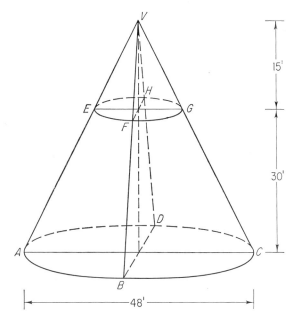

Problems 16-46 to 16-50

16-49. Find the total area of cone V-$ABCD$.
16-50. Find the lateral area of cone V-$EFGH$.

V-RST is a right circular cone.   Plane $PQL \parallel$ plane RST.

16-51. Find the volume of V-RST.
16-52. Find the volume of the solid $PRSTLQ$.

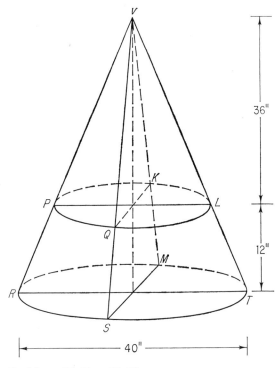

Problems 16-51 to 16-55

16-53. Find the lateral area of V-PQL.
16-54. Find the total surface area of V-RST.
16-55. Find the total area of the solid $PRSTLQ$.

16-17 The Sphere. A *sphere* is a closed surface every point
of which is equidistant from a fixed point within, called the *center*
(see Fig. 16-18).   If a circle is rotated about one of its diameters,
the solid generated is a sphere.

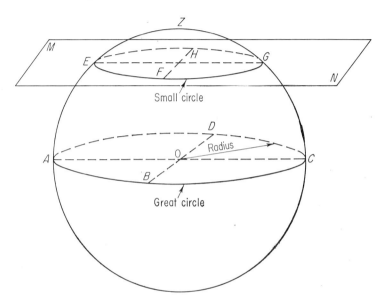

Fig. 16-18.   Sphere.

A *radius* of a sphere is a line segment joining the center to any
point of the sphere.

A *diameter* of a sphere is a straight-line segment through the
center and having its ends on the sphere.   The measure of the
diameter is twice that of the radius.

If a plane intersects a sphere, the intersection is a circle.   If
the plane contains the diameter of the sphere, the circle is a *great
circle;* otherwise the circle is a *small circle*.   All great circles of
a sphere are equal.   Every great circle bisects the sphere into
surfaces called *hemispheres*.

The portion of a sphere cut off by a plane is called a *segment* of the sphere. *Z-EFGH* of Fig. 16-18 is a segment.

16-18   The Surface Area of a Sphere.   The surface area of a sphere is equal to four times the area of the great circle of the sphere.

▶ *Formula*

$$\text{Area of sphere} = 4 \text{ times area of great circle}$$
$$S = 4\pi r^2$$

16-19   Volume of a Sphere.   The volume of a sphere is equal to $\frac{4}{3}\pi$ times the cube of the radius of the sphere.

▶ *Formula*

$$\text{Volume of sphere} = \tfrac{4}{3}\pi \text{ (radius)}^3$$
$$V = \tfrac{4}{3}\pi r^3$$

16-20   Torus.   If a slender rod, such as Fig. 16-19*a*, is bent into a ring (Fig. 16-19*b*), the solid formed is called a *torus*.   The

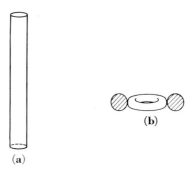

(b)

(a)

Fig. 16-19.   Torus.

surface of the torus will equal the lateral surface area of the cylinder.   Since $h = 2\pi R$, we can find the surface area by multiplying the circumference of the center line of the torus by the circumference of its cross section.

▶ *Formula*

$$\text{Surface area of torus} = 2\pi r h$$
$$S = 2\pi r(2\pi R)$$
$$= 4\pi^2 r R$$

In like manner, the volume of the torus is equal to the volume of the cylinder. Thus, the volume of the torus is found by multiplying the circumference of the center line of the torus by the area of the cross section.

▶ *Formula*

$$\text{Volume of torus} = 2\pi R(\pi r^2)$$
$$V = 2\pi^2 r^2 R$$

PROBLEMS

16-56. Find the volume of a sphere having a 10-ft diameter.

16-57. Find the surface area of a sphere with a diameter of 8 in.

16-58. The area of the great circle of a sphere is 75 in.^{2} What is the surface area of the sphere?

16-59. Find the radius of a sphere with a volume of 84.82 in.^{3}

16-60. Find the diameter of a sphere with a surface area of 201.0 in.^{2}

16-61. Find the volume of a sphere whose surface area is 64 ft^2.

16-62. A sphere just fits in a cube whose volume is 5830 in.^{3} What is the volume of the sphere?

16-63. A hollow spherical metal ball has an outside diameter of 13 in. and is $\frac{1}{2}$ in. thick. Find the volume of the metal in the ball.

16-64. Find the volume enclosed in the figure.

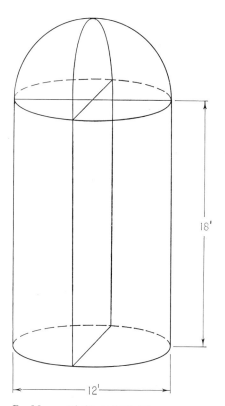

Problems 16-64 and 16-65

16-65. Find the total surface of the figure. Include the lateral surface of the cylinder, the area of the base, and the area of the hemisphere.

16-66. Find the surface of the torus with an inside diameter of 16 in. and an outside diameter of 18 in.

16-67. Find the volume of the torus of Prob. 16-66.

Answers to Odd-numbered Problems

Chapter 1

1-1. 11,427

1-3. 13,923

1-5. 101,570

1-7. 27,271,294

1-9. 10,054

1-11. 89,533

1-13. 8,097 ft

1-15. 1,446 ft

1-17. 320,130 mi²

1-19. $1,518.03

1-21. 52

1-23. 817

1-25. 2,482

1-27. 61,305

1-29. 56,566

1-31. 468,379

1-33. 86,151

1-35. 1,345 kwhr

1-37. 20,250

1-39. $4,395

1-41. 787

1-43. 10,620

1-45. 827,904

1-47. 31,316,857

1-49. 4,044,301,002

1-51. 1,417,426,956

1-53. 9,000

1-55. 91

1-57. $91.20

1-59. $1,664

1-61. Car X, 6 miles

1-63. 73

1-65. 45

1-67. $202\frac{13}{404}$

1-69. $27\frac{18}{8,493}$

1-71. 100,308

1-73. $30,047\frac{53}{309}$

1-75. $100,406\frac{562}{653}$

1-77. 459

1-79. $690.54

1-81. 43 lb

1-83. 120

1-85. $249\frac{1}{5}$

1-87. 1,152

1-89. 6

1-91. 2

1-93. 2

1-95. 5

1-97. 12

1-99. 10

1-101. 54

Chapter 2

2-1. 15

2-3. 32

2-5. 3

2-7. 52

2-9. 47

2-11. $6\frac{1}{3}$

2-13. $11\frac{1}{4}$

2-15. $1\frac{5}{12}$

2-17. $3\frac{7}{12}$

2-19. $3\frac{1}{4}$

2-21. $\frac{15}{8}$

2-23. $\frac{50}{11}$

2-25. $\frac{25}{9}$ **2-27.** $\frac{31}{4}$

2-29. $\frac{48}{5}$ **2-31.** $\frac{3}{5}$

2-33. $\frac{5}{6}$ **2-35.** $\frac{2}{9}$

2-37. $\frac{5}{9}$ **2-39.** $\frac{37}{53}$

2-41. $2 \cdot 2 \cdot 3 \cdot 3$ **2-43.** $2 \cdot 2 \cdot 2 \cdot 3 \cdot 5$

2-45. $2 \cdot 3 \cdot 3 \cdot 5 \cdot 5$ **2-47.** $3 \cdot 3 \cdot 7 \cdot 11$

2-49. $2 \cdot 2 \cdot 2 \cdot 5 \cdot 5 \cdot 13$ **2-51.** 60

2-53. 240   **2-55.** 1,200

2-57. 210   **2-59.** 1,848

2-61. $\frac{2}{3}$ **2-63.** $\frac{7}{12}$

2-65. $\frac{3}{5}$ **2-67.** $1\frac{2}{3}$

2-69. $1\frac{5}{24}$ **2-71.** $\frac{11}{20}$

2-73. $\frac{137}{270}$ **2-75.** $4\frac{5}{24}$

2-77. $4\frac{323}{720}$ **2-79.** $\frac{421}{7,350}$

2-81. $40\frac{3}{8}$ **2-83.** $15\frac{5}{24}$

2-85. $14\frac{233}{270}$ **2-87.** $8\frac{1}{12}$

2-89. $10\frac{191}{270}$ **2-91.** $49\frac{1}{2}$ yd

2-93. $33\frac{3}{4}$ lb   **2-95.** $1\frac{19}{64}$ in.

2-97. $\frac{9}{16}$ in.   **2-99.** $\frac{1}{2}$

2-101. $\frac{35}{96}$ **2-103.** $\frac{7}{12}$

2-105. 8   **2-107.** $\frac{16}{27}$

2-109. $\frac{3}{10}$ **2-111.** 1

2-113. $\frac{368}{4,059}$ **2-115.** 22

2-117. 3   **2-119.** $18\frac{6}{7}$

2-121. $52\frac{4}{5}$ **2-123.** $4\frac{4}{5}$ hr

2-125. $\frac{2}{7}$ **2-127.** $10\frac{2}{3}$

2-129. $1\frac{1}{7}$ **2-131.** $\frac{25}{27}$

2-133. $\frac{15}{28}$ **2-135.** $\frac{9}{10}$

2-137. $1\frac{3}{7}$ **2-139.** $6\frac{150}{161}$

2-141. 12   **2-143.** $\frac{11}{24}$

2-145. $\frac{21}{32}$ **2-147.** $\frac{3}{8}$

2-149. $52\frac{1}{2}$ **2-151.** $2\frac{4}{87}$

2-153. 5   **2-155.** $17\frac{1}{2}$

2-157. $\frac{25}{27}$ **2-159.** $\frac{85}{98}$

2-161. $1,079\frac{23}{33}$ **2-163.** 108

2-165. 150

Chapter 3

3-1. (*a*) 0.642   (*b*) 14.108   (*c*) 18.004   (*d*) 0.056   (*e*) 87.0605
       (*f*) 2002.200   (*g*) 8.3   (*h*) 47.013   (*i*) 0.73   (*j*) 0.9451
       (*k*) 4.8039

3-9. 0.7500   **3-11.** 0.6250

3-13. 0.2812   **3-15.** 0.5469

3-17. 0.4444   **3-19.** 0.2727

3-21. $\frac{3}{8}$

3-25. $\frac{16}{125}$

3-29. $\frac{135}{16}$

3-33. 472.626

3-37. 35.2533

3-41. 9.869

3-45. 1235.4

3-49. 12.73484

3-53. 0.918271809

3-57. 0.075

3-61. 89.012

3-65. 75.8125

3-69. 63.90

3-73. 1.7

3-77. 850

3-81. 1.63×10^6

3-85. 3.91

3-23. $\frac{33}{8}$

3-27. $\frac{23}{32}$

3-31. 18.995

3-35. 12.5031

3-39. 10.498

3-43. 15.280

3-47. 10,050.4

3-51. 1.683879

3-55. 0.01028376

3-59. 0.50

3-63. 2,000

3-67. 14.1

3-71. 15

3-75. 315

3-79. 8.5

3-83. 0.220

3-87. 14.35

Chapter 4

4-1. 0.11

4-5. 1.375

4-9. 0.004

4-13. 3.745

4-17. 0.9%

4-21. 0.04%

4-25. 1200%

4-29. 28,300%

4-33. 31.25%

4-37. 65%

4-41. $231\frac{1}{4}\%$

4-45. $2312\frac{1}{2}\%$

4-49. $5\frac{12}{25}$

4-53. $\frac{7}{8}$

4-57. $\frac{191}{400}$

4-61. 32

4-65. $4,500

4-69. 800

4-73. $195\frac{35}{37}$

4-77. 200%

4-81. 3387.6

4-85. 3.20

4-89. $122\frac{2}{3}$

4-93. $14\frac{6}{7}$

4-97. 675

4-3. 0.084

4-7. 0.0025

4-11. 0.00007

4-15. 0.000625

4-19. 25%

4-23. 760%

4-27. 8.0045%

4-31. $58\frac{1}{3}\%$

4-35. 14.0625%

4-39. $791\frac{2}{3}\%$

4-43. 178%

4-47. $\frac{5}{4}$

4-51. 15

4-55. $\frac{33}{80}$

4-59. $\frac{1}{150}$

4-63. 9.6

4-67. 113.6

4-71. $3\frac{1}{3}\%$

4-75. 1,057.548

4-79. 1,176

4-83. 432

4-87. $504

4-91. 0.00907872

4-95. 1200%

4-99. $21\frac{7}{833}\%$

4-101. $4.08   4-103. $100,000
4-105. 28,000 watts   4-107. $225.62
4-109. $24.80; $25.42   4-111. 12%
4-113. $45.83   4-115. $270; $2,070
4-117. 27 lb; 24 lb; 15 lb; 300 lb   4-119. $120,000
4-121. $100   4-123. 6.4%

Chapter 5

5-1. 7.68   5-3. 5.55
5-5. 2,770   5-7. 164,400
5-9. 433,000   5-11. 53,900
5-13. 10.24   5-15. 0.01266
5-17. 2.12   5-19. 5.04
5-21. 3.02   5-23. 846
5-25. 0.0721   5-27. 857
5-29. 4,020   5-31. 0.272
5-33. 130.9   5-35. 4.36
5-37. 0.00001554   5-39. 0.0563
5-41. 1,186   5-43. 0.259
5-45. 0.1145   5-47. 0.1948
5-49. 0.306   5-51. 0.746
5-53. 0.01823   5-55. 1.326
5-57. 57.5   5-59. 0.000363
5-61. 21.3   5-63. 2,230
5-65. 0.523   5-67. 4.02
5-69. 6.49   5-71. 0.488
5-73. 6.86   5-75. 0.1044
5-77. 1.503   5-79. 0.855
5-81. 43.5   5-83. 0.0476
5-85. 14.90   5-87. 52.6
5-89. 2,210   5-91. 69,900
5-93. 63.3   5-95. 500
5-97. 1821   5-99. 0.0286
5-101. 8   5-103. $\frac{1}{8}$
5-105. 14   5-107. 7
5-109. $\frac{2}{8}$ 5-151. 29
5-153. 148   5-155. 429
5-157. 719   5-159. 97.4
5-161. 0.878   5-163. 0.0615
5-165. 0.0293   5-167. 387
5-169. 0.571   5-171. 5.29
5-173. 75.7   5-175. 1815
5-177. 77,300   5-179. 0.00728
5-181. 7.48   5-183. 16.06

5-185. 28.6

5-187. 214

5-189. 0.340

5-191. 55.2

5-193. 2.44

5-195. 3.63

5-197. 0.783

5-199. 8,090

5-201. 22.0

5-203. 0.238

5-205. 0.0566

5-207. 576,000

5-209. 0.000691

5-211. 1.965

5-213. 8.31

5-215. 0.879

5-217. 0.330

5-219. 44.3

5-221. 8.82

5-223. 1.704

5-225. 0.443

5-227. 7.72

5-229. 0.588

Chapter 6

6-1. 0.283 m

6-3. 0.0593 mm

6-5. 8.732 gm

6-7. 6.115 l

6-9. 3150 in.

6-11. 15,153.6 ft

6-13. 1.4395 short tons

6-15. 7.325 bushels

6-17. 115.5 in.^{3}

6-19. 0.0593 dm^2

6-21. 0.0000835 m^3

6-23. 54 in.^{2}

6-25. $831\frac{7}{8}$ yd^3

6-27. $0.0144 \frac{m}{hr}$

6-29. $875,000 \frac{kg}{m^3}$

6-31. $\frac{35}{54} \frac{oz}{in.^3}$

6-33. 31.75 m

6-35. 5.45 lb

6-37. $110,000 \frac{cm}{min}$

6-39. $0.0742 \frac{lb}{in.^2}$

6-41. $2.17 \frac{gm}{cm^3}$

6-43. $18,070 \frac{mg}{mm^2}$

6-45. $25.9 \frac{km}{min}$

Chapter 7

7-17. 5

7-19. 8

7-21. 48

7-23. -27

7-25. -13

7-27. 0

7-29. 0

7-31. -11

7-33. -5

7-35. 10

7-37. 30

7-39. -45

7-41. -35

7-43. -33

7-45. 7

7-47. -0.9

7-49. 0

7-51. 13

7-53. -6	**7-55.** 18
7-57. -334	**7-59.** -59
7-61. -24	**7-63.** 9
7-65. -12.11	**7-67.** -13
7-69. 22	**7-71.** 39
7-73. -19	**7-75.** -87
7-77. -9	**7-79.** 23
7-81. -59	**7-83.** 12
7-85. -1.20	**7-87.** -30
7-89. 63	**7-91.** 4
7-93. $\frac{1}{4}$	**7-95.** $\frac{4}{9}$
7-97. 20	**7-99.** -28
7-101. $-\frac{3}{4}$	**7-103.** 120
7-105. -5	**7-107.** -72
7-109. -15	**7-111.** $-4\frac{3}{4}$
7-113. -6	**7-115.** -20
7-117. -2	**7-119.** $-1\frac{28}{175}$

Chapter 8

8-19. -5	**8-21.** 4
8-23. 10	**8-25.** $1\frac{1}{7}$
8-27. -7	**8-29.** 9
8-31. 20	**8-33.** 0
8-35. 0	**8-37.** 11
8-39. -1	**8-41.** -13
8-43. $-3k$	**8-45.** $-8ab$
8-47. $5cd$	**8-49.** $-6bd$
8-51. $10r^2t^2$	**8-53.** $6b^3c^2$
8-55. $-2.9xy$	**8-57.** $6a^3 - 3a^2b - ab^2 - 2b^3$
8-59. $-8r^2s^2 - 11rs + 13$	**8-61.** $-3a^3 - 2ab + 3b^3$
8-63. $-11a$	**8-65.** $12k$
8-67. $67rs$	**8-69.** $4lm$
8-71. $-3ab$	**8-73.** $9a + 2$
8-75. $4x^2y + 5x + 3xy$	**8-77.** $13a - 7c$
8-79. $-3x^2y + 15xy$	**8-81.** $-9x^2$
8-83. x^2y^3	**8-85.** $(8a)^5$
8-87. a^8	**8-89.** u^{12}
8-91. $12x^2$	**8-93.** $-20y^5$
8-95. $24r^2s^2t^2$	**8-97.** $-30a^4b^3c^4$
8-99. $2x^3$	**8-101.** $9z^3 - 4z^2$
8-103. x^3z^6	**8-105.** $25x^4y^6$
8-107. $16x^4y^8z^{12}$	**8-109.** $6b^2c$
8-111. x^2	**8-113.** $-\dfrac{3d}{k^2m}$

8-115. 3^{13}

8-117. ab^2

8-119. y^3

8-121. $\dfrac{-c^6}{a^{12}b^3}$

8-123. $-15a^3b^2 + 5a^2b^3 - 20ab^4$

8-125. $4k^4 - 8k^3 + 20k^2 - 28k$

8-127. $-3u^5v^2 + 12u^4v^3 - 21u^2v^4$

8-129. $-6a^3b^2 + 12a^2b^3 + 6ab^4$

8-131. $a^2 + 2a - 15$

8-133. $z^2 - 4z - 77$

8-135. $6a^2 - 31a + 35$

8-137. $4x^2 - 49$

8-139. $15m^4 - 26m^3 + 8m^2$

8-141. $2x^3 - 7x^2y + 7xy^2 - 2y^3$

8-143. $x^4 - x^3y - 8x^2y^2 + 5xy^3 + 15y^4$

8-145. $a^4 - a^3 - 5a^2 + 27a - 30$

8-147. $2a^4 - 3a^3b - 2a^2b^2 + ab^3 - 2b^4$

8-149. $6a^4 - a^3b - 2a^2b^2 + 3ab^3 - 2b^4$

8-151. $4x^4 + x^3y - 26x^2y^2 + 17xy^3 + 7y^4$

8-153. $a^3 - 7a^2 + 4a + 12$

8-155. $3a^3 + 16a^2 + 15a - 18$

8-157. $2a^3 + 3a^2b - 32ab^2 + 15b^3$

8-159. $5a^3 - 3a^2 + 4a - 2$

8-161. $x - y - 2y^2$

8-163. $10xy^2 + 7 - 6y^2 - 5y^3$

8-165. $x + 3$

8-167. $3x^2y - z$

8-169. $z - 6y$

8-171. $x^2 + 2x + 3$

8-173. $2x - 3$

8-175. $3y - 2z$

8-177. $4a^2 - 3ab - 2b^2$

8-179. $a^2 - 2ab + 3b^2 + \dfrac{-8b^4}{a^2 + 3b^2 + 2ab}$

8-181. $x + 2y + z$

8-183. $3k^2 - 7k + 4 + \dfrac{6}{k^2 - 8k + 6}$

8-185. $3a^2 - 6ab - 5b^2$

8-187. $7c^2 - 5d^2 + \dfrac{5d^4}{6c^2 - 9cd - 7d^2}$

Chapter 9

9-1. 8

9-3. -3

9-5. 6

9-7. $\frac{1}{2}$

9-9. -4

9-11. 4

9-13. -2

9-15. $\frac{10}{3}$

9-17. 2

9-19. $\frac{1}{2}$

9-21. 2

9-23. -5

9-25. -5

9-27. -3

9-29. 4

9-31. -3

9-33. No solution

9-35. $\frac{19}{5}$

9-37. $13\frac{1}{2}$

9-39. 4

9-41. 3

9-43. $-\frac{18}{7}$

9-45. $-\dfrac{5a}{2}$　　　　　　　　　　**9-47.** $\tfrac{3}{10}d$

9-49. $\dfrac{15a^2}{4a-1}$ ~~$5a$~~　　　　　　**9-51.** $\dfrac{ab+ac}{5}$

9-53. $\dfrac{V}{lh}$　　　　　　　　　　**9-55.** $\dfrac{S-\pi r^2}{2\pi r}$ $\dfrac{S-2\pi r^2}{2\pi r}$

9-57. $\dfrac{3V}{\pi r^2}$　　　　　　　　　**9-59.** $\dfrac{v^2}{2g}$

9-61. $\dfrac{6M}{h^2}$　　　　　　　　　**9-63.** $\dfrac{33{,}000H}{LAN}$

9-65. $\dfrac{l-a}{n-1}$　　　　　　　　**9-67.** $2A-b$

9-69. $\dfrac{Wv^2}{Fg}$　　　　　　　　**9-71.** v_0+at

9-73. $\dfrac{RR_1}{R_1-R}$　　　　　　　**9-75.** Rod, \$15; reel, \$20

9-77. Length, 31 yd; width, 28 yd　　**9-79.** $\tfrac{6}{10}$
9-81. $54\tfrac{3}{4}$ in., $51\tfrac{3}{4}$ in., $48\tfrac{3}{4}$ in., $45\tfrac{3}{4}$ in.
9-83. Father, 40 yr; son, 20 yr　　　**9-85.** \$4920
9-87. $41\tfrac{2}{3}$ gal, 8% sol; $58\tfrac{1}{3}$ gal, 20% sol　　**9-89.** $33\tfrac{1}{3}$ gal
9-91. 48 mi/hr　　　　　　　　　**9-93.** $6\tfrac{3}{7}$ hr
9-95. (a) 16 hr　(b) 240 mi　　　**9-97.** 28 days

Chapter 10
10-33. $30°$　　　　　　　　　　**10-35.** $130°$
10-37. $109°$　　　　　　　　　**10-39.** $164°$
10-41. Scalene, obtuse　　　　　**10-43.** Isosceles, acute
10-45. Isosceles, acute　　　　　**10-47.** Equilateral, equiangular
10-49. Scalene, right
10-53. $\overleftrightarrow{AB}$ and $\overleftrightarrow{CD}$; $\overleftrightarrow{AC}$ and $\overleftrightarrow{BC}$　　**10-51.** Scalene, right
　　　　　　　　　　　　　　　10-55. $\angle H$ and $\angle K$
10-65. (a) $150°$　(b) $115°$　(c) $90°$　(d) $45°$　(e) $180-\alpha°$

Chapter 11
11-1. Yes　　　　　　　　　　**11-3.** No
11-5. Yes　　　　　　　　　　**11-7.** Yes
11-9. Yes　　　　　　　　　　**11-11.** Yes
11-13. Yes　　　　　　　　　**11-15.** No
11-21. ASA　　　　　　　　　**11-23.** No
11-25. Hypotenuse-acute angle　　**11-27.** Hypotenuse-acute angle

11-29. Hypotenuse-leg

11-31. ASA

11-33. SAS

11-35. No

Chapter 12

12-1. Yes

12-3. Yes

12-5. Yes

12-7. No

12-9. No

12-11. $45°$

12-13. $140°$

12-15. $l_2, l_3; m_1, m_2, m_3$

12-21. $60°$

12-23. $45°$

12-25. $70°$

12-27. $135°$

12-29. $48°$

12-31. $20°$

12-33. $90°$

Chapter 13

13-1. $60°$

13-3. $20°$

13-5. $m = 106°; m\angle \alpha = 37°$

13-7. $45°$

13-9. $m\angle \alpha = 69°; m\angle \beta = 69°$

13-11. $44°$

13-13. $50°$

13-15. $110°$

13-17. $m = 50°$

13-19. $15°$

13-21. $58°$

13-23. $m = 100°; m\angle \alpha = 25°;$
$m\angle \beta = 25°$

13-25. $61°$

13-27. $15°$

13-29. $108°$

13-31. $32°$

13-33. $92°$

13-35. $m\angle \alpha = 90°; m\angle \beta = 25°$

13-37. $m = 120°; m\angle \alpha = 25°$

13-39. $m = 80°; m\angle \alpha = 20°;$
$m\angle \beta = 55°$

Chapter 14

14-1. (a) $\frac{2}{3}$ (c) $\frac{8}{9}$ (e) $\frac{1}{6}$ (g) $\frac{24}{5}$

14-5. (a) 18   (c) 10   (e) 14.4 in.

14-7. (a) $4:3$ (c) $5:2$ (e) $b:a$

14-9. (a) 6   (c) 10   (e) $\frac{1}{3}$

14-11. 14,400

14-13. 7

14-15. 10

14-17. 40

14-19. 16

14-21. 15

14-23. 40

14-25. 6

14-27. 15

14-29. 6

14-31. 19.2

14-33. 6

14-35. 15

14-37. 31.2

14-39. 4

14-41. 40

14-43. 8

14-45. 30

14-47. 10

14-49. 9

14-51. 9.6   **14-53.** 16
14-55. 2.5   **14-57.** 14

Chapter 15
 15-1. (*a*) 11.6 yd   (*c*) 6.007 mi   **15-3.** (*a*) 1.4 ft   (*c*) 2.000 yd
 15-5. 17.5 ft²   **15-7.** $199\frac{3}{4}$ ft²
 15-9. \$323.49   **15-11.** 54 in.²
 15-13. 512 in.²   **15-15.** $7\frac{7}{8}$ ft²
 15-17. $139\frac{1}{4}$ in.²   **15-19.** $361\frac{7}{8}$ ft²
 15-21. 560 yd²   **15-23.** 158.6 in.²
 15-25. 512 in.²   **15-27.** $63\frac{15}{16}$ ft²
 15-29. 16 in.   **15-31.** 240 ft²
 15-33. 54 ft²   **15-35.** 7.79 ft
 15-37. 175.5 in.²   **15-39.** 384 ft²
 15-41. 36.4 in.²   **15-43.** $132\frac{1}{2}$ ft²
 15-44. (*a*) 9.42 in.   (*c*) 11.31 in.   **15-45.** (*a*) 118.0 in.²   (*c*) 70.68 in.²
 15-46. (*a*) 13.04 in.²   (*c*) 88.5 in.²   **15-47.** 85.84 in.²
 15-49. 235 in.²   **15-51.** 8 in.²
 15-53. 141 in.   **15-55.** 350 in.²
 15-57. 61.25 in.²   **15-59.** 16

Chapter 16
 16-1. 160 yd³   **16-3.** 3375 in.³ or $\frac{125}{64}$ ft³
 16-5. 2295 in.³   **16-7.** $\sqrt[3]{3456} \approx 15.12$ in.
 16-9. 640 in.²   **16-11.** $20\sqrt{455} \approx 427$ in.²
 16-13. 610 lb   **16-15.** 1,132 in.²
 16-17. 112,200 gal   **16-19.** 125%
 16-21. 15,030 gal   **16-23.** 1,130 ft²
 16-25. 14.36 in.   **16-27.** 562 lb
 16-29. 194   **16-31.** 7,050 gal
 16-33. 810 in.²   **16-35.** 240 in.²
 16-37. $944\frac{4}{9}$ lb   **16-39.** 304 in.²
 16-41. 333 in.²   **16-43.** 3,820 in.²
 16-45. 1,005 ft³   **16-47.** 1,005 ft³
 16-49. 5,650 ft²   **16-51.** 11.64 ft³ or 20,106 in.³
 16-53. 1,838 in.²   **16-55.** 3,390 in.²
 16-57. 201 in.²   **16-59.** 2.72 in.
 16-61. 48.1 ft³   **16-63.** 246 in.³
 16-65. 1,018 ft²   **16-67.** 42.0 in.³

Index